Roots of Change

Farming and the Landscape in East Anglia, c.1700–1870

Susanna Wade Martins and Tom Williamson

The Agricultural History Review
Supplement Series 2

BRITISH AGRICULTURAL HISTORY SOCIETY
1999

From time to time *Agricultural History Review* has published supplements where the history of an aspect of rural economy and society has required a longer treatment than could be achieved within the confines of an article. Proposals for supplements should be directed in the first instance to the editors of the *Review*. This is the second supplement: the first to be published was Adrian Hall, *Fenland Worker-Peasants. The economy of smallholders at Rippingale, Lincolnshire, 1791–1871* (1992).

Enquiries about the work of the society, applications for membership and orders for its publications should be directed to the Society c/o the Department of History, University of Exeter, Amory Building, Rennes Drive, Exeter, EX4 4RJ.

The society is indebted to the Centre of East Anglian Studies, University of East Anglia, and the Norman Scarfe Trust for grants in aid of the publication of this volume.

ISBN 0 9536668 0 8

The cover illustration is taken from an early eighteenth-century map
of Earsham Park Farm, Earsham, Norfolk,
reproduced by kind permission of the owner, Nicholas Meade Esq., of Earsham.

Published by The British Agricultural History Society, Department of History, University of Exeter,
Amory Building, Rennes Drive, Exeter
Typeset by Carnegie Publishing, Chatsworth Road, Lancaster
Printed and bound by The Alden Press, Oxford

Contents

Figures

Tables

Abbreviations

AgHR	*Agricultural History Review*
BPP	*British Parliamentary Papers*
EcHR	*Economic History Review* (second ser., 1948 –)
ESRO	East Suffolk Record Office
JRASE	*J. Royal Agricultural Society of England*
NRO	Norfolk Record Office
NRS	*Norfolk Record Society*
PP	Parliamentary Papers
PRO	Public Record Office, Kew
WSRO	West Suffolk Record Office

Acknowledgements

We would like to thank colleagues and students at the Centre of East Anglian Studies and the School of History, University of East Anglia, for help, information, and encouragement: especially the late Jim Holderness, A. Hassell Smith, Richard Wilson, Adam Longcroft, Jonathan Theobald, Anthony Stacey, Robert Liddiard, Jo Parmenter, Sarah Birtles, Keith Bacon, Anthea Taigel, and – above all – Kate Skipper, who carried out much of the documentary research concerning the Broads marshes and the central claylands.

The research presented here was principally funded by a generous grant from the ESRC, although various component projects were supported by Norfolk County Council, Suffolk County Council, the Broads Authority, and the University of East Anglia. The research on farm buildings was mainly carried out by a Community Service Programme team, co-directed by the late Alan Carter. The diagrams were drawn by Philip Judge.

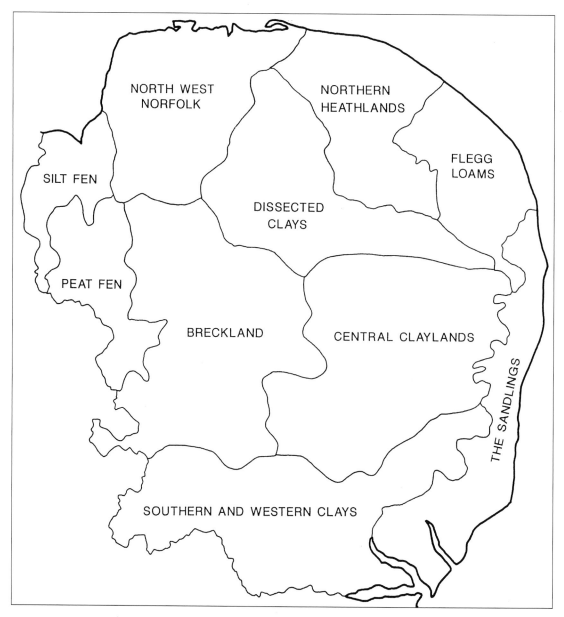

1. The principal landscape regions of East Anglia, as discussed in this volume.

CHAPTER I

The Farming Landscapes
of Norfolk and Suffolk

1. Debating the 'Agricultural Revolution'

The nature, timing and even the existence of an 'Agricultural Revolution' has been the subject of much debate over the past few decades. The traditional view, expressed by Ernle in his classic survey of 1912, was that the 'revolution' was essentially a phenomenon of the eighteenth and early-nineteenth centuries: an interconnected bundle of agrarian improvements initiated by a clique of progressive landowners, characterised by enclosure, and by a range of new husbandry practices, featuring new crops and rotations and improved breeds of livestock. The widespread adoption of these improvements raised yields and brought new land into cultivation, and thus allowed the expanding cities of the industrial revolution to be fed.[1]

The orthodox view of the eighteenth-century 'revolution' was challenged in the 1960s by Eric Kerridge. He suggested that the sixteenth and seventeenth centuries were, in fact, the period which saw the decisive break with medieval husbandry practices. The key developments were the introduction of convertible husbandry, the adoption of new crops, the drainage of marshland, and the construction of irrigated water meadows: in his view, the main force of change was spent before 1670.[2] Subsequent scholars attempted to do what Kerridge could not: quantify the scale of productivity increase, and demonstrate the extent to which the adoption of such practices actually raised crop yields. In the 1970s and 1980s Overton, Glennie, and Allen all used the evidence of probate inventories to calculate actual trends in crop yields during the early modern period, and all have showed that – with differing chronologies in the different regions which each was studying – yields were indeed rising significantly during the sixteenth and seventeenth centuries.[3]

Thompson meanwhile had distinguished a first agricultural revolution in the eighteenth century, involving enclosure and improved husbandry techniques; and a second, characterised by the buying-in of inputs such as animal feeds and artificial fertilisers, associated with the

[1] Lord Ernle (R. E. Prothero), *English Farming, Past and Present* (sixth edn, 1961).

[2] E. Kerridge, *The Agricultural Revolution* (1967); E. Kerridge, 'The Agricultural Revolution Reconsidered', *Agricultural Hist.*, 43 (1969), pp. 463–76.

[3] P. Glennie, 'Continuity and change in Hertfordshire agriculture, 1550–1700: trends in crop yields and their determinants', *AgHR* 36 (1988), pp. 145–61; id, 'Measuring crop yields in early modern England', in B. M. S. Campbell and M. Overton (eds), *Land, Labour and Livestock.*

Historical studies in European agricultural productivity (1991), pp. 255–83; R. C. Allen, 'The growth of labour productivity in early modern English agriculture', *Explorations in Economic History* 25 (1988), pp. 117–46; M. Overton, 'The determinants of crop yields in early modern England', in Campbell and Overton (eds), *Land, Labour and Livestock*, pp. 284–322; id, 'Estimating crop yields from probate inventories: an example from East Anglia 1585–1735', *JEcH* 39 (1979), pp. 363–78.

capital-intensive 'high farming' of the mid-nineteenth century.[4] According to this view, it was in the period after 1830 that the most significant improvements in agricultural productivity were achieved. Indeed, Mingay went further, seeing the hundred years up to 1850 merely as 'a base, or rather a preparation ... for the greater changes yet to come'.[5] At the other end of the chronological scale, however, Bruce Campbell demonstrated that even in the medieval period remarkable improvements could be made in the practice of agriculture. In parts of thirteenth-century Norfolk, fodder crops, principally peas and beans, were substituted for year-long fallows; fertilisers were assiduously applied; and high labour inputs provided yields which were well up to those of the post-medieval centuries.[6]

Not surprisingly, perhaps, in the light of all this research some scholars (notably Joan Thirsk) have come to question whether the term 'agricultural revolution' now has any real meaning.[7] Yet to see agricultural improvement as continuous or at least recurrent over the long term is not to deny that certain periods were characterised by particularly rapid rises in productivity; and whatever the scale of agricultural improvement in earlier centuries, the period between 1750 and 1850 was unquestionably one of these. As Beckett has argued, 'The primary task of the farming community was to feed the population, and if this is taken as the essential criterion for defining an agricultural revolution, the concept is clearly justified' in this period; and he continues by reminding us of Chambers and Mingay's argument that there must have been a phenomenal increase in food supplies between the mid-eighteenth and the mid-nineteenth centuries because the population of Britain increased by some 6.5 million, and yet was fed with the help of only minimal imports.[8] Indeed, Holderness has suggested that increases in output over this period were in the order of 225 per cent for wheat, 68 per cent for barley, and 65 per cent for oats.[9] The volume of livestock products displayed an equivalent rise: according to Beckett, 'An increase in output from slightly less than 6 million hundredweight a year in 1750 to over 12 million is not out of the question and may indeed be an under-estimate since it suggests a decline in per capita consumption'.[10] True, there remain a number of scholars, such as Robert Allen, who would emphasise the superior achievements of the previous two centuries.[11] But on the whole modern scholars agree that the traditional period of the agricultural revolution – c. 1700 – c. 1850 – was a time of momentous change, in which the output of English agriculture increased by a factor of around 3.5.[12]

What is also important is that these gains were achieved at the same time as an increase in labour productivity, which rose faster in England than elsewhere in Europe. Although the agricultural workforce probably expanded significantly in the period of the industrial revolution,

[4] F. M. L. Thompson, 'The second Agricultural Revolution', *EcHR* 21 (1968), pp. 62–77.

[5] G. E. Mingay (ed.), *The Agrarian History of England and Wales*, VI (1989), p. 971.

[6] B. Campbell, 'Agricultural progress in Medieval England: some evidence from East Norfolk', *EcHR* 36 (1983), pp. 26–46.

[7] J. Thirsk, *England's Agricultural Regions and Agrarian History, 1500–1750* (1987), pp. 57–8.

[8] J. V. Beckett, *The Agricultural Revolution* (1990), p. 9.

[9] B. A. Holderness, 'Prices, productivity and output', in *Agrarian History* VI, p. 145.

[10] Beckett, *Agricultural Revolution*, p. 55.

[11] R. C. Allen, 'The two English Agricultural Revolutions, 1450–1850', in Campbell and Overton (eds), *Land, Labour and Livestock*, pp. 236–54. R. C. Allen, *Enclosure and the Yeoman. The agricultural development of the south Midlands, 1450–1850* (1992).

[12] R. C. Allen, 'Agriculture during the Agricultural Revolution', in R. Floud and D. McCloskey (eds), *The economic history of Britain since 1700* (2 vols, second edn, 1994), I, p. 102.

it nevertheless did so at a slower rate than that involved in industry. In 1760 the output of each agricultural worker could feed around one other person: but by 1841 it could feed another 2.7. In short, the agricultural revolution allowed the industrial revolution to happen.[13]

Where did all the additional food come from? In part it came from the extension of good-quality agricultural land at the expense of unimproved 'waste'. Most authorities, however, agree that raising yields on *existing* arable land was the principal feature of the period, although there remains some disagreement about how this was achieved. Writers like Ernle or Chambers emphasised the key importance of more efficient farming practices resulting from the enclosure of open fields, and placed particular stress on the adoption of new crops, especially turnips and clover or 'artificial' grasses, combined in the classic Norfolk four-course rotation. These increased the amount of nitrogen – the key chemical removed by cropping – in the soil. Clover fixed nitrogen directly; turnips indirectly, by increasing the amount of stock which could be kept and thus the amount of dung (which also contained a range of other key chemicals) put on the land. The central importance of the new crops and rotations has, in effect, passed into historical orthodoxy: with O'Brien, for example, arguing that 'at the core of a protracted process was a set of fodder crops which offered a solution to the age-old problem of how to raise the capacity of farmland to carry more animals' – and thus increase the supply of manure.[14] A minority of scholars has, however, placed rather less emphasis on crops and rotations, stressing instead a wider range of improvements. Allen, for example, has suggested that a whole range of innovations contributed to increased yields in the eighteenth and early nineteenth centuries: better seeds; greater inputs of manure; marling and draining; and the use of seed drills and other improved farm machinery. 'Historians have not yet been able to pin down the relative importance of these factors, but together they were responsible for the rise in corn output'.[15]

With a few exceptions, recent explorations of agrarian change have tended to take the form *either* of grandiose econometric models, based in large measure on sources (such as the speculations of Gregory King) of at best uncertain value; *or* of detailed statistical studies of particular areas, utilising single bulk data sources, principally probate inventories. The research presented in the following pages adopts a rather different approach. It is our belief that because farming systems are related in infinitely complex and subtle ways not only to social and economic structures, but also to aspects of the natural environment, their development cannot really be understood by taking a broad-brush approach and juggling figures and statistics embracing the whole country. England in 1750 was still a highly regionalised economy. Indeed, even today generalisations about English agriculture as a whole are often misleading, or meaningless. Detailed study of a particular area also allows a range of different kinds of evidence – archaeological, as well as documentary – to be examined. This is particularly important because historians utilising single sources have tended to concentrate on single 'causes' of change. For example, those who have used probate inventories to study crop yields have, understandably enough, tended to explain any observed changes in terms of the other categories of information offered by this source: that is, in systems of cropping and livestock densities. Using a wider

[13] Beckett, *Agricultural Revolution*, p. 60.

[14] P. K. O'Brien, 'Agriculture and the home market for English industry, 1660–1820', *Eng. Hist. Rev.* 100 (1985), p. 781.

[15] Allen, 'Agriculture', p. 113.

range of sources allows us to examine a greater range of possibilities: and doing this within a limited area, and informed by a wider knowledge of its human and natural geography, permits us to move beyond sweeping generalisations and to focus on the practicalities of agriculture 'on the ground'. To some historians, such an unashamedly 'plough and cow' approach will at times seem excessively descriptive and insufficiently quantitative: and it is true that we have not attempted to quantify the unquantifiable, or build complex mathematical models on uncertain data. Statistical refinement is misleading where the data is patchy or its character uncertain. Doubtless some will criticise this volume for its lack of statistical rigour: but we would maintain that the regionally focused, multi-source approach adopted here can make a real contribution to our understanding of the processes of agricultural change. Others may believe that we have embraced wholeheartedly a conventional agricultural and economic agenda, paying insufficient attention to social aspects, to the lives of the poor: there may be some justification in this criticisim, but the latter matters have been admirably dealt with by other writers,[16] and social aspects will become relevant in the latter sections of this work.

In the study that follows we shall begin by describing East Anglia, and the characteristics of its various subregions, in the late seventeenth century. The subsequent chapters examine the pattern of change during the period of the classic 'agricultural revolution'. Chapter II deals with change in the *farming framework*: the physical environment, material culture, and organisational structure of farming. In this we discuss enclosure, changes in land-use, drainage, marling, tools and implements, farm buildings and changes in farm size. Chapter III, in contrast, examines *farming practice*: the kinds of crops grown, the rotations employed, and the organisation of livestock husbandry. We freely admit that this division between 'framework' and 'practice' is somewhat arbitrary, and to some extent cuts across that more familiar distinction, between the fixed capital and infrastructure supplied by the landlord, and the working capital supplied by the tenant. The reasons behind our choice of categories will, we hope, become apparent in the course of what follows. In Chapter IV the distinction between 'framework' and 'practice' is abandoned when the development of agriculture during the 'High Farming' period is discussed, for reasons which should again become evident. In Chapter V we consider the achievement of East Anglian agriculture across the whole period, from 1660 to 1870, examining what was gained, in terms of extending the cultivated acreage and raising crop yields. The last two chapters evaluate the contribution made by different kinds of 'improvement', and by different sections of the farming community, and attempt to explain East Anglia's prominence in the agricultural improvements of the eighteenth and early nineteenth centuries.

2. The Agricultural Revolution in East Anglia

The reputation of Norfolk as the most advanced agricultural county in England was established early: in 1742 an anonymous contributor to the *Gentleman's Magazine* was already singing the county's praises, and by 1771 Arthur Young was able to list the elements which made up a

---

[16] See J. M. Neeson, *Commoners. Common right, enclosure and social change in England 1700–1820* (1993); K. Snell, *Annals of the labouring poor. Social change and* *agrarian England, 1660–1900* (1985). For a criticism of 'conventional' concerns, see K. Snell, review of *Agrarian History VI*, in *J. Hist. Geog.* 17 (1991), pp. 195–203.

distinctive Norfolk 'system' of husbandry.[17] William Marshall was also convinced of the central role played by Norfolk in agricultural improvement, although he differed from Young in his interpretation of precisely who was responsible for the main innovations.[18] A succession of later historians, beginning with Lord Ernle, similarly emphasised the central role of Norfolk, and of certain pioneering aristocrats, especially Viscount Townshend in the 1730s and 1740s, and Thomas William Coke in the decades after 1776. Although the role of these aristocratic improvers has not, perhaps, stood the test of time, the pre-eminent role of the county in eighteenth-century agriculture has remained unchallenged: in Beckett's words, 'Norfolk led agricultural change just as Lancashire was in the forefront of industrial change'.[19]

Although Norfolk's importance has thus long been recognised, the only book entirely devoted to the county's agriculture in this period is Naomi Riches' *The Agricultural Revolution in Norfolk* of 1937. Riches relied heavily on the printed reports of Kent, Marshall and Young, as well as on the archives at Holkham. In a number of ways her work queried some of the assumptions made by Ernle. She supported the view, earlier expressed by Saunders, that Ernle had been mistaken in his assertion that turnip cultivation was effectively introduced by Townshend; or that marling was only practised in the period after 1730. Nevertheless, she endorsed (with some reservations) his more general assertions regarding the importance of Townshend and Coke.[20] The emphasis on the great estates of north west Norfolk was continued by Plumb, who in 1952 showed that on the Houghton estate, too, the cultivation of turnips had been established on a significant scale by the early eighteenth century.[21]

Parker, in an article of 1955 and – more comprehensively – in a book of 1975, presented evidence that challenged some aspects of the accepted story. He showed that while Coke may have been an 'eminent and successful landlord', whose estate was a model of the best farming practice, he could not be regarded as an innovator: his real role was as a public relations man, promoting new methods at his annual 'sheep shearings'.[22] If Coke's reputation thus underwent some further revision, his importance as an influence, if not as an innovator, remained; and the standing of that other noted 'improver', 'Turnip' Townshend, has escaped more or less unscathed, with Rosenheim's 1989 study showing him as a keen agriculturalist, actively encouraging the adoption of new rotations among his tenants, and embarking on ambitious and successful schemes of land improvement.[23]

There has, however, long been an alternative tradition, emphasising the agricultural importance of other districts of East Anglia. As early as 1787 Marshall suggested that it was *north east* Norfolk – a district of comparatively small estates – which had first pioneered the new rotations. More recently, in 1956 Kerridge showed how turnips and clover were being cultivated on a large scale on the claylands of south Norfolk and north Suffolk by the second half of the seventeenth century. Holderness, in the fifth volume of the *Agrarian History of England and Wales*, argued

[17] *Gentleman's Magazine* 12 (1752), p. 502.

[18] W. Marshall, *The Rural Economy of Norfolk* (2 vols, 1787), I, p. 2.

[19] Beckett, *Agricultural Revolution*, p. 68.

[20] N. Riches, *The Agricultural Revolution in Norfolk* (1937); H. W. Saunders, 'Estate management at Raynham, 1661–86 and 1706', *Norfolk Arch.*, 19 (1917), pp. 39–67.

[21] J. H. Plumb, 'Sir Robert Walpole and Norfolk husbandry', *EcHR* 5 (1952/3), pp. 86–9.

[22] R. A. C. Parker, *Coke of Norfolk: a financial and agricultural study, 1707–1842* (1975), p. 72.

[23] J. M. Rosenheim, *The Townshends of Raynham. Nobility in transition in Restoration and early Hanoverian England* (1989).

that the new rotations were first pioneered, probably from the 1680s, in east Norfolk: they were in use by the 1720s on all the good loams of the region, although whether they were standard practice 'remains doubtful'.[24] Mark Overton, using the evidence of probate inventories, likewise argued that the cultivation of turnips was first established, in the later seventeenth century, in north east Norfolk and on the claylands of north Suffolk and south Norfolk. But, working in part with Bruce Campbell, Overton has made a number of other, more important suggestions regarding the progress of East Anglian agriculture.[25]

Firstly, Overton has argued convincingly that turnips were originally grown, not by arable farmers in an attempt to increase supplies of manure and thus enhance yields, but by cattle farmers, looking for new sources of fodder. Only very gradually was the new crop adopted in predominantly arable, sheep-corn areas of East Anglia. Secondly, he pioneered the use of the information contained in probate inventories to chart actual changes in crop yields. His analysis suggested that cereal yields rose steadily though the seventeenth century, and were rising fast in the 1720s and 30s. In the period 1680–1709, average yields per acre in East Anglia of wheat and barley were 15.9 and 16.1 bushels respectively. Over the period 1710–1739, in contrast, the figures were 19.2 and 20.8 – a significant increase. He also looked ahead to the situation later in the century. By the 1760s, according to information presented in Arthur Young's *Farmer's Tour*, wheat yields had reached 26.5 bushels and barley 32.5 bushels per acre, although by 1801, according to the House of Lords *Report on the Dearth of Provisions*, they had dropped back to 22.4 and 32 respectively, and shortly afterwards – in 1804 – Young estimated that the average yield for wheat from the county as a whole was 24 bushels per acre. Thereafter yields continued to climb.[26]

Overton was cautious in offering any explanation for this impressive rise in yields. The large scale adoption of clover and turnips must have been a factor but cannot provide the entire explanation.[27] By the middle decades of the eighteenth century the cultivation of both crops was (to judge from inventory evidence) widespread, but the proportions of the cropped acreage devoted to each (3 per cent for clover, 8 per cent for turnips) were low.[28] Moreover, the full potential of the new crops was only realised when they were combined in regular rotations like the 'Norfolk four-course', but the available evidence suggests that such rotations were only very sparingly adopted before 1800. We shall see later that while many of Overton's suggestions are confirmed by a close examination of sources other than probate inventories, some may require modification.

Not surprisingly, perhaps, given the region's fame during the 'long' eighteenth century, few historians have paid much attention to the development of East Anglian farming in the middle decades of the nineteenth century. Contemporaries were certainly interested in the state of the region's agriculture, as is shown by R. N. Bacon's survey of Norfolk agriculture of 1844 or the Raynbirds' similar examination of Suffolk farming of 1849: but neither these sources, nor such material as the submissions made to the various Royal Commissions on agriculture, have been

[24] B. A. Holderness, 'East Anglia and the Fens', in J. Thirsk (ed.), *The Agrarian History of England and Wales*, V (i) (1984), pp. 197–238.

[25] Overton, 'Determinants'; B. M. S. Campbell and M. Overton, 'A new perspective on medieval and early modern agriculture; six centuries of Norfolk farming *c.* 1250–1850'. *Past and Present* 141 (1993), pp. 38–105.

[26] Overton, 'Determinants', pp. 298–305.

[27] Overton, 'Determinants', p. 314.

[28] *Ibid.*, p. 312.

much used by modern historians. The most important exceptions are Philip Roe, who in the early 1970s made an important study of 'High Farming' in Norfolk, based largely on the questionnaires collected from Norfolk farmers by Bacon to provide information for his book.[29] In addition, J. P. Dodd has used the agricultural statistics collected in 1854 by John Walsham to examine the state of East Anglian agriculture in the mid nineteenth century.[30] Mention should also be made of the invaluable maps presented by Kain in his *Tithe Atlas* of 1986, based on the information collected in the 1830s in connection with the commutation of parochial tithes.[31] As we shall see, the development of East Anglian agriculture in this period not only has an importance of its own: it also throws important light on the real character of 'improvement' in the previous period.

3. The background: farming regions in the late seventeenth century

Agricultural historians studying the eighteenth and nineteenth centuries have generally eschewed the kind of regional approach adopted by colleagues working in the early modern period.[32] The volumes of the *Agrarian History of England and Wales* covering the periods 1500–1640, and 1640–1750, were largely structured around a regional framework – unlike that more recently published, spanning the years 1750–1840. Nevertheless, the concept of the region remains problematic, as a comparison of, for example, the classificatory schemes proposed by Joan Thirsk and Eric Kerridge demonstrates.[33] Most regions have been defined through a combination of contemporary descriptions and documentary sources, of which probate inventories are the most important. But their configuration has usually been based on a study of geology or topography. That is, once a *general* impression of farming within a district is obtained, the *boundaries* of the 'region' are defined through a consideration of soil maps.

This issue has recently been considered by a number of historical geographers. In particular, Mark Overton has argued, in a study of East Anglian probate inventories, that farming practices did not, in fact, fall easily into spatially discrete 'regions', but instead exhibited a more complex and mixed pattern of distribution.[34] Nevertheless, while Overton's research does indeed demonstrate the spatial complexity of husbandry in the early modern period, an explicitly 'regional' approach will be adopted here. There are two reasons for this.

Firstly, to a large extent the diversity of farming enterprises highlighted by Overton is a consequence of the fact that, in terms of soils and topography, few regions represent homogenous topographic zones. Rather, the *essence* of regions is that they constitute two or more different types of terrain, found together within the same area and often interdigitated in highly complex ways. Thus, for example, regions of clay soil can combine level, poorly-draining

[29] P. Roe, 'Norfolk Agriculture in 1850' (unpublished M.Phil thesis, University of East Anglia, 1975).

[30] J. P. Dodd, 'Norfolk agriculture in 1853–4', *Norfolk Arch.* 36 (1976), pp. 252–64; id, 'Suffolk crop returns of 1854', *Proc. Suffolk Institute of Archaeology* 35 (1982), pp. 303–15.

[31] R. J. P. Kain, *An atlas and index of the tithe files of mid-nineteenth century England and Wales* (1986).

[32] See M. Overton, 'The Critical Century? The *Agrarian History of England and Wales 1750–1850*', [review in] *AgHR* 38 (1991), pp. 185–9.

[33] Thirsk, *Agricultural Regions and Agrarian History*.

[34] M. Overton, *Agricultural Regions in early modern England: an example from East Anglia*, (University of Newcastle upon Tyne, Dept. of Geography seminar papers 42, [nd])

plateaux *and* valleys which contain lighter soils: two very different topographic zones which are too intimately mingled to be disaggregated into separate 'regions', but which give rise to different landscapes and often interdependent agrarian practices. Secondly, a regional approach is adopted here because, as we shall argue, agricultural progress in the eighteenth century involved the gradual triumph over a range of 'limiting factors'. These varied from place to place, but included aspects both of the natural environment – of soils and topography – and of the human. In one area productivity might be limited by aspects of soil chemistry, in another by poor drainage, in a third by the nature of field systems, in a fourth by all three. These limiting factors were intimately related to aspects of the natural environment not only directly, but also indirectly: for the systems of agrarian organisation, including field systems, which the eighteenth-century 'improvers' inherited from the medieval past were themselves largely a response to the character of the local environment. It is, therefore, to drift geology, soils and related concerns that we must first turn.

East Anglia, as strictly and correctly defined, comprises the two most easterly counties in England, and the driest. No part of Norfolk or Suffolk receives (on average) more than 70cm of rainfall per year: parts of the Breckland regularly receive less than 55cm.[35] Moreover, the two counties have a geology characterised by relatively soft young rocks which have, in yet more recent times, been rubbed smooth by glacial erosion and smothered under glacial and periglacial deposits.[36] The resultant deep soils and muted terrain, combined with a dry climate, ensured that by later Saxon times this was the wealthiest, the most densely populated, and most economically precocious area in England, and Norwich the country's second largest city. These circumstances also ensured that wealth was widely distributed through society in the early medieval period, and that the power of manorial lords was relatively limited.

Largely as a consequence of all this the pattern of settlement and the organisation of field systems differed in a number of significant ways from the Midlands.[37] Nucleated villages, surrounded by open-fields carefully regulated by communal decision, were rare.[38] Even the most regulated field systems, in the west of the region, were more flexible than was usual in the Midlands: elsewhere communal regulation was often negligible and nowhere were the holdings of owners and tenants spread evenly across the arable territory of the vill, clustering instead in more restricted areas. And in parts of the region – most notably in southern Suffolk – open fields seem always to have been of limited extent. This absence of developed communal agriculture was mirrored in the pattern of settlement. Over much of the two counties village nucleations were rare and farms were widely scattered across the landscape, often hugging the edges of commons and greens.

East Anglia remained a prosperous and populous region right through the Middle Ages, although by the fourteenth century its wealth was based as much on textiles as on agriculture. At the start of our period, in *c.*1700, it was still economically buoyant and Norwich remained the second largest city in the kingdom although its position was now being challenged by Bristol.

---

[35] A. Grove, 'Climate', in F. Briers (ed.) *Norwich and its Region* (1961).

[36] G. Larwood and B. Funnell, *The Geology of Norfolk*, (1970); C. Hodge *et al.*, *Soils and their Uses in Eastern*

England (1984); H. Edlin, *East Anglian Forests* (1972), p. 5; T. Williamson, *The Origins of Norfolk* (1983), pp. 4–5.

[37] Williamson, *Origins*, pp. 105–136, 167–78.

[38] Campbell, 'Agricultural Progress'.

In the city the textile industry continued to flourish into the nineteenth century, but in rural areas it was in steady decline throughout the middle and later decades of the eighteenth century: in an important sense, East Anglia was a deindustrialising region during the period studied here. Rural population growth continued inexorably into the middle decades of the nineteenth century: under- and unemployment were the social background to all the changes in farming which will concern us in the chapters that follow.

In the final analysis East Anglia's geology determined the character of its various agrarian economies. The region's basic structure comprises a series of sedimentary deposits which were laid down in sequence and then raised and tilted so that the earliest are only exposed in the north-west of Norfolk – as a narrow and varied strip of country forming a low escarpment between Hilgay and Hunstanton.[39] The latest of these deposits, and that forming the main body of this escarpment, is the chalk which, dipping towards the south and east, is buried ever deeper beneath more deposits. In the east it is obscured by as much as 200 metres of Crag deposits – a varied collection of Pliocene and Pleistocene gravels, clays, and shelly sands – except in the extreme south east of Suffolk, where it is masked by other Tertiary deposits, sands and gravels and London clay.

This simple basic pattern is, however, largely obscured by a diverse range of glacial deposits. Across the centre of East Anglia, in a great curving band which extends south westwards into Essex and Hertfordshire, a thick mantle of boulder clay forms a slightly tilted plateau, dissected to varying degrees by river valleys. The clays themselves are of varied composition, in places containing quantities of chalk, elsewhere sandier and more acid in nature. To the north and west of this clay belt, and to the south and east, the glaciations had a different effect. Here meltwaters and high winds deposited a range of sands and gravels which gave rise to an equally diverse range of soils. In the extreme east and west of East Anglia, in the Fens and in the area generally known as the Norfolk Broads, still more recent deposits determine the character of the local soils, marine and alluvial silts, and peat.

In the following pages we define ten regions, associated with these varied soil patterns, which provide the framework for much of the discussion that follows. Not only did each of these regions display a distinctive repertoire of landscapes, and farming patterns, in the early modern period; each also followed its own trajectory of development in the eighteenth and early nineteenth centuries – experiencing, as it were, its own 'agricultural revolution'.

(i) North-West Norfolk

North-West Norfolk, as defined in Figure one, occupies an area of *c.* 950 square kilometres. It is an area of light, freely-draining soils which was already, by the late seventeenth century, dominated by large landed estates like Holkham, Houghton, Hunstanton, and Raynham. This is, in essence, the area described by Arthur Young in 1804 as the 'Good Sands' district and it exemplifies, in a striking manner, the principle that agricultural regions often comprise two or more quite distinct kinds of natural terrain. The underlying chalk outcrops on the northern and western fringes of the region, beside the coast, and also in the valleys of the principal rivers. It gives rise to the deep and well-drained soils of the *Newmarket 2 Association* and, along the

---

[39] Edlin, *Forests*, p. 5; Larwood and Funnel, *Geology of Norfolk.*

north coast, the particularly fertile soils of the *Hunstanton Association*.[40] Elsewhere, however –
in the 'uplands' – the chalk is overlain by acid, sandy drift, giving rise to the less fertile soils
of the *Barrow Association*.[41] The uplands were settled later than the valleys: problems of lime
deficiency were compounded by the absence of reliable water supplies, for water could only be
obtained from ponds formed in the patches of boulder clay that sporadically occur within the
sandy drift. While some of the settlements in upland locations are, and have long been, sizeable,
many – and especially those whose parishes largely comprise plateau drift rather than calcareous
soils – are small. Many, indeed, had experienced drastic shrinkage in late medieval and early
and post-medieval times. It was here that the large estates which characterised the region in
post-medieval times – Holkham, Houghton, Raynham and the rest – normally had their
heartlands.

It is this distinction, between the acid, waterless uplands, and the more fertile lowlands, which
structures the history of the region and which explains some otherwise curious features of its
development. In particular, it goes a long way towards explaining the region's superficially
contradictory enclosure history. North-West Norfolk is often considered as the main arena of
mid-eighteenth-century improvement, and contemporary visitors like Young reported a landscape of large enclosed farms. Yet this is also the region with the highest incidence of late
eighteenth-century parliamentary enclosure in East Anglia.[42] The explanation for this apparent
contradiction lies, of course, in the distinction between upland and valley. The early-enclosed
farms generally lay in parishes largely composed of the poorer upland soils, which had usually
experienced a degree of late medieval depopulation: in such places open fields and commons
had often completely disappeared by the start of the period being studied here.[43] Most parishes
with extensive areas of calcareous valley soils, in contrast, remained populous and largely
unenclosed at the end of the seventeenth century, and usually for long after: places like
Hunstanton, shown on a map of *c.*1700 (Figure 2); or North Creake, where a survey of 1600
shows a landscape almost entirely occupied by open fields or, on the higher ground, open
commons. Some piecemeal enclosure had taken place here, but the parish remained largely
open until 3,600 acres were enclosed by parliamentary act in 1809.

Sedgeford is a typical example. The village is located in the upper part of the valley of the
Heacham River. The soils of the lower ground are calcareous loams of the *Newmarket 2
Association*: the higher ground, towards the periphery of the parish, consists of the acid soils of
the *Barrow Association*. A parliamentary Survey of the Dean and Chapter lands, which occupied
some 1585 acres of the total of 4140 acres in the parish, was drawn up around 1649.[44] This
shows that there was very little meadow and enclosed pasture land in the parish: only 36.75
acres, *c.*2.5 per cent of the Chapter's holding, consisted of grass closes (one had recently been
converted to arable). Most of the land lay in strips 'intermixed and undivided with customary
and other lands'. These were divided between the 'infield lands' on the better soils, and the

[40] Hodge *et al*, *Soils*, pp. 225–7, 268–9.

[41] *Ibid.*, pp. 107–11.

[42] M. Turner, 'Parliamentary Enclosure', in P. Wade-
Martins (ed.), *An historical atlas of Norfolk* (1993),
pp. 124–5.

[43] See in particular the maps of Rougham, 1713 (in

private ownership: reproduced in part in A. Taigel and
T. Williamson, 'Some early geometric gardens in Nor-
folk': *J. Garden Hist.* 11 (1991), p. 109); Houghton 1720
(Houghton Ms, Map 1); Holkham 1728 (Holkham Ms, 5);
West Acre High House 1726 (NRO, BL 14/28).

[44] NRO, LeStrange OC 1; DCN 51/91.

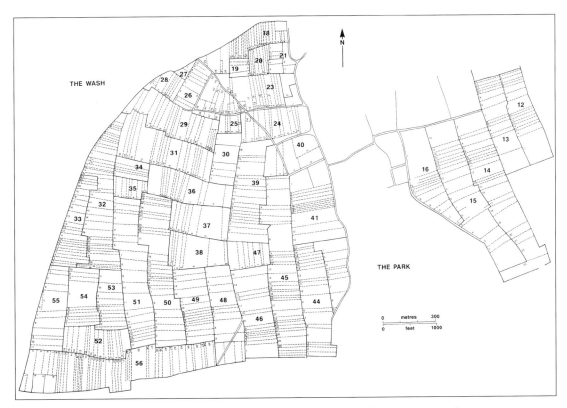

2. The open fields of Hunstanton in north-west Norfolk, as shown on a map of *c.* 1700.

'brecks', or areas of temporary cultivation, five-eighth of which were under cultivation at any one time. Open heathland covered some 18 per cent of the area of the manor; the outfield brecks occupied 58 per cent; the permanent arable less than 20 per cent.

The same survey informs us that there was a *foldcourse* for 1200 sheep belonging to the manor

> which are to be kept in this manner, viz partly upon the common ... partly upon the shack of all the arrable ground whether they be customary, freehold or demesne lands ... and partly on the lands or unplowed ground of the said Brecks whereof five parts of the whole into eight being divided are every year to lye and lay for pasture ...

It was the foldcourse which distinguished East Anglian sheep-corn husbandry from that practised in other light-land regions of England, such as the South Downs or Wessex. In all such systems, arable cultivation was dependent upon large flocks, grazed by day on the upland heaths and by night systematically folded or 'tathed' on portions of the arable, thus ensuring a continuous flow of nutrients onto the easily-leached soils. In the East Anglian foldcourse system, however, arrangements for folding were highly systematised, and firmly controlled by the manorial lord.[45] The flocks were dominated by the stock of the lord (or his lessee) which

---

[45] K. J. Allison, 'The sheep-corn husbandry of Norfolk in the sixteenth and seventeenth centuries', *AgHR* 5 (1957), pp. 12–30; M. Bailey, *A Marginal Economy? East Anglian Breckland in the later middle ages* (1989).

ranged over both heath and arable land when it lay fallow or before sowing in autumn or spring. Because there was often more than one manor in a village, the fields and commons were divided into separate, normally continuous blocks known as 'foldcourses' which, like the East Anglian manor itself, often extended across parish boundaries. Originally devised as a way of ensuring that the demesne arable received more than its fair share of manure, in post-medieval times the essence of the institution changed. The foldcourse became a way of keeping large commercial flocks, from which the manorial lord or his flock-master lessee excluded the stock of the tenants.

We shall discuss in more detail the kinds of arable husbandry practised in the open fields at the start of the period: suffice to say at this juncture that barley was the dominant crop on the better soils, rye was largely restricted to the poorer. Wheat and peas were extensively grown and clover was already a common crop. Land was usually fallowed every four or five years. Less is known about the husbandry practices on the enclosed upland farms of the region but some at least seem to have consisted largely of pasture ground. These farms, often marking the sites of deserted medieval hamlets and villages, could be very extensive. Waterden Farm, for example, occupied in 1713 more or less the whole of the area of the parish, a total of 805 acres.[46]

At Sedgeford, as we have seen, only *c.* 20 per cent of the land area was under permanent cultivation in the mid-seventeenth century, and although the cropped area of the brecks would have contributed a further 36 per cent it seems likely, allowing for fallowing, that less than 40 per cent of the land area was under crops at any one time. In other parishes the relative proportions of heath, breck and infield might vary but the area under crops seldom exceeded 50 per cent, unless – as at Hunstanton – the parish lay almost entirely within an area of calcareous loams.

(ii) *Breckland*

Our second main region, Breckland, lies to the south of that just discussed and, as defined in Figure one, occupies an area of around 1530 square kilometres. It was, and is, the least fertile region in East Anglia. Problems of low rainfall and sharp late frosts are compounded by the nature of the local soils. Acid sands lie directly upon the ice-weathered surface of the porous chalk: droughtiness and acidity were the key problems faced by arable farmers.[47] The soils fall mainly within the *Newmarket 1* and *Worlington Associations*, although those of the *Newport 4* and *Methwold Associations* are also prominent.[48] Worlington and Newport soils occupy the higher ground: they are strongly acid and very permeable. Newmarket and Methwold soils, characteristic of the valley sides, are more amenable to early agriculture: they are formed in part in the chalk or chalky drift but are nevertheless fairly acid, due to excessive leaching. This basic distinction between the moderately poor soils within the principle valleys, and the *very* poor soils on the interfluves, structured land use: the arable was largely located in the former locations, the latter were occupied by heaths or, in some places, manorial rabbit warrens. It must be stressed, however, that even the better soils of Breckland were poor by East Anglian standards, and often unstable, prone to wind erosion. Thus an agreement made between George

---

[46] NRO, MS 21130 179 X 4.
[47] Williamson, *Origins*, pp. 11–13, 21, 35, 125.

[48] Hodge *et al*, *Soils*, pp. 265–7, 277–9, 368–70.

Foxe, tenant of a farm near Merton Park, and the Walsingham estate in 1782 noted: 'In consideration of Lord Walsingham's permission to break up the north part of Mill Hill Break, I do hereby promise to pay all expenses of clearing land that may blow from the said piece of land into the park'.[49]

In terms of agricultural practices, this region is best considered as a more extreme version of that just discussed. Here, too, seventeenth-century agriculture was structured around the foldcourse and the outfield breck.[50] Given the relatively poor nature of the arable land, and the importance of sheep in the economy, foldcourses were of considerable importance to their owners. In 1624 Robert Lord derived the staggering sum of £522 from his Elveden foldcourse (£31 for skins and pelts, £259 for hoggets and lambs, £83 for crones and £149 for 79 stone of wool).[51]

Breckland also exhibits the contrast we have already noted in North-West Norfolk, between areas of comparatively early, and those of comparatively late, enclosure. There were many parishes from which the population had haemorrhaged in the fifteenth and sixteenth centuries, and which were already completely enclosed before the end of the seventeenth: parishes like West Tofts, Buckenham Tofts, Lynford or Santon Downham. Some contained little or no arable, such as Wordwell, which consisted of a single farm in 1736, 'the chief profits whereof arise from a flock of sheep, the soil being for the most part a barren dry heath a very bleak place'.[52] Such parishes often formed the core of large landed estates, which systematically bought out small proprietors in neighbouring parishes, often gaining complete control of these (and effecting total enclosure) in the course of the eighteenth century. Elsewhere, however, viable agricultural communities survived: such places sometimes experienced little piecemeal enclosure before enclosure by parliamentary act in the late eighteenth or early nineteenth centuries.

Today, the soils of Breckland are mainly classified as Grade 4 or Grade 5 agricultural land. Even at the end of the eighteenth century, to judge from the county maps published by Faden (Norfolk, 1797) and Hodskinson (Suffolk, 1783), around 40 per cent of the land area was occupied by heaths and warrens (Figure three). At the start of the eighteenth century this figure was probably in excess of 65 per cent. Here indeed the agricultural improvers found a worthy challenge, a desert waiting to bloom.

(iii) *The Northern Heathlands*

Modern historians, when discussing the agrarian regions of Norfolk, often group the whole of the north east of the county together as a single region, one of 'fertile soils'. Earlier generations knew better. Marshall for example, writing in 1787, made a distinction between the excellent soils of the 'southern hundreds' – that is, the hundreds of East and West Flegg, South Walsham, and Blofield – and the 'less genial soils' which characterised the rest of the region. Although there were areas with a 'stronger, fertile' soil in the latter district, much was light and shallow, and there were extensive areas of 'barren heaths and unproductive sands'.[53] This general

[49] NRO, WLS LXI/1/7 430 X 5.

[50] W. G. Clarke, *In Breckland Wilds* (1925); M. R. Post-gate, 'The field systems of Breckland', *AgHR* 10 (1962), pp. 80–101; idem., 'Historical Geography of Breckland 1600 to 1850' (unpublished MA thesis, University of London, 1960).

[51] ESRO, Iveagh MS, HD 1538/212/1.

[52] C. Paine, 'West Suffolk: a study of village decay and depopulation' (unpublished typescript held by WSRO).

[53] Marshall, *Rural Economy*, II, p. 188.

3. The landscape of Breckland in the late eighteenth century, as depicted on William Faden's map
of Norfolk, 1797.

distinction was mirrored by Arthur Young in 1804[54] and is echoed in the tithe files of 1838/9, which enthuse about the Flegg soils, but which often emphasise the poor quality of those in parishes further west. Heydon, for example, is described as a parish in which

> The land is most of it very inferior, the best of it near the village is a thin soil and that at a distance is either a sharp gravel or a mixture of black land neither of which will produce much corn and the turnips are also very bad.[55]

The distinction made by these sources corresponds, in broad terms, with the categories mapped by the Soil Survey of England and Wales. Marshall's 'southern hundreds', together with most of Happing and Tunstead, and parts of Erpingham, are dominated by soils of the

---

[54] A. Young, *General View of the Agriculture of Norfolk*   [55] PRO, IR 18/6336.
(1804), pp. 12–14.

Wick 2 Association: deep, fertile, loamy soils formed over sandy glacio-fluvial till and coverloam. These soils also occur in the north and west of the area – in the hundreds of Taverham, Holt, across much of North and South Erpingham, and through the eastern side of Eynsford – but they here constitute a smaller proportion of the land surface, which is dominated instead by soils of the *Wick 1 Association* – similar but shallower and more stony soils – and by those of the *Newport 1, 2,* and *3,* and the *Felthorpe Associations*: shallow sandy soils, acid and infertile, similar to those found in Breckland.[56] The distinction between these two broad regions is compounded by the fact that the area of the 'southern hundreds' includes extensive areas of low-lying and fen, whose presence had an important effect on the development of the local agrarian economy.

As defined in Figure one, the less fertile of these two regions – the *Northern Heathlands* – covers an area of *c.*800 square kilometres. The extensive areas of poorer soils on the principal interfluves, and on the Holt-Cromer ridge in the north of the district, were still in the late eighteenth century occupied by vast tracts of heath, dividing the ribbons of more fertile soils in the principal river valleys (those of the Ant, Bure, Wensum and their principal tributaries). The floors of the latter contained large areas of meadow land, and in general the region was a well-watered one (in contrast to Breckland and much of the North-West Norfolk), with few places more than 1.5 kilometres from reasonable supplies of running water. The settlement pattern has, since medieval times, been predominantly dispersed, taking the form of common-edge settlements, many strung out along the edge of the valley-floor meadows. In spite of the poverty of the soil the region was densely populated by late medieval times, and also wealthy, largely on account of the textile industry which developed in the vicinity of Aylsham, North Walsham and Worstead.[57]

Unlike North-West Norfolk or Breckland, both of which became increasingly dominated in the course of the post-medieval period by very large landed estates, the Northern Heathlands was characterised by a more complex mixture of landholding units, including both large estates (Blickling, Wolterton, Gunton) and smaller gentry properties. The poor quality and low price of land here, coupled with an essentially arable-based economy, ensured the gradual attrition of small owner-occupiers. Yet at the same time the region's proximity to Norwich ensured that it was a popular place for the gentry to reside: William Faden's map of the county (Figure 3) shows it peppered with their houses and parks.

Marshall in 1786 stressed the essentially arable nature of the region: '… viewing the District at large, the grassland bears so small a proportion to the arable, that its distinguishing characteristic is that of an arable country'. Yet, while this may have been the case if we consider only the relevant acreages of particular farms, taking the region as a whole the statement is misleading. Analysis of Faden's map of 1797 suggests that less than 65 per cent of the region was actually under arable cultivation. A substantial area – no less than 13,000 hectares (*c.*17 per cent of the total area) – was still occupied by common land, comprising some low-lying fen grounds but mainly open heathland. It is difficult to estimate the proportion of arable at the start of the

---

[56] Hodge *et al, Soils*, pp. 345–9.
[57] K. J. Allison, 'The Norfolk worsted industry in the sixteenth and seventeenth centuries', *Yorkshire Bulletin of* *Economic and Social Research* 12 (1960), pp. 74–82; 13 (1961), pp. 61–77.

period covered by this study, but it can hardly have been more and may well have been significantly less. The extent to which such land lay in open fields also remains unclear. Early maps suggest considerable variation. On the one hand, there were some parishes – such as Horstead, surveyed in 1699 – which were already entirely enclosed by this time.[58] Following the pattern we have already noted in other regions, these were usually small parishes, with a single proprietor, sometimes in marginal locations. On the other hand, there were many places in which extensive areas of open field, as well as commons, survived until the end of the eighteenth century: Horsford for example still had 1022 acres of open arable as late as 1802.[59] Most parishes, however, lay between these extremes: they had generally experienced a significant degree of piecemeal enclosure at the start of the period, yet still retained large tracts of open arable. A map of Cawston, for example, dating to *c*.1600, shows that only half of the arable remained in open fields (Figure 4).[60] The rest lay in enclosures whose sinuous boundaries indicate that they had been enclosed piecemeal from the open field furlongs. Indeed, the map distinguishes between lands enclosed within the previous forty years, and those more anciently enclosed.

The region's agriculture in the early modern period was broadly similar to that of North-West Norfolk or the Breckland – that is, it was based on the cultivation of wheat, rye and especially barley – although farmers here seem to have maintained rather larger numbers of bullocks and milking cattle, due no doubt to the extensive areas of meadows and marsh on the floors of the principal valleys. There was, however, an important institutional difference between the Northern Heathlands and the regions so far discussed. Although sheep flocks were grazed by day on the heaths and folded by night upon the arable, foldcourses *per se* were of minor importance. Although they existed in a number of parishes – Cawston, for example, had one – even in medieval times they had been absent from many vills, a circumstance which has generally (and plausibly) been attributed to the relative weakness of manorial authority here.

In common with Breckland and North-West Norfolk the main environmental problem facing arable farmers here was the extreme acidity of much of the soil. Indeed, sampling by MAFF between April 1950 and March 1951 singled out the Aylsham-Sheringham-Mundesley-North Walsham district as the most seriously lime-deficient area of Norfolk.[61]

(iv) *The Flegg Loams*

This region, covering an area of *c*.590 square kilometres, could scarcely be more different. The soils of Flegg and the 'southern hundreds' were renowned in the eighteenth century. Arthur Young's comments were typical:

> One of the most interesting circumstances in the husbandry of Norfolk, is the soil of Flegg hundred; and much in Blowfield and Walsham hundreds is of the same quality; it is sandy loam, from two to three feet deep, and much of it as good at bottom as on the surface; of so happy a texture that almost any season suits it ... So fertile a soil I have very rarely seen of so pale a colour ...[62]

---

[58] Private collection: reproduced in Taigel and Williamson, 'Some early geometric gardens in Norfolk'.

[59] W. E. Tate, *A Domesday of English Enclosure Acts and Awards* (1978), p. 179.

[60] NRO, MS4521, map box 6.

[61] PRO, MAFF 105: Eastern Region Records. Report of the County Agricultural Officer [Norfolk], April 1952.

[62] Young, *Norfolk*, p. 12.

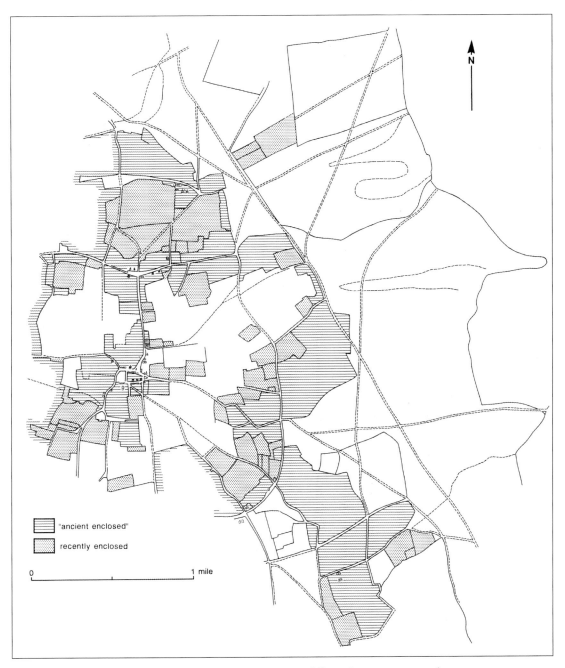

4. The progress of enclosure in Cawston, Norfolk, as shown on a map of *c.*1600.

Even today the soils of the *Wick 2 Association* are rated among the best arable land in England, almost all classified as Grade 1 by MAFF. Not surprisingly, the region was one of the most densely settled regions in medieval England. Moreover, as Campbell has demonstrated, by the thirteenth century it also boasted one of the most advanced agricultural systems in the country, in which the ground was thoroughly prepared for cultivation, crops systematically weeded, and livestock stall-fed on both hay and fodder crops. As a result crop yields were raised to levels which were not to be surpassed until the eighteenth century. The area was weakly manorialised, foldcourses were largely absent, and cropping extremely flexible. Open fields were ubiquitous – occupying almost all the land except the commons, and some limited areas of enclosed demesne – but they were very poorly regulated, 'common' only to the extent that tenants had the right to graze after the harvest shack

Open fields continued to dominate the landscape well into the post-medieval period. Thus a map of Herringby and Stokesby, surveyed in 1659, shows most of the two parishes occupied by open-field strips, interspersed with only occasional closes, and the same is true of a 1582 map of Smallburgh.[63] Indeed, in many places large areas of open fields persisted into the nineteenth century. Most of Scratby remained unenclosed until the 1840s, while almost all the arable land in Winterton remained open until the enclosure of 1811.[64] By the seventeenth century there was very little woodland in the region. Heaths and other upland commons of were also of limited extent, a reflection of the good quality of the upland soils, and of the area's long history of dense settlement.

Eighteenth-century commentators claimed that this was an area in which small proprietors were very thick on the ground, and while something of an exaggeration, this was nevertheless not an area dominated by large unitary landed estates. Indeed, William Faden's map of 1797 shows an almost complete absence of landscape parks in this region, in stark contrast to the Northern Heathland district to the west.

By the sixteenth and seventeenth centuries the area was densely settled but much less industrialised and urbanised than the Heathlands to the west. Probate inventories show it as a district in which sheep were of some importance, but in which dairying (and in particular butter-production), together with the fattening of young cattle, were of the greatest significance. In part, this reflected the existence of extensive fens and marshes in the area now known as 'Broadland'. The main area of marsh occupied a great triangular wedge of silts and clays, a former estuary, where the principal rivers draining eastern Norfolk (the Yare, Bure, Waveney, Thurne, Ant and Chet) having gradually joined, discharge into the North Sea. This area, often referred to for convenience as the Halvergate 'triangle', had long been held in severalty and reasonably well drained. Defoe, writing in 1722, described this area in glowing terms:

> In this vast tract of meadows are fed a prodigious number of black cattle, which are said to be fed up for the fattest beef, though not the largest in England; and the quantity is so great, as they not only supply the city of Norwich, the town of Yarmouth, and the county adjacent, but send great quantities of them weekly in all the winter season to London.[65]

The records of the Sea Breach Commission – established in 1609 to maintain the sea defences around the headwaters of the River Thurne between Happisburgh and Winterton – indicate that in the seventeenth century the bulk of the marsh was already privately owned. Indeed, the minute books for 1616, and lists of rate payers for 1702 and 1715, suggest that at this time there

[63] NRO, Acc. 4.3.86: above P152A.

[64] K. Bacon, 'Enclosure in East Norfolk' (unpublished MA Dissertation, Centre of East Anglian Studies, University of East Anglia, 1993), pp. 14–28.

[65] D. Defoe. *The Tour through the Whole Island of Great Britain, 1722* (Penguin edn, 1976), p. 88.

was roughly the same amount of common land as there was to be at the start of the nineteenth century. The same records suggest that land ownership and tenure within the marshes was highly fragmented, and that at the start of our period the situation described by Marshall in 1787 apparently already pertained:

> The inclosures, or 'marshes', run from ten to fifteen to forty or fifty acres each; belong to a variety of owners; and are rented by a still greater number of occupiers; almost every farmer, within fifteen or even twenty miles, having his marsh.[66]

Because of this, the construction and maintenance of banks and sluices was usually a co-operative endeavour. Thus, for example, a document of 1675, relating to marshes in Raveningham (in the extreme south of the Halvergate 'triangle') describes

> The Severall Marshes with theire Quantities which have theire Drayn through the Sluice Lyinge between Glover Denny gent. and Francis Langley and ought to be Chargeable toward the Renewinge and repayers of the Sayd Sluice'.

Fourteen different landowners, with holdings ranging in size from four to sixty five acres, contributed (the total cost was £4 2s. 6d., the total amount collected – at 6d. per acre – came to £4 6s. 6d. leaving 4s. 6d. in hand).[67]

This fragmented landholding pattern, together with the extensive area of the marsh, explains the vital importance of the marshmen in the local economy. Marshall described in 1787 how

> The stock are under the care of *marshmen*, who live in cottages scattered over the Marshes: – each having his district, or "level of marshes", to look after. His perquisite is a shilling upon the pound-rent, which is sometimes paid by the landlord but more generally by the tenant.[68]

The system was a long established one, and isolated 'marsh houses' existed in medieval times – a number are known as a result of recent archaeological fieldwork, and they are sporadically referred to in documentary sources.[69] In the medieval period sheep were the principal animals grazed on the marsh, but by the sixteenth century they were being displaced by cattle. Already in 1589 Nicholas Bishop of Halvergate died owning 16 'neates', 16 yearlings, three steers and a 'bolle': while the following year John Dymonde of Halvergate possessed, among other stock, '5 bullockes boughte at Hopton fayre', together with '3 milche neate and a bull'.[70] By the following century, the practice of buying in store cattle, many from highland areas of Britain, was well-established. Defoe in 1722 described how most of the 'prodigious number of black cattle' fed on the marsh were Scots 'runts', brought down yearly to Horsham fair.[71]

Whereas the broad expanses of marsh in the Halvergate 'triangle' had, for the most part, always been held as private property, in the upper valleys of the main rivers the majority of the land – some on silts and clays, some on acid peat – remained as common until well into the post-medieval period. Some of these areas – especially those occupying the silt deposits –

[66] Marshall, *Rural Economy,* II, p. 278.
[67] NRO, KNY 27.
[68] Marshall, *Rural Economy,* II, p. 280.
[69] T. Williamson, *The Norfolk Broads: a landscape history* (1997), pp. 40–50.
[70] NRO, 9/96 Inv 5/131; Inv 9/197.
[71] Defoe, *Tour,* p. 88

were primarily used as grazing marsh. Others – those on the damper peat – were principally mown, for a variety of products, and here grazing was a subsidiary use. As Marshall explained in 1787:

> The produce and principal use of a fen are totally different from those of a grazing marsh. The profits of a fen arise, in general, from Reed and gladdon, cut for thatch for buildings. Sedge and rushes, for litter; and thatch, for hay and corn-ricks, and sometimes for buildings. Coarse grass, for fodder, and sometimes for pasturage; – and Peat for fuel.[72]

Large areas were cut for 'marsh hay', a mixture of fen grasses and rushes (principally *Juncus subnodulosus* and *Juncus effusus*), which was used for cattle fodder or litter: some sections were mown for sedge (*Cladium mariscus*) and for reeds (*Phragmites australis*) used for thatching. Rushes were cut for lights, and for domestic flooring; 'gladdon' or lesser reed-mace (*Typha angustifolia*) and yellow flag (*Iris pseudacorus*) were harvested for basket-making. The commons were also extensively cut for peat, although on a more casual basis than in the early middle ages, when intensive extraction had led to the formation of the large lakes or 'broads' which give the district its popular name.

Eighteenth- and nineteenth-century agricultural writers regularly bemoaned the poor management of the Broadland commons but – as keen advocates of enclosure and 'improvement' – they exaggerated their deficiencies. Far from being waterlogged quagmires which it was no-one's business to drain, they were generally well-regulated, and the grazing marshes often carefully drained and protected. At Beccles, in 1552 alone 950 rods of dyke, all belonging to 'the comen fenne', were 'drawne and skorrede'. Numerous payments were also made for maintaining the causeways which provided access to it; while the 'dams', walls and principal drainage dykes were reinforced with faggots.[73] In most parishes a rate was levied to pay for such maintenance works. At Martham in the sixteenth century this was raised specifically for 'casting, carting, or other repairing or drayning of the common'.[74] At Cantley in the early eighteenth century all commoners had to pay three shillings a year for each bullock grazed on the common marsh, 'for the repairs of the Walls, Banks, Sluices, Ditches Drains Gates and Fences of the Said Common'. This custom was changed in 1728 to a more flexible system, by which a committee of five (one of whom was always the rector), chosen by the commoners, would decide each year what works were required, and levy a rate accordingly.[75]

Compared with other regions of East Anglia, there were few 'limiting factors' constraining the agricultural productivity of the Flegg Loam Region, and comparatively little opportunity for expanding the area under cultivation. The arable soils of the uplands were deep, fertile, and well drained, and suffered to only a limited extent from acidity. The marshes provided excellent grazing, although capable of some improvement through better drainage. It was the fens of the upper valleys which, as we shall see, contemporary improvers thought capable of better use, although their activities were to meet with only limited success.

[72] Marshall, *Rural Economy*, I, pp. 319–20.
[73] Beccles Town Hall, Beccles Fen reeves account, 1552.
[74] B. Cornford, 'The commons of Flegg in the medieval and early modern periods', in M. Manning (ed.), *Commons in Norfolk* (1988), pp. 14–20.
[75] NRO, MC 76/1.

(v) *The Central Claylands*

The East Anglian claylands occupy, in all, some 3900 square kilometres in a great arc running through the centre of the region. They do not, however, constitute an homogenous zone. There are important differences between central Norfolk (highly dissected, gently rolling, with muted relief and extensive areas of sandy and gravelly soils); southern and western Suffolk (more deeply dissected and undulating, and with more calcareous soils); and the central heart of the region, in north Suffolk and south Norfolk. It is this latter district which we will first consider.

This *Central Clayland* region – a total of *c.*1560 square kilometres – comprises a low drift-covered plateau, seldom rising above 55 metres OD, which is dissected by the valleys of the Waveney, Tas and Dove, together with the various streams, such as the Broome Beck, feeding in to these. The soils on the sides of the principal valleys are lighter, and often sandier, than those on the more level interfluves, generally falling within the *Burlingham 1* and *3*, the *Ashley*, and the *Hanslope Associations*. Because they lie on a gradient they are easier to drain with furrows and field ditches, and therefore more amenable to early agriculture, than those of the level interfluve areas.[76] The latter, in contrast – those of the *Beccles III Association* – are heavy and particularly poorly-draining, especially where slight concave depressions occur in the plateau surface. They are also mildly acidic in their natural state, due to the high water table. When effectively drained, however, all the clayland soils are reasonably fertile and today all are classified as Grade 2 or Grade 3 arable land.

Early maps, such as that of Scole in Norfolk, of *c.*1590 (Figure 5), show that the medieval landscape in the principal valleys largely consisted of arable open fields.[77] Documentary and cartographic evidence suggests that some of the heavier land on the interfluves was also farmed as subdivided arable, although here a greater proportion was occupied by enclosed fields (arable or pasture) or by areas common grazing, managed woodland, or deer parks.[78] Some of the closes had been reclaimed direct from the 'waste' at a relatively late stage in the colonisation process, and often occupied extensive areas: a survey of Redgrave in 1540 described 'One Close called Great Stubbynges … containing by estimation 72 acres'.[79]

Like the open fields elsewhere in East Anglia, those of the claylands were of 'irregular' type, and the pattern of settlement was correspondingly dispersed, consisting for the most part of scattered farms and hamlets, often forming girdles around the margins of greens and commons.[80] There were few village nucleations and – as a consequence of settlement mobility in the early middle ages – parish churches often stood on the edge of settlements, or quite isolated in the midst of fields.[81]

By the sixteenth century, the economy had come to specialise, to a greater degree than

[76] Hodge *et al, Soils*, pp. 117–23, 132–8.

[77] ESRO, MD 417/61 4074/47.

[78] A. Davison, 'The evolution of settlement in three parishes in south east Norfolk', *East Anglian Archaeology* 49 (1989). K. Skipper, 'Wood-Pasture: the landscape of the Norfolk Claylands in the early modern period' (unpublished MA dissertation, Centre of East Anglian Studies, University of East Anglia, 1989). D. Yaxley,

'Medieval Deer Parks', in Wade-Martins (ed.) *Historical Atlas*, pp. 54–5.

[79] WSRO, Acc. 1066. From the Old English *stubb*, 'tree stump': a term usually interpreted to mean 'clearing'.

[80] P. Warner, *Greens, Commons and Clayland Colonisation: the Origins and Development of Green-side Settlements in East Suffolk* (1987).

[81] Williamson, *Origins*, pp. 167–71.

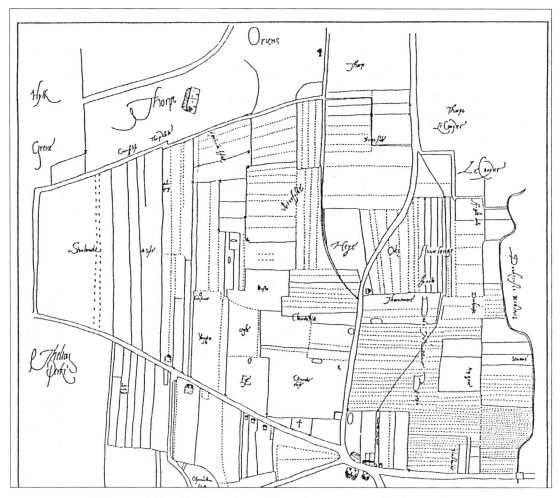

5. The open fields of Scole, south Norfolk, as shown on an undated map of c.1590.

formerly, in cattle fattening and dairying. Probate inventories suggest that most farmers kept milking cattle, fattened bullocks, and possessed cheese-making equipment. Few farms had more than 25 per cent of their area in tilth. By the second half of the seventeenth century clover and nonsuch were being sown as part of arable rotations, and turnips were appearing in the fields. As well as wheat, barley, peas and vetches, industrial crops were cultivated on a small scale. Thomas Proctor of Gissing died in 1621 owning, *inter alia*, 'five sacks and 5 pound hops', while in 1591 William Mases of Gissing had 'two stone and three querters of hempe'.[82] In common with most 'wood-pasture' areas, the Central Claylands were not for the most part characterised by large landed estates and although early deer parks were fairly numerous here, eighteenth-century landscape parks were comparatively rare.

The late-medieval shift towards a more pastoral economy was accompanied by the gradual, piecemeal enclosure of the region's open fields. Sixteenth-century surveys, such as the 1589

[82] NRO, INV 8/120; 50B/105; 31/42B

extent of the manor of Shelfhanger, describe a complex mixture of closes and open field strips. A late sixteenth century map of Scole in Norfolk similarly shows a landscape still dominated by open fields, although a number of blocks of enclosed land had been established. Tithe documents and other sources show that enclosure progressed fast in the following century, and the majority of seventeenth-century maps from the region show a largely enclosed landscape, although some areas of open fields continued to exist into the eighteenth and even the early nineteenth century. Common land, however, survived longer. As commons were not physically divided between proprietors, but exploited by right, they could not easily be removed by private agreements. Most were enclosed by parliamentary acts in the decades around 1800.

As the open arable of the valleys was gradually subdivided by hedges, the extensive areas of *private* pasture on the interfluves – large grazing grounds and deer parks – were gradually being split up. An undated late seventeenth-century note in the Denton glebe terrier, for example, describes how

> Richard Skeet late of Alburgh did usually pay Eighteen pence for the Tyth of a Great Close lying within the Town of Alburgh in Possession of Anthony Freston & in the Occupation of Butcher which Close is now divided in four several pieces ...[83]

The size of fields, and hence the density of hedges, created by the various post-medieval changes in the landscape seems to have varied greatly from area to area but on the smaller farms, in particular, the mesh of hedgerows could be tight indeed. A manorial survey for Diss, dating to 1589, refers to closes ranging in size from 40 acres down to 3 rods or less: the smaller closes were, as often today, normally referred to as *pightles*.[84] A 'Particular of Mr Rodwell's Farm' in Diss, made in 1771, described 21 fields with an average size of *c.* 2.86 acres.[85] This was an extreme case: but maps and surveys nevertheless suggest that on many farms the average field size in the seventeenth and early eighteenth century was less than five acres, although some large 'grazing grounds' continued to exist.

Woodland was a significant feature of the post-medieval clayland landscape. As well as large woods, there were numerous smaller woods and copses, groves or *grovets*. Yet although seventeenth-century topographers referred to the claylands as 'woodland' countryside, the region was not very densely wooded when compared with districts like the Weald of Kent, or the Chilterns. The term 'woodland' derived, in fact, from the large numbers of non-woodland trees: maps of the Channons Hall estate in Tibbenham (1640) (Figure 6), of the Ditchingham Hall estate (1615), and of the demesne lands of Hedenham manor (1617), show hedges well-endowed with trees and large amounts of free-standing timber.[86] At Denham in Suffolk a farm survey of 1651 suggests that there was an average of 15.4 trees per acre, while in Thorndon one of 1742 implies a density of no less than 29 per acre.[87] Most were oaks. Thus at Langley in 1676, 70 per cent of the trees recorded on the estate were oaks, with 30 per cent ash; at Thorndon in 1742

---

[83] NRO, PD 136/35.

[84] NRO, PD 80/90.

[85] NRO, NRS 12793 3F F8.

[86] All NRO, respectively, Acc. Barnes 1.5.86 Map Tree 4; Bedingfield 27.7.65 P 153 B; and Bedingfield 27.7.65 P 153 B/3.

[87] For more information about the development of the Suffolk clayland landscape in the seventeenth century, see J. Theobald, 'Changing landscapes, changing economies. Holdings in woodland High Suffolk, 1600–1840' (unpublished MA dissertation, Centre of East Anglian Studies, University of East Anglia, 1993).

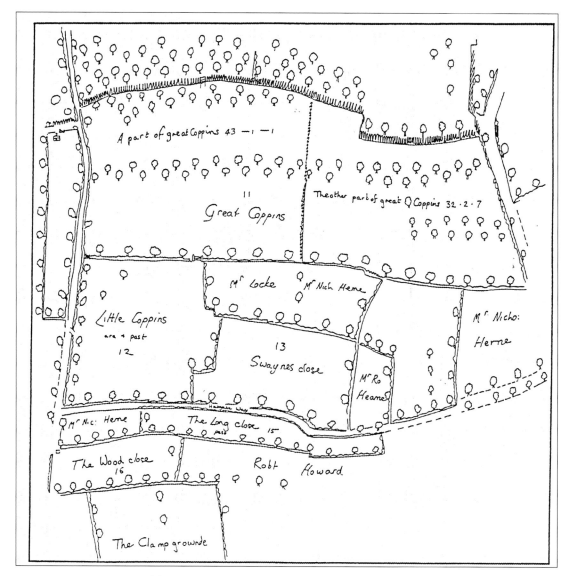

6. Detail from a map of Channons Hall, Tibenham, south Norfolk, 1640.

67 per cent were oak, 16 per cent ash, 17 per cent elm.[88] Most trees were managed as pollards. Thus the 1540 Redgrave survey described how

> In the seyd woods and park land about the scytuacons of the seyd mannor and dyvers tenementes there and in other the hamlettes aforseyd and in the lands perteyning in the same be growing 1,100 okes of 60, 80 and 100 years growth parte tymber parte usually cropped and shred.[89]

[88] NRO, NRS 11126; WSRO, T1/1/16.   [89] WSRO, Acc. 1066.

Of the trees mentioned in the Thorndon (Suffolk) survey of 1742, for example, no less than 82 per cent were pollards, only 13 per cent were classified as saplings and a mere 5 per cent were timber trees. At Debenham, the figures were less striking, but pollards nevertheless dominated: 57 per cent of the trees here were so classified, 27 per cent were saplings, and only 16 per cent described as timber. Leases frequently refer to pollards, the cuttings or 'loppings' from which were usually allowed to the tenant, although unrestricted cutting was forbidden.

Where closes were permanently used as pasture, trees might be scattered throughout their area. Many, however, were sporadically ploughed and it was therefore customary to concentrate pollards and timber in strips along their periphery. Such features are well represented on a map of an estate in Hedenham, dated 1769, which also shows similar (though narrower) lines of trees running through the centre of some of the fields (Figure 7). Sixteenth and seventeenth-century documents often refer to these features as 'grovetts': thus in 1633 the glebe terrier for Denton described 'the Churchyard with a Pightell & a little Grovett above that Close towards the south', and 'Two Closes joineing together Westward called South Crofte – the first Close hath a Grovett above'.[90] The more usual term for these pollard strips, however, was 'rows'.

Peripheral strips of pollards were one aspect of a more general phenomenon in the old wood-pasture landscape. The cropped area of arable fields frequently did not run right up to the boundary hedge but instead there was often a strip, left uncultivated, which was mown for hay, or used for grazing tethered cattle. Thus the tithe accounts for Denton in Norfolk in the seventeenth and eighteenth centuries refer to payments received for hay grown 'in ye borders in ye plough'd close', in the 'Borders of his severall ploughed lands', and in '3 several borders'.[91] The Denton glebe terrier offers some explanation for the practice:

> Item every Occupier of Arable Lands enclosed or in the Fields paying Tyth of Corn there growing in consideration thereof pays no Tyth Grass or Hay of so much of the Headlands & side lands & Borders as is convenient for the Team for the Turning of his horses Plough & Harrows in the Tillage of such arable lands.[92]

The fact that the inhabitants of Denton *did* sporadically pay tithe on grass borders indicates that these were often wider than would be required simply for turning the team. Such mown strips in fact had a number of functions: they supplied extra fodder, but also provided access to ditches, hedges and pollards while corn was growing in the fields.

(vi) *The Southern and Western Clays*

There are important differences in the landscape, economy and historical development of 'high' Suffolk – included above as part of the Central Claylands region – and the clayland areas lying to the south and west. South of the Gipping valley the terrain is more undulating and the soils less naturally acid: those of the *Ashley Association* are only slightly acidic while those of the *Hanslope Association* are formed in chalky till and are alkaline to the surface. Waterlogging is much less of a problem here than in the Central Claylands, partly because of the more rolling nature of the terrain: it was much easier to remove surface water through furrows and field

[90] NRO, PD 136/35.   [92] NRO, PD 136/35.
[91] NRO, FEL 553X2.

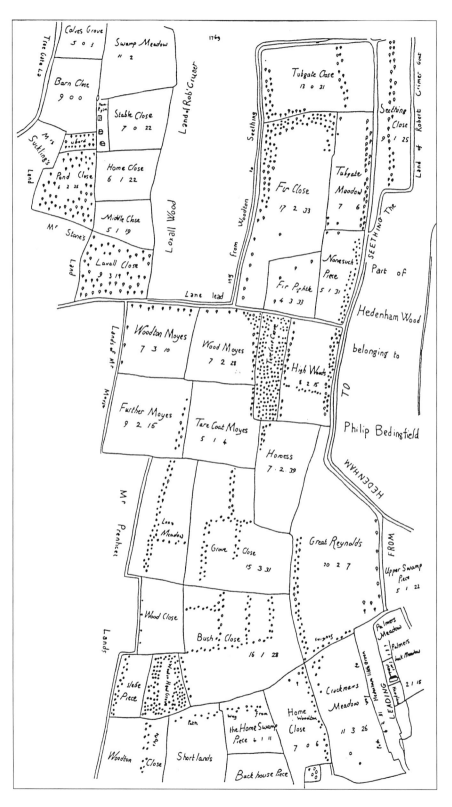

7. Detail from a map
of Hedenham, south
Norfolk, 1769.

ditches. All these factors helped ensure that, in early modern times, arable farming was of greater importance in this district, and dairying and bullock-fattening of less significance (most of the area is today classed as Grade 2 agricultural land). Reyce and other seventeenth-century commentators thus distinguished between the north-east of Suffolk – 'which cheifly consist upon pasture and feeding' – and the south-west, the 'midle parts', which although 'enjoying much medow and pasture, yett far more tillage doe from thence raise their cheifest mainten-ance'.[93] Cartographic evidence supports their observations. Thus a map of Kentwell Manor in Long Melford, surveyed in 1613,[94] indicates that around 50 per cent of the land was under arable cultivation. This was also a region in which the gentry were more prominent than in the Central Claylands, although large estates were not as noticeable a feature of the landholding pattern as they were in the areas of acid soils, like Breckland.

Nevertheless, it must be emphasised that not all the differences between these two clayland regions can be attributed in any simple or direct way to post-medieval agrarian practices. In many ways the medieval landscape of this region formed an extension of that of Essex and eastern Hertfordshire: it was more like the Home Counties than East Anglia proper. In par-ticular, open-field agriculture seems never to have been so firmly entrenched, even on the most amenable soils, except along the western fringes of the region. Early maps, such as those for Alpheton and Acton (1580 and 1613), Chattisham (1595), or Long Melford (1580), show almost no open field land, and even open commons and 'tyes' were limited both in number and extent.[95] Moreover, although the settlement pattern was highly dispersed, its character differed noticeably from that of the Central Claylands. Village nucleations were more prominent and the dispersed element took the form of isolated farms, and small hamlets clustered around pocket-handkerchief greens, rather than large common-edge agglomerations. The area was also more urbanised than the Central Claylands, largely because of the importance of the textile industry here in late medieval and early post-medieval times: today the picturesque 'wool towns' of Long Melford, Hadleigh, and Sudbury form a prominent feature of the landscape. In addition, there were (and are) more woods than in the Central Claylands, but fewer farmland trees – presumably because of the arable bias of the local economy. Yet if the landscape here was less 'bosky' than in the Central Claylands, it was no less densely hedged. In Long Melford, for example, the map of 1580 suggests that (excluding the Park, and closes attached to dwellings) the average field size was slightly less than four hectares.[96]

Although they differed in some aspects of their early history, it is convenient to group the claylands of west Suffolk with the relatively narrow strip of loamy clay soils running across the south-east of the county. Here, from Framlingham to Claydon, dissected terrain and the dominance of Hanslope Association soils similarly ensured a bias towards cereal production, and a corresponding lack of interest in dairying and fattening. Also included within this region is the area of loamy soils around Ipswich, and along the valley of the Stour. The region of the *Southern and Western Clays* thus somewhat arbitrarily defined covers an area of *c.*1400 square kilometres.

[93] Lord F. Hervey (ed.), *Suffolk in the Seventeenth cen-tury: the Breviary of Suffolk by Robert Reyce* (1902), p. 29.
[94] Private collection: Long Melford Hall archives.

[95] WSRO, 2130/1; 2130/2; ESRO, HA 167 3050/131.
[96] ESRO, HA 167 3959/131.

(vii) *The Dissected Boulder Clays*

A further subdivision of the East Anglian claylands can be identified. In central Norfolk the plateau is more dissected, by rivers with wide shallow valleys. While extensive spreads of *Beccles Association* soils do occur here, they are interrupted by tracts dominated by the sandier, more amenable soils of the *Burlingham Association*. In addition, the higher ground of the plateau is locally covered by sandy or gravelly drift. In the seventeenth century these areas of acid soil were occupied by areas of heathland, most of which remained unenclosed until the early nineteenth century. As defined in Figure 1, this distinctive area covers, in all, *c.* 980 square kilometres.

In the seventeenth century this region displayed features which allied it both with the Central Claylands to the south, and with North-West Norfolk to the west. Like the former, it had a dispersed pattern of settlement, with farms and cottages strung around greens and commons: but like the areas lying to the west there was much arable land here, some still in open fields. Maps of Brisley (1622), Morley (1629), Longham (1595), Raveningham (1632) and Weasenham (1590) suggest that between 25 per cent and 45 per cent of the land lay in open fields, and although much enclosure took place in the course of the seventeenth century some open arable survived into the eighteenth and, sporadically, into the nineteenth.[97] Moreover, in some parishes foldcourses appear to have existed. In a manner reminiscent of Breckland and North-West Norfolk regions, moreover, there were a handful of parishes which had already been enclosed: parishes which, in the course of the later Middle Ages, had fallen under the domination of single landowning families. On the higher ground, in particular, shrunken or depopulated villages could be found – Godwick, Testerton, Oxwick, Little Bittering, Pattesley, Croxton, Fulmondestone, and Great Palgrave – in which common fields and rights had long been completely extinguished. Fulmondestone, for example, had no open fields at all by 1614. In such situations most of the land appears to have been put down to pasture and used for large-scale cattle-ranching.[98]

Probate inventories confirm that this was a more arable area than the Central Claylands, although significant numbers of stock were also kept, especially cattle. The main limits to cultivation arable arose from the poorly-draining nature of the local soils. The *Burlingham Association* soils which dominate the area, while generally lighter than those of the *Beccles Association*, are for the most part only slowly permeable and suffer from some degree of seasonal waterlogging. In addition, the constituent series of both Associations are naturally acidic and still require regular applications of lime, as do the soils formed in the pockets of acid sand and gravel drift on the higher land.

(viii) *Fenland*

Although many historians have discussed the East Anglian Fens as a single topographic unit, they in fact comprise two quite distinct geographical entities. The southern or *Peat Fens* is today

---

[97] NRO, 402/7; PD3/108 (H); Holkham Hall archives, uncatalogued; Raveningham Hall archives, uncatalogued; NRO, Acc. 20.5.70, P150 B/4.

[98] Williamson, *Origins*, pp. 181–2; Parker, *Coke of Norfolk*, p. 43.

a wide, flat, and empty landscape punctuated only by the occasional isolated farmstead, or by rows of poplars. It covers – within the counties of Norfolk and Suffolk, and excluding much larger areas in the adjacent counties – a total of c.480 square kilometres. The northern Fenland, or *Marshland*, was and is a very different landscape, full of sprawling villages, as well as containing numerous isolated farms. This, as defined in Figure one, covers an area of only c.330 square kilometres in Norfolk and Suffolk.

The peat fens comprise deposits built up in a former estuary of the Ouse, Nene and other Midland and East Anglian rivers. The complex sequence of sedimentation and transgression need not detain us here, but it is important to note that in many areas the peat overlies marine clays and silts of very different chemical and physical composition. In medieval times the fens were exploited from their margins, or from islands of older rock within them. The land was invariably waterlogged during the winter months, and in some areas for much of the year. While some areas of peat, close to the upland margins, seem to have been under cultivation during the middle ages, most comprised common fen, exploited in the kinds of ways already described for the Broadland fens. Grazing occurred for some of the year but large areas were principally mown, for hay or litter; or cut for reeds and saw sedge. Some sections were cut for peat, and the fish and wildfowl were systematically exploited. The area was not a wilderness, in any meaningful sense of the word. Thousands of years of intensive exploitation had fundamentally altered its ecology, and as in Broadland the use of the fens was carefully controlled by manorial courts.[99] By the seventeenth century cattle were the most important stock kept by the fen farmers, but sheep were also grazed. Thomas Cox described in 1700 how 'The Soil is so fat that Tilney-Smeethe alone is said to feed 30,000 Sheep which would be a great Advantage to the Inhabitants did not the Overflowings of the Sea much lessen it'.[100]

In the early seventeenth century large-scale schemes of drainage, financed largely by outside capital, were initiated. As a result of the General Drainage Act of 1600 it was possible for large landowners to overrule local proprietors and suppress any common rights which obstructed the path of drainage schemes. Under the direction of the Dutch engineer Vermuyden, a system of drains and diversion channels was dug within the area which became known, after the scheme's principal financial backer, as the Bedford Level.[101] The project met with considerable local opposition, but was initially successful, and large areas of fen were enclosed and in some cases ploughed (although as Dugdale emphasised in 1662, 'there are many great meres and lakes still continuing').[102] Walter Blith described the practice of 'denshiring': ploughing off the turf with a light plough, burning it in heaps and spreading the ashes across the surface, to improve fertility.[103] The ashes were alkaline, and thus helped neutralise the natural acidity of the peat. Land so treated was usually cropped for a few years and then returned to grass, under a form of convertible husbandry. Nevertheless, the majority of reclaimed land was too wet to be successfully cultivated and remained under permanent grass, although the quality of the sward was improved by drainage. Moreover, arable land use declined in the second half of the century, for the condition of the reclaimed lands deteriorated: in Darby's words, 'What seemed a

[99] H. C. Darby, *The Draining of the Fens* (second edn. 1956).

[100] H.C. Darby, *The Changing Fenland* (1983), p. 138.

[101] Darby, *Changing Fenland*, p. 130.

[102] W. Dugdale, *The History of Inbanking and Drayning of Diverse Fens and Marshes* (London, 1662), p. 267.

[103] Darby, *Changing Fenland*, p. 92.

promising enterprise in 1652 had, by 1700, become a tragedy. Disaster abounded every-where'.[104] The engineers and adventurers had failed to anticipate the shrinkage of the peat which followed drainage. The surface of the land fell below that of the rivers and had to be progressively embanked. Windpumps were linked to a complex system of channels and lifted the water into the rivers and other major watercourses. The mills were simple structures, wooden smock mills, often erected on piles for stability, with four wood and canvas sails driving a scoop wheel.

The construction of mills prevented widespread inundation but arable land-use remained at a low level in the early eighteenth century – in part, of course, a consequence of low cereal prices. The extent of ploughland was limited by other factors. As in the Central Claylands, landlords were usually absentees and estates were small and fragmented, so it was hard to supervise the farming operations of tenants: there was a widespread concern that excessive cultivation would waste the fen soils. Landowners followed the path of caution, issuing leases that allowed only limited conversion to tilth, so that most farms had no more than a quarter of their land under the plough.

The landscape history of the silt fens, or 'Marshland', is very different. The silt was laid down by successive marine transgressions in late prehistoric and Roman times over a sequence of peat and clay deposits which had, earlier in the prehistoric period, accumulated in the mouth of the estuary. Changes in relative sea levels led to extensive colonisation in the Roman period, with farms and small arable fields strung out along the firmer and slightly higher ground provided by old creek ridges. The area seems to have been largely abandoned for settlement in the late Roman period, due to changes in relative land/sea levels, but by Middle Saxon times recolonisation had occurred. In later Saxon and early post-Conquest times expansion took place inland, onto the lower silt ground, with the new fields being protected by 'walls' or banks. The oldest fields, concentrated around the principal villages, are of irregular shape, but later Saxon and medieval expansion created a pattern of more regular fields, generally in the form of thin strips, seldom more than twenty metres in width and often considerably narrower: in extreme cases these could be as much as two kilometres in length.[105] Archaeological and documentary evidence makes it clear that reclaimed land was used in a variety of ways. Some fields were permanent pasture, but many were under arable cultivation.[106] In post-medieval times, so far as the evidence goes, the relative extent of grazing and arable fluctuated in accordance with market conditions but grassland predominated. At the start of the period studied here, the majority of the area seems to have been under pasture. The nature of the local soils, reflecting the varied nature of the superficial geology, was a major determinant of the extent of arable land use. As Young noted in the early nineteenth century, 'The stiffer clays are the worst arable; the more mild and temperate ones, the best and easiest worked of course; but the strongest clay is best for grass'.[107]

Although the majority of the silt fens was already held in severalty in medieval times, areas of common land also existed, normally occupying pockets of poorly-draining peat within the silt matrix. These were often shared between numerous parishes. Limited areas thus required

---

[104] Ibid., p. 106.
[105] R. Silvester, 'The Fenland Project, Number 3. Marshland and the Nar Valley, Norfolk', East Anglian

Arch. 45 (1988).
[106] Silvester, 'Fenland Project', pp. 164–5.
[107] Young, Norfolk, p. 14.

enclosure and draining in the post-medieval period, such as the 30,000 acres intercommoned by the inhabitants of Tydd St Giles, Tydd St Mary, and Newton which was reclaimed in 1632.[108] But although around 20 per cent of the region was effected by parliamentary enclosure acts, the majority of Marshland, like the peat Fens, was held in severalty at the end of the seventeenth century.

(ix) The Sandlings

Sandlings is the name traditionally given to the strip of light, acid soils which runs down the east coast of Suffolk, between the Central Claylands and the sea. Generally between 5 and 10 kilometres wide, and nowhere more than 16 kilometres, this agriculturally marginal area extends over some 740 square kilometres and displays a range of soils similar to those of Breckland or the Northern Heathlands. Most fall within the *Newport 4 Association*: deep, well-drained but acid. The Sandlings district differs, however, from these regions in that all the parishes within it possessed at least one other kind of terrain within their boundaries. The majority had areas of coastal marsh, which were progressively embanked and improved in the course of the post-medieval period. Others extended out onto the claylands to the west, and thus included areas of fertile if heavy soils. Some parishes, especially towards the north of the region, contained portions of all three environmental zones, clay, sand and marsh.

In the middle ages the region's landscape had comprised a mixture of heathland, unimproved coastal marsh, and open-fields of the usual East Anglian 'irregular' kind.[109] By the seventeenth century these had often experienced a degree of piecemeal enclosure and early maps – like those for Benacre (1580) or Sutton (1629) – generally show a complicated mixture of open fields, closes, and enclosed plots subdivided into strips.[110] The extent of enclosure varied considerably from parish to parish, however. By 1613 in Trimley and Falkenham all the arable land was enclosed, but Felixstowe in the same period still lay almost entirely open. Most parishes, however – like Somerleyton in 1652 – seem to have consisted largely of enclosed land: here strip cultivation extended over only around 25 per cent of the arable area.[111]

Not only do the region's open fields appear to have been extensively enclosed by the end of the seventeenth century, the heaths, too, were largely held in severalty. Some were demesne land, others held as copyhold; the former was often leased, sometimes in extensive, continuous 'walks' like the 1068 acres held by one tenant in Chillesford in 1601. Copyhold tenants usually occupied smaller portions, typically between four and ten acres. All this was also true of the coastal marshes, although here there were fewer large leasehold blocks and much was held in very small portions.[112] In the parish of Walton, for example, 170 acres of the Mayestone Level was leased in 1613 to separate tenants in four blocks; a further 254 acres was copyhold, and held by seven tenants. As Burrell has noted, in some parishes fragmentation was extreme. In Reydon the salt marshes were held by nine tenants, in a number of separate portions – some as small as a rood – while the Fresh Marsh 'was held by 12 tenants with an even larger number of subdivisions, the smallest block of land being 20 perches and the largest 20 acres'.[113]

[108] Darby, *Changing Fenland*, p. 67.

[109] E. D. R. Burrell, 'Historical Geography of the Sandlings of Suffolk, 1600 to 1850', (unpublished MSc thesis, University of London, 1960), pp. 20–25.

[110] ESRO, 50/19/1, 6; TG 31C.

[111] Burrell, 'Sandlings', p. 33; ESRO, 295; 942.64 Som.

[112] Burrell, 'Sandlings', pp. 34–45.

[113] *Ibid.*, p. 32.

The early enclosure of the marsh grounds should perhaps be expected, given what has already been said about the similar areas further north, in Broadland. The generally enclosed nature of the heaths and arable, however, is more surprising (especially when compared with other areas of acid soils in East Anglia). It may in part have been a consequence of the general absence of foldcourses in the region: these are sporadically referred to in medieval documents but few seem to have been in operation by the end of the seventeenth century.

The pattern of agriculture in the region in the early modern period has been discussed in detail by Burrell.[114] Rye, as in other acid soil regions, was extensively grown on the poorest soils. Norden's map of Sir Michael Stanhope's estate in the area between the rivers Alde and Deben, surveyed in 1600–1, has a note across an area of unreclaimed heathland: 'some of this is reasonable good rye ground; so more of the heath if it were used accordingly'.[115] Barley and wheat were grown on the better land, as also was hemp, which is frequently mentioned in inventories (a 1613 survey of the manor of Walton-cum-Trimley notes no less than 84 hemplands).[116] Livestock husbandry was also important, however, with large herds of dairy cows and bullocks on the grazing marshes. Between Easter and Michaelmas 1601, 1200 barrels of butter and 1198 cheeses were shipped to London from Walberswick and Southwold alone.[117] Cattle were also grazed on the heaths, but here sheep were more important, often kept in huge flocks, as on the Friston Hall estate in 1690s where there were over 1000.

(x) *Conclusion*

In the late seventeenth century East Anglia thus comprised a complex mosaic of regions. Indeed, the foregoing discussion has to some extent simplified regional geography: additional, smaller regions could easily have been defined and discussed. The nature of field systems, the relative proportions of enclosed and unenclosed land, and the extent of commons and wastes, all varied considerably from district to district, and with them the particular character of agrarian arrangements. Given that the extent of climatic variation within the two counties was limited, this diversity of agrarian structures seems largely to have been a consequence of topography and geology, although the proximity of markets must also, to some extent, have been influential. Some of the environmental factors operated directly upon the practice of early-modern agriculture. Others operated indirectly, in the sense that the institutional structures which they had engendered in the remote past persisted into modern times, fundamentally effecting the practice of farming, as, above all, in the case of the foldcourse.

Yet while the overwhelming impression is one of diversity, both within and between regions, certain generalisations can be made. One of the most striking, to anyone familiar with the modern countryside of Norfolk and Suffolk, is that very large areas were occupied by permanent or semi-permanent grassland. The Fens were at this time a largely pastoral region, so too the Central Claylands. Rather less than a quarter of the land area of both was probably under cultivation in *c.*1700. It is true that in the other clayland districts the proportion of pasture was less (perhaps in the vicinity of 40–45 per cent) but in the various acid soil districts there were vast tracts of unploughed land, made up in the main of unimproved heath. Even in the fertile

---

[114] *Ibid.*, p. 49.
[115] British Library Map Room, 5210 (3).

[116] Burrell, 'Sandlings', p. 50; ESRO, 50/1/74(1).
[117] Burrell, 'Sandlings', p. 52.

Flegg Loam District there were extensive areas of low-lying marsh and fen. Although it is difficult, given the nature of the available evidence, to make any very reliable estimate of the area under arable cultivation in the two counties in *c.*1700, it was certainly less than half: 40 per cent would be a reasonable estimate (counting non-cultivated 'breck' as pasture).

The second general observations is that the regions with the greatest areas of unenclosed land – whether common or open-field – tended to be those on the lighter and more acid soils – Breckland, the Northern Heathlands, the Sandlings and North-West Norfolk. The clayland areas and the Fens, in contrast, were already (by and large) enclosed landscapes, at least in a legal and tenurial sense. More important, perhaps, is the observation that taken as a whole East Anglia was already, by the end of the seventeenth century, a land of enclosures. Probably around two thirds of the two counties was already technically enclosed in 1700. The following century and a half were to see the removal of almost all remaining open land: but other changes in the structure of the landscape, and in the physical framework of farming, were to be of greater significance in the development of husbandry.

CHAPTER II

The Farming Framework, *c.* 1700–1830

Recent discussions of the 'Agricultural Revolution' have placed particular emphasis on farming *methods*, and especially on the use of new crops and rotations. Contemporaries, however, were aware that increases in production were also achieved by changes in the farming *framework*. Arthur Young, for example, emphasised the importance of improvements in farm equipment and plant; the enclosure of commons and open fields and the amalgamation of 'small, trifling enclosures'; the construction of better farm buildings; improvements to grassland, through irrigation and drainage; assiduous application of marl; and more diligent drainage of arable land.[1] We will argue here that while some of these improvements in the organisational structure and material culture of farming were of marginal significance in raising output, others were at least as significant as the adoption of improved rotations or the selective breeding of livestock. Some, indeed, were the necessary precondition for the adoption of such 'improved' farming practices.

1. Enclosure, reclamation, and changes in land use

Just as each region within East Anglia had its own enclosure history in the period up to the late seventeenth century, so too did each have its own experience in the course of the eighteenth and early nineteenth centuries; experiences moulded both by contemporary circumstances and by the institutional and tenurial structures inherited from the deep past.

(i) *North-West Norfolk and Breckland*

In North-West Norfolk the contrast between the acid-soil 'uplands' and the calcareous soils of the valleys and coastal strip was maintained throughout the eighteenth century. In the former, the area of enclosed ground, already extensive by *c.*1700, increased steadily – usually as one of the large estates gradually bought out other proprietors. The removal of open fields and commons was thus usually achieved without a parliamentary act. The extensive open fields on the more calcareous soils experienced, in contrast, only slow attrition. In the parish of Sedgeford, already discussed, less than 10 per cent of the arable appears to have been enclosed by 1649, if the holding of the Norwich Dean and Chapter was typical.[2] A plan of the fields and brecks drawn up in 1736 shows that there was little change in the following ninety years: about 1720 strips existed in the open fields and the property of the Dean and Chapter was still scattered amongst them.[3] An estate map of 1783 suggests that consolidation progressed during the middle and later decades of the century, associated with some engrossment of holdings. Nevertheless,

---

[1] Young, *Norfolk, passim.*
[2] NRO, DCN 51/91.

[3] NRO, Church Commissioners 11002.

most of the land in the parish still lay open in 1797, when 4139 acres – well over 75 per cent of the total land area – was enclosed by parliamentary act. By this time the Dean and Chapter were the largest landowner but held only 38 per cent of the total area of the parish. Four other owners each had over 100 acres (the LeStranges of Hunstanton with 360 acres, P. Glover with 800 acres, and Rolfe of Heacham with 176 acres) and there was a long 'tail' of small proprietors (indeed, as late as 1840 there were still fourteen landowners, although the Dean and Chapter now had 2060 acres, the Rolfes 820 and the Stylemans (owners of the Hunstanton estate) 658).[4]

The experience of the parish of Snettisham was similar. When enclosed by parliamentary act in 1766 the majority of the land still lay in open fields and commons.[5] During the preceding decades the consolidation of holdings had been more significant than enclosure. A terrier of 1727 in the Kings Lynn borough archive lists the scattered strips which made up the borough's Red Barn Farm. Although 70 acres of the farm were consolidated into enclosed fields, the remaining 730 acres lay in 146 pieces scattered through 80 furlongs.[6] Here, too, ownership remained fragmented at the time of the enclosure. In addition to the three main landowners (Styleman with 2,415 acres, Elizabeth Cobbs with 488 acres, and Kings Lynn Borough with 745 acres), there was once again a long 'tail' of smaller proprietors.

The late enclosure of such parishes was a function not merely of the more fragmented tenurial structure in such places but also of the institution of the foldcourse. Numerous legal cases attest the determination of foldcourse owners to resist their erosion by the proliferation of hedged closes, which could exclude the flocks from their customary grazing on the fallows and shack. Thus in 1673 a dispute between James Coldham and Richard Potter was resolved 'by the examination of ancient witnesses as also by the reading of a certain description of witnesses made in the High Court of Chancery … that the said close is a shack close and so has been anciently used'.[7] The borough of Kings Lynn in 1690 similarly asserted that rights of shackage had existed for the past 40 years over certain closes that were now being fenced off and sown with clover in Snettisham, where it had a foldcourse for 800 sheep.[8] Not only piecemeal enclosure, but also *general* enclosure, might be discouraged and retarded by the existence of foldcourses. The largest proprietor was usually a manorial lord and foldcourse owner. The costs and legal complexities (as well as the potential gains in rental income) of enclosure had to be weighed against the income derived from having a flock ranging for much of the year over other peoples' land. Against this, we need to note that the sums to be made from direct exploitation of such rights, or from leasing them to another party, were not huge; at Snettisham the Kings Lynn borough's foldcourse for 800 sheep was valued at only £48 per annum in 1690;[9] the Anmer course was let for as little as £25 in 1758.[10] In part this was because some landowners were reluctant to exploit their rights to the full because of the antagonism their exercise raised amongst tenant and neighbours. In 1802, when Mr Hare of Hillington was worried about the amount of compensation he might receive for the loss of his foldcourse should the proposed enclosure of Docking proceed, he admitted that 'through neglect and timidity it had not been fully exercised'.[11] It is hardly surprising, then, that as the farm rents began to rise after 1750,

4 NRO, Gun 63; NRO 300.
5 NRO, C/Sca/2 265.
6 NRO, Af 112.
7 NRO, MC40/64.

8 NRO, Af 231.
9 NRO, Af 231, 17.
10 NRO, MC40/104.
11 NRO, MC50/77/4.

and parliamentary enclosure became a more familiar tool, large-scale enclosure proceeded apace in this region. Alone in East Anglia, North-West Norfolk has a parliamentary enclosure experience comparable to that of Midland counties like Leicestershire or Northamptonshire, in that the bulk of acts were passed before the outbreak of the Napoleonic Wars, peaking in the 1770s.

Of course, the neat picture presented here – of pre- or non-parliamentary enclosure on the acid soils where most parishes were absorbed by large estates, and of parliamentary enclosure on the calcareous soils where ownership was more fragmented – has a number of exceptions. These, however, tend to confirm the central importance of patterns of ownership, and of the institution of the foldcourse. A map of Heacham – a coastal parish largely composed of calcareous soils – surveyed in 1620 shows that the bulk of the parish lay in open fields, brecks and sheep walks.[12] A subsequent map shows that by 1765 considerable piecemeal enclosure of the arable had occurred, and sections of the sheepwalk had also been enclosed.[13] However, the fact that the latter is specifically described as 'Lord's Allotment' implies that the Rolfes, the manorial lords, had agreed to forego some of their foldcourse rights and allow piecemeal enclosure in return for the right to enclose parts of the common. Nevertheless, such enclosures were limited in area and the act of 1780 affected 3300 acres of 'open-field land, brecks, commons and wastes'.[14] Hunstanton is another exception which confirms the general rule. Although largely composed of calcareous soils, enclosure had taken place by the end of the century without parliamentary act (an act of 1857 merely removed a small common of 84 acres).[15] Unusually for a parish so located, however, Hunstanton was dominated by a single landowner. From the late fifteenth century it was almost entirely owned by the Le Strange family and by 1670 it was completely in their possession.[16] At this time almost the whole of the parish (excluding the park) consisted of open fields and commons, and an undated early eighteenth-century map shows a similar picture, with the parish divided into 56 furlongs containing around 50 pieces each.[17] Although in many cases holdings had been consolidated, comparatively little enclosure had taken place. A map of 1765, however, shows that further consolidation, and some enclosure, had occurred. By 1819 there were only five farms and the parish was – with the exception of the common – completely enclosed.[18]

To judge from surviving maps (and making due allowances for potential bias in this source) it seems likely that around 35 per cent of the land in North-West Norfolk was enclosed before c.1660. Parliamentary enclosure effected another 30 per cent of the region, suggesting that around 35 per cent was enclosed by other means in the period after 1660. These are very approximate estimates but nevertheless provide *some* indication of the region's enclosure experience. However and whenever it occurred, enclosure (in the period after c.1760 at least) was usually associated with a major change in land use and environment. Heaths and sheepwalks

[12] NRO, LeStrange OB2.

[13] NRO, GUN 94 Map Cabinet III.

[14] At this time 55 commonage rights still existed, 21 of which were held by owners of less than 10 acres, and seven by owners of between 11 and 50 acres. The largest landowners, the Stylemans, had 1541 acres but this was still less than half the parish. The Rolfes owned 747 acres, and there were a further four landowners with between

50 and 200 acres – together with the customary 'tail' of smallholders.

[15] NRO, NCH.

[16] C. Oestmann, *Lordship and Community: the Le-Strange family and the village of Hunstanton, Norfolk, in the first half of the sixteenth century* (1994), pp. 45–55.

[17] NRO, LeStrange H1.

[18] NRO, LeStrange OA3, M5–6.

were ploughed and the outfield brecks were subjected to more regular and intensive cropping. By 1840, according to the tithe award maps, less than 15 per cent of the land area was under permanent grass, largely restricted to the valley floors of the major rivers like the Stiffkey, Burn or Heacham River; the few, large, landscape parks; and the coast, where the larger estates were, throughout the eighteenth century, involved in the embanking and reclamation of areas of salt marsh. Outside the large parks and plantations surrounding great country houses like Holkham, Houghton, or Raynham this was, by the mid nineteenth century, a landscape of almost unrelieved arable, of large rectangular fields bordered by flimsy hawthorn hedges marching relentlessly across the gentle slopes.

The experience of Breckland parallels in many ways that of North-West Norfolk. Enclosure came late to the more populous parishes on the least impoverished soils: elsewhere enclosed land proliferated in the course of the eighteenth century as large estates systematically bought out smaller proprietors, often to save the expense of a parliamentary enclosure. Thus a series of maps for Sapiston shows the gradual purchase and exchange of freehold strips and glebe land by the Dukes of Grafton from 1667 to 1789.[19] The parish was completely enclosed without a parliamentary act and the map accompanying the act for the neighbouring parish of Honington (1801) refers to Sapiston as 'recently enclosed'.[20] Between 1760 and 1798 Lord Cornwallis set out to buy the parishes of Culford, Ingham, Timworth, and West Stow. By 1800 the estate controlled the entire area of all five parishes: they were surveyed, and then divided into nine new farms, mostly covering more than 1000 acres each.[21] Enclosure continued in this way throughout the seventeenth and eighteenth centuries. But Breckland was nevertheless effected, more than any other region in East Anglia, by parliamentary enclosure. Of the 126 parishes in the region, 66 had enclosure acts. Moreover, these were not restricted to residual areas of waste: in more than two-thirds of these cases, over 50 per cent of the area of the parish was enclosed, and the majority of acts dealt with open fields as well as with commons.[22] In all, between 50 and 60 per cent of the total land area of the region was probably enclosed by parliamentary act.

As in North-West Norfolk, parishes enclosed by act usually had complex pattern of land-ownership. When Saham Tony was enclosed in 1797 the land was shared between 62 allottees. The largest single allotment, 1393 acres (45.0 per cent of the parish), went to one James Crowe; but another large allotment accounted for 521 acres (17 per cent of the parish area), a further three allotments covered more than 100 acres each, and there was a long 'tail' of smaller proprietors, with a total of 11 allottees gaining 183 acres in blocks of between 10 and 100 acres, and a further 174 acres (5.5 per cent of total parish area) going in blocks of less than ten acres.[23] The parish of Croxton, enclosed by an act of 1813, was similar. Here 52 per cent of the allotted acreage went to the Master and Fellows of the School and Hospital at Thetford, but four other large allottees (two receiving over 700 acres each) received a further 44 per cent of the enclosed area. The remaining 4 per cent was divided between ten recipients.[24]

[19] WSRO, HA 513/28/13, 14, 16, 17.
[20] WSRO, HA513/28/9/1.
[21] C. Paine (ed.), *The Culford Estate 1780–1935* (1993).
[22] A. Stacey, 'Parliamentary Enclosure in Norfolk 1720–1870' (unpublished MA Dissertation, Centre of East Anglian Studies, 1993), pp. 35–8.
[23] NRO, C/Sca2/127.
[24] NRO, C/Sca2/84.

The chronology of parliamentary enclosure in Breckland was in some ways similar to that in North-West Norfolk, in that there were a number of relatively early acts (eleven in the Norfolk Breckland alone before 1795). Here, however, there was a greater concentration of activity during the Napoleonic War years, accounting for nearly 70 per cent of the total acreage enclosed by act. Impressive though these figure are, there is no doubt that they underestimate the extent and intensity of wartime enclosure: for engrossment and piecemeal enclosure continued alongside enclosure by act right through this peak period, and into the nineteenth century. Faden's map of Norfolk, surveyed around 1794, has the words 'common fields' emblazoned prominently across the parishes of East Wretham, Brettenham, Kilverstone, Riddlesworth, Gasthorpe, West Harling, and Bridgeham. By the late 1830s, to judge from the tithe awards maps, all common grazing and open arable had been removed from these parishes, but only one – Bridgeham – was enclosed by a parliamentary act (in 1804).[25]

The continued importance of enclosure by non-parliamentary means is, above all, a manifestation of the importance of large estates in the Breckland in the eighteenth century. The records of one of these estates – the Walsingham estate, based at Merton – are particularly complete, and provide a good illustration of the varied processes of enclosure and reclamation. Especially informative are the letters written by Thomas de Grey, who acted as agent for his brother William, Chief Justice of Common Pleas from 1771.

The de Grey family were established at Merton by 1600 and gradually added to their estates: by 1870 these totalled 12,120 acres in Norfolk, mainly concentrated in the parishes of Merton, Thompson, Tottington, Stanford and Sturston, together with a further 1075 acres in Suffolk. In 1771, two years after they had been purchased, Stanford and Sturston were surveyed. All the arable land – around 850 acres – was already enclosed, but some 2200 acres of sheepwalk and heath, although technically in severalty, remained unreclaimed.[26] Both parishes had been largely depopulated by the sixteenth century (in 1729 the manor of Stanford had consisted of only four tofts).[27] When the estate was purchased, William Smith was tenant of Sturston Farm, which also included much of Stanford parish. The estate planned to renegotiate the lease and reclaim large areas of heath. 'A great part of the land is capable of improvement', Thomas de Grey wrote to his brother in 1769.[28] The original plan was to let all of Sturston, with 744 acres of Stanford, as one great farm totalling 2625 acres on a 31 year lease. If possible, 670 acres were to be ploughed, the landlord paying for the costs of spreading marl and manure. He would also build a barn and a stable for ten horses, the tenant paying 5 per cent of the cost.[29]

These plans seem to have come to nothing, however, and Smith's old lease continued to run until 1782. As the date for its expiry approached further plans for improvement were formulated. Ralph Cauldwell, the steward of the Holkham estate, was asked about the feasibility of improvement: his report was not very hopeful. 'When I rode about your estates I observed the best soils towards the extreme parts of your land, and could it be considered to enclose and cultivate for corn and cattle some of those parts and leave the worst for rabbits, it might suit every

[25] NRO, NCH.

[26] NRO, CC Petre Mss Box 8 (e).

[27] And one watermill, one dovehouse, ten gardens, 2000 acres of 'lands', 40 acres of meadow, sixty acres of

pasture, and 200 acres of furze and heath: NRO, WLS XXIX/1, 416 X 4.

[28] NRO, WLS XXIX/4/5 416 X 4.

[29] NRO, WLS XXIX/2/2 416 X 4.

purpose'.[30] Thomas de Grey, however, was more optimistic, although interestingly he thought that the only way of realising the full potential of the land was to take it in hand:

> An enterprising man on the spot who could give his mind to such an employment would take the estate into his own hands for 4 or 5 years and might then let it according to its true value – Mr Tass did thus at Bodney – a medium cannot so well be drawn from the tenants to make improvements over such a waste of a country; it is an arduous affair, if it were not, there would not be an occasion to send so far for a doctor.[31]

There was much discussion about whether the two parishes should be organised into one farm, or two: eventually a plan for two farms was agreed. But it proved difficult to value the land as it might be in an improved state, and thus to set the rent. An attempt was made, on the assumption that there would be 1200 acres of arable (600 on each farm), 600 of which was to be sown with corn yearly, 300 under one or two-year lay, 300 in turnips. The produce would be 4 combs per acre for cereals, and 600 sheep, 20 cows, 30 head of young stock and 24 horses would be kept.[32]

To begin with, Smith was keen to lease both of the proposed farms and a rent of £630 for 23 years was being considered. But there were disputes about the amount of ground to be left under turnips at the end of the tenancy, and de Grey was keen to split the land into two separate tenancies. 'I have not the least wish that Mr Smith should not continue a tenant, but I think it a pity that such a tract of country should remain in one man's hand's totally unimproved'.[33] There was much haggling over the rent, with Smith offering 3*s*. an acre and De Grey wanting 5*s*. Four shillings was eventually agreed. Smith continued to make demands, and although de Grey was prepared to make 'some indulgence believing him to be a substantial farmer and well calculated to that sort of farm', he was not prepared to agree to a barn as large as Smith demanded.[34] When the lease was signed in 1782 Smith had got most of what he wanted, including more lenient husbandry clauses.[35]

All this left the problem of what to do with the remaining land in Stanford. In spite of the comparative buoyancy of the agricultural markets, the agent John Andrews – echoing the earlier comments by Cauldwell – felt that it was best used as a warren, noting that 'to make it more of a warren will require less money to be laid out and more rent made of the premises'. The prospective tenants, however – one Mr Bidwell and his nephew – also clearly intended that the holding should operate as an arable farm, for they complained that under Smith's tenancy the place had deteriorated. It had been let under poor covenants which had allowed Smith to grow two years of grain crops in succession, 'too much at any time on that poor land'. Moreover, 'it does not appear that there will be any turnips this year'.[36]

We have discussed this example at length because it illustrates well the character of improvement in many marginal parishes in the late eighteenth century, which had been acquired in their entirety by large landowners. Enclosure might be the prerequisite for improvement, but

[30] NRO, WLS XXIX/6/15 416 X 4.

[31] NRO, WLS XXIX/1/7 416 X 4.

[32] NRO, WLS XXIX/2/30 416 X 4.

[33] NRO, WLS XXIX/2/30 416 X 4.

[34] NRO, WLS XXIX/2/9 416 X 4.

[35] NRO, WLS XXIX/2/34 416 X 4.

[36] NRO, WLS XXIX/2/50 416 X 4.

even in parishes long in severalty, large areas of heath remained unreclaimed. Enclosure and reclamation were not synonymous.

We noted earlier that engrossment and piecemeal enclosure continued on a large scale even during the peak period of parliamentary enclosure. The same estate's activities in the neighbouring parish of Tottington go some way towards explaining why. Most of the land here had been owned by the de Grey family since the early eighteenth century. In 1763 Robert Knopwood, the owner of about 80 acres and the second largest proprietor in the parish, agreed to exchange land:

> Whereas ... such lands ... do lay intermixed with and are inconvenient to each party and at a greater distance from their several farm houses and for the better convenience and improvement of their said estates ... agree to exchange such lands as lay convenient and contiguous to the enclosed lands of Knopwood in exchange for the several lands of Knopwood as lay convenient and contiguous to and intermixed with the land of the said Thomas de Grey ...[37]

In 1765 a report was compiled on the 'unimproved parts of ... Tottington together with proposals for dividing and improving the same'.[38] Open fields still survived but de Grey was anxious to avoid the expense of an enclosure act: given the marginal quality of the land here, the costs were unlikely to be recovered quickly through enhanced rents. Walsingham was therefore keen to buy out the remaining owners. The 83 acres formerly owned by Knopwood, but now in the hands of trustees for his son, were purchased for £2000. The 43 acres owned by one Mrs Duffield, scattered in 33 pieces, were acquired with more difficulty. In 1771 she was offered £1000: but 'she says (and with some truth) she can increase the rents, though I cannot, because she can let her little scraps to such tenants of mine with whom they are intermixed and they must give her a full price or suffer by the refusal'.[39] There was trouble, too, with the smallest owners, those with less than ten acres, who were led by one Peter Dent (owner of nine acres). Thomas de Grey described to his brother how 'The little owners are led by Dent, who is well-calculated by his air of importance to lead a rabble'.[40] This opposition forced Walsingham to seek an enclosure act, although by 1774 – the year the act was passed – there were only four remaining proprietors, Mrs Duffield and two of the smaller owners having sold out. These individuals did not really represent a residual peasantry holding out against an engrossing landlord. Only Daniel Noil was resident in Tottington: Dent lived at Cranwich, about ten miles to the east, Thomas Levett lived in Thompson while William Balls, a carpenter, lived in Newmarket.[41] Prior to enclosure Walsingham's holding in the parish had been organised into three farms: following enclosure his much larger holding was divided into five farms, let on new leases.

Enclosure, brought about in a variety of ways, was thus a major factor in Breckland. Indeed, it seems likely that more than 70 per cent of the region's land area passed from open fields and commons, to land held in severalty, between 1700 and 1820. The majority of this enclosure, moreover, occurred after 1770, and mostly during the period of the Napoleonic Wars. What is

37 NRO, WLS XXVII/19 415 X 5.
38 NRO, WLS XXVII/19 415 X 5.
39 NRO, WLS XVII/20 415 X 5.

40 NRO, WLS XXVII/20/24 415 X 5.
41 NRO, WLS XXVII/19 415 X 5.

less clear, however, is the extent to which enclosure was necessarily associated with an extension of the area under arable cultivation; nor how far such activities were, in the long term, financially viable. In 1774 Thomas de Grey bemoaned the costs of the Tottington enclosure:

> The expense of improving is much greater than is generally understood. Hicks bill [the solicitor] £500, making fences, £200, roads £50.[42]

In the unusually favourable conditions of the Napoleonic Wars the farms here, and in other Breckland parishes, were viable. But subsequently it was often hard to find tenants. Even in the good years of the 1860s, before the onset of agricultural depression, four of the estate farms were in hand.[43] The extreme marginality of the local soils exacerbated the climatic extremes which characterised the region. In 1786 de Grey remarked:

> Our farms in the open country have suffered much by two dry summers and a winter unusually severe. I will venture to assert they are worth less by 20 per cent than three years ago.[44]

In 1828 John Worledge of Ingham described the farms in his area to a House of Lords Committee as 'principally of poor sandy soil and gravelly land, the produce of which in corn is very precarious, amounting in dry seasons to little or nothing'.[45] In fact, in contrast to the situation in North-West Norfolk, enclosure in Breckland was not necessarily accompanied by the large-scale ploughing of sheepwalks and the more intensive cropping of outfield breaks. The tithe maps of the late 1830s and early 1840s make it clear that large areas of heath survived within the new gridiron network of hawthorn or pine hedges. Some of this grassland was the result of post-Napoleonic War recession. Thus Mr Crosbie of West Stow Hall described in 1824 how

> When I hired my farm there was in cultivation upwards of 500 acres of the old outfield, but I found it was impossible with any advantage to keep so large a quantity of very bad land under the plough. I therefore determined with the sanction of the late Lord Cornwallis to select certain parts of the outfield which were rather better, to give them a good dressing of clay and to farm them upon the four-course system, which I have done, and to lay down for some years a very considerable part of the outfield, about 200 acres ... this additional quantity of new sheep walk it may be called gives a greater range for my stock in the summer.[46]

Much, however, had never been put to the plough. Indeed, improvers did not necessarily assume that enclosure would be followed by universal tilth. In part, the continued existence of extensive tracts of grass reflected the need to maintain large flocks of sheep so that the thin poor soils could be kept in cultivation. In part, however, it simply reflected the fact that much of Breckland were submarginal for cultivation in any circumstances, even those of the Napoleonic Wars.

Other aspects of the old agricultural regime survived within the new landscape. The tithe award maps show numerous outfield 'breaks', although these now took the form of consolidated fields bounded by straight hedges of pine or hawthorn, rather than areas of intermingled strips. Warrens, too, continued to operate within the enclosed landscape. In March 1784 William Smith

42 NRO, WLS XXVII/20/15 415 X 5.

43 NRO, WLS XVIII/17 411 X.

44 NRO, WLS XLI/2/20 430 X 5.

45 BPP, 1828, VIII, p. 544

46 Paine, *Culford Estate*, p. 30; Buckinghamshire RO, D/E By C44.

was given permission to 'add to his present warren in Sturston 48 acres of the arable lands belonging to the farm of the said Wm Smith adjoining to the north side of his warren bank and use the land as a warren during the continuation of his lease'. Many of the warrens were massive concerns: that at Stanford covered more than 537 acres. In the 1820s it was stocked with 7200 rabbits, but with the rabbits taken from the adjoining arable and sheepwalk the numbers were greater: nearly fifteen thousand were taken between 17 August 1824 and 1 March 1825, a yield which was considered about average.[47] The existence of such feral populations could in turn discourage reclamation. When the future of the Walsingham's Stanford farm was being debated in 1782 it was specifically stated that, because it was bordered by the warrens of Wretham and Sturston, it was likely that 'the greater part of it will be made a rabbit farm'.

In addition to all this, estate owners often preserved areas of heathland, even after enclosure, to provide cover for game. In 1780 Abel Smith, a tenant of the Walsingham estate, was accused of having cleared 'all the furze off Wether Heath, which leaves it as naked as Lincolns Inn Fields for the protection of game'. One of the complaints made in 1817 about Mr Sewell, another difficult Walsingham tenant, was that he had ploughed up areas of heath land without permission and thus damaged game cover.[48] Rabbit-farming and game-shooting might, to an improving agriculturalist, appear to be archaic or wasteful uses of land, but in this hostile environment they represented fairly rational forms of land use. In 1877, at the start of the agricultural depression, game and rabbits combined contributed no less than £1774 16s. 6d. to the income of the Merton estate.[49]

It was partly to provide game cover (particularly for the pheasant) that much woodland was planted in Breckland in the late eighteenth and early nineteenth centuries. Notable examples included the great belt of trees at West Tofts, embracing not only the park but also the home farm and a portion of heathland, which was planted in the 1770s: it consisted of a variety of trees, although principally conifers, and covered an area of around 100 hectares.[50] Arthur Young reported in 1804 that Sylvanus Bevan, a noted agricultural improver, had planted no less than 966,000 trees on his estate at Riddlesworth.[51] Afforestation often followed hard on the heels of enclosure acts. Thus a Walsingham estate memorandum detailing 'Business for 1779' begins with 'To complete the present Plantations at Tottington Heath', later continuing 'The six acres on Tottington Heath to be set out between the two Ten Acre pieces and Tottington Water, each to be broken up and lie so 'till it can be planted'.[52] Plantations also provided shelter in this bare and open landscape, and aesthetic considerations were also important. The most extensive plantations were associated with the parks laid out around the many gentlemen's residences located in the region. Contemporaries were also well aware of the economic benefits of planting. The West Tofts belt was up for sale with the rest of the estate in 1780, and the Particulars asserted that:

The number of trees that will remain in the Plantations, after they are thinned so as to leave them at a proper distance, to facilitate their Growth, will be about Six Hundred Thousand:

[47] NRO, WLS LXI/23 436 X 6.
[48] NRO, Petre Box 17, bundle 1.
[49] NRO, WLS XXIV.

[50] N. Kent, *A General View of the Agriculture of Norfolk* (1796), p. 92
[51] Young, *Norfolk*, p. 383.
[52] NRO, WLS XVII

which in the Course of a few years, will at least be worth a shilling a Tree, and consequently amount to Thirty Thousand Pounds.[53]

Even allowing for the customary exaggerations of sale catalogues, there can be no doubt that on marginal land like this large-scale tree-planting offered a better return in the medium term than agricultural rents: the 'shilling a tree' quoted in 1780 refers to semi-mature specimens. When mature the trees would fetch as much as twenty times this amount. We should, however, remember that on these light and sandy soils planting might be a risky business: trees were susceptible both to drought and to attacks by the ubiquitous rabbits. Letters relating to the Buckenham Tofts and West Tofts estates in the 1780s describe attempts to keep rabbit numbers down prior to planting: they remained 'beyond belief', considering that the owner, Payne Galway, had a warrener employed full time on the problem with 'ferrets and near a hundred traps'.[54]

We have dwelt at some length on the development of Breckland because it epitomises the process of reclamation on the poorest soils of East Anglia. On the one hand, this was a region transformed in the period of the Agricultural Revolution, in which perhaps 70 per cent of the land area was enclosed (from open field or heath) in the century and a half after 1700. Yet on the other hand, much of this land remained unimproved, or reverted to rough grazing after only a short period of cropping. All the enthusiasm of a Bevan, or a de Grey, could not triumph over the circumstances of nature.

(ii) *The Northern Heathlands and the Sandlings*

These two regions, as we have seen, in many ways resembled Breckland and North-West Norfolk: they were characterised by acid soils and, at the start of the period studied here, contained extensive areas of heathland. Yet there were differences. In particular, while in both these regions extensive areas were already owned in large units at the start of the eighteenth century, neither came to be dominated by the kind of very large estate common in North-West Norfolk or Breckland. These were, instead, landscapes moulded by a prosperous gentry. Furthermore, in neither area was the foldcourse a significant institution: some parishes in the Northern Heathlands had them,[55] but the majority did not, while in the Sandlings they were virtually unknown.

It was probably due to this latter circumstance that in the Sandlings, as we have seen, the majority of the arable land, and most of the heaths and marshes, were in severalty from an early date. Moreover, piecemeal engrossment and enclosure continued throughout the following century. In Alderton, for example, the court rolls document the acquisitions of the Woolnaugh family through the period from 1729 to 1768. Vast numbers of strips were purchased, many less than half an acre in size. Some strips survived as late as 1844 but they did so in a largely enclosed landscape.[56] Parliamentary enclosure, in contrast, was of minor significance in the region, effecting less than 3 per cent of the total land area, principally small patches of common heath

---

53 Sale catalogue, Norfolk Local Studies Library.

54 NRO, Petre Box 17 DR1: 13 Dec. 1787.

55 Thus, for example, leases for foldcourses in Heydon, Corpusty and Cawston survive from the 1750s and 1780s.

A lease for a farm in Oulton with 'liberty of sheep walk over lands in other's possession' was signed in 1758: NRO, BUL 11/310.

56 Burrell, 'Sandlings', p. 45.

and marsh. Only occasionally were more extensive areas of common removed, like the 233 acres of waste enclosed in Foxhall in 1804, or the 501 acres of 'heaths, plains, commons and waste grounds' removed in the same year at Bucklesham.

Of more importance than enclosure *per se* was the extension of the cultivated acreage. The frontier of cultivation was expanding in the early seventeenth century, but this process slowed after 1650. Indeed, in the years around 1700 the depressed prices of cereals encouraged some reversion to heathland, as on the Rous estate in 1700, where 150 acres of former arable were converted to a warren.[57] Stray references suggest that arable expansion recommenced in the course of the eighteenth century: thus the steward of the Friston Hall estate noted in 1729 that he had 'cleared about 30 acres of broom and furzes and hopes to have a good deal of corn there this year'.[58] But this process clearly intensified in the last decades of the century, and in 1795 Young, describing the 'extensive wastes of Sutton', commented:

> Having long ago called on the farmers publicly to cultivate them, I cannot but recollect the answers I then received – that it would not answer – and that they were fit only for what they gave – coarse sheepwalk. I have now the pleasure to find my old opinion confirmed, for great tracts have been broken up within these twenty years, and are found to answer well ...[59]

The reduction in the area of heaths was often considerable. Thus a map of estates of Sir Michael Stanhope in the parishes of Eyke, Bromeswell, Rendlesham, Tunstall, Chillesford, Sudbourne and Orford, surveyed in 1601, shows extensive areas of heathland which had, by 1840, been reduced by more than 75 per cent.[60] Nevertheless, conversion was by no means total, and many of the greatest heaths, such as Reydon, Foxhall, and Martlesham, survived largely untouched into the twentieth century: and many smaller areas of heath continued to exist within the bounds of ring-fence farms. Even with assiduous applications of marl, manure, and 'crag' – a Pleistocene deposit of shelly calcareous material which occurred in limited areas around Woodbridge – the viability of much reclaimed land was precarious. As in Breckland, when agricultural prices slumped after the Napoleonic Wars arable tended to revert once more to grass. In 1822 the agent of the Middleton estate reported that 'crops in general have been scanty' on the estate's Sandlings farms, and so rent reductions were needed.[61] Another survey described Denham Bridge Farm as 'light poor and uncertain land' and reported – significantly – that Purdis Farm consisted of poor land, more suited to stock than to arable, that had been ploughed too much.[62]

The pattern of change in the Northern Heathlands was in several respects similar to that in the Sandlings. Unhampered by the existence of foldcourses, piecemeal enclosure of open arable had usually proceeded a long way by the start of the eighteenth century. The map of Cawston surveyed around 1600 shows, as already noted, the open arable in an advanced state of attrition.[63] Here, as elsewhere, piecemeal enclosure continued during the next two centuries. By 1780, according to a Heydon estate map, Woodgate Field had entirely disappeared, along with

[57] ESRO, HA11 L9/22.
[58] BL, Add. Ms 22,249.
[59] A. Young, *A General View of the Agriculture of Suffolk* (1795), p. 38.

[60] Burrell, 'Sandlings', pp.107–9.
[61] ESRO, HA 93/3/126.
[62] ESRO, HA 93/3/155.
[63] NRO, Ms 4521, Map Box E.

Windmill Field and South Hawe. By 1801, only a few residual strips remained, although some 1300 acres of common land survived, and were removed by a parliamentary act in that year.[64] This late survival of large areas of common heath was typical. Over half the parishes in the region experienced some parliamentary enclosure, almost exclusively in the War years.[65] Around a half of these had 'combined' acts which included areas of open-field arable, but a sample examined in detail shows that the latter made up only 55 per cent of the total area enclosed.[66] Given that the acts relating to other parishes in the region dealt exclusively with common land, it is evident that parliamentary enclosure in this region was overwhelmingly concerned with open heaths.

Nevertheless, the pattern of enclosure was complex. There were some parishes in which rather more extensive areas of open field survived to be enclosed by act. Conversely, there were distinct groups of parishes where even the commons had been removed before the end of the eighteenth century. Almost without exception the latter lay within the bounds of one of the principal landed estates: great estate centres at Wolterton, Gunton, Blickling and Heydon were all surrounded by a penumbra of such parishes. It was, on the whole, those parishes lying at the interstices of the large estate blocks in which open fields and commons survived late, often until enclosure by act: a pattern not dissimilar to that already described in North-West Norfolk. The large estates were, however, busy building up their holdings even here and individual farms often included portions of both enclosed and open land. In 1742 Heath Farm, straddling the boundary between North Walsham and Worstead, covered 201 acres of enclosed closes, 86 acres of 'enclosed brecks', and 180 acres of open field land.[67] A series of maps and plans of the Heydon estate, compiled between 1770 and 1790, illustrates this complexity well.[68] The parishes of Heydon, Salle and Oulton – all on acid upland soils – were entirely enclosed: but in Corpusty and Cawston – larger, more populous parishes with more fertile soils – the estate lands lay in a mixture of open field strips and closes.

Cawston, as we have seen, lost its residual areas of open field through parliamentary enclosure but this did not happen in Corpusty. The Heydon map book suggests that around 50 per cent of the parish probably remained unenclosed in the 1770s or 1760s, but piecemeal enclosure was continuing, and notes in an estate memoranda book show that much land was being purchased in the parish in the late 1790s: in 1797 £1450 was spent on buying Mr Bowle's estate, and £1000 on Mr Elwyn's.[69] This still left several small holders as well as Lord Orford (26 acres), the Rev Pitman (51 acres), and Jeremiah Ives (420 acres). Unenclosed strips were still in evidence in 1802, when a lease for one of the farms contained husbandry and marling clauses specifically relating to both enclosed land and land lying in open strips.[70] Significantly, however, it also stated that the landlord had the right to exchange lands during the duration of the lease. Presumably piecemeal exchange and purchase led to the final eradication of the open arable, for the enclosure act of 1863 dealt with only a tiny area of common meadow. Corpusty's experience was shared by other parishes. In Saxthorpe, which adjoins it to the north, the

[64] NRO, MF/RO 334/1, 3.

[65] Stacey, 'Parliamentary Enclosure', pp. 39–42.

[66] Cawston 1802 (NRO, C/Sca2); North Walsham 1814 (NRO, Norwich Bishopric estates 164,380); Sheringham 1809 (NRO, C/Sca2/251); Edgefield 1815 (NRO, C/Sca2/

101); Tuttington 1821 (NRO, C/Sca2/261).

[67] NRO, BCH 72.

[68] NRO, MF/RO 334/1,3.

[69] NRO, MC 335 BUL 16/4.

[70] BUL 11/293/9

Wolterton estate was busy acquiring lands in the early nineteenth century: one purchase included 35 acres in 'diverse parcels of arable, meadow and pasture', another sixteen acres of 'half year lands'.[71] By 1840, according to the tithe award map, all trace of open fields had disappeared from the parish.[72]

The importance of engrossment and piecemeal enclosure in the region both before and during the 'parliamentary' period makes it difficult to estimate the overall chronology of enclosure. A reasonable estimate – based on an examination of 20 estate maps – would suggest that around half the region lay in enclosures at the start of our period; that another 25 per cent (mainly open field land) was enclosed by the late eighteenth century; and that another 25 per cent (of which around half was common land and half open fields) was removed by parliamentary act, or other means, in the period after *c.* 1790.[73] Given the nature of the evidence, this must be a very approximate estimate, but it is probably broadly correct.

Following enclosure, much common heath was put to the plough, and at the same time there were many attempts to improve and cultivate various areas of demesne heathland which, in the technical, legal sense, had been long enclosed. Thus the 700 acre Cawston Park on the Heydon estate was surveyed in 1789 and divided into large rectangular fields.[74] Initially parcelled out between three estate farms, it was later leased as a unit in its own right. By 1820 an up-to-date farm, complete with regular courtyard plan, had been built in the centre of this new landscape. It seems, however, that many attempts at converting heathland to arable were – as in Breckland – comparatively short-lived and unsuccessful. Following the enclosure of Cawston Heath in 1801 new farms were created and the land systematically marled and drained. But by 1804 much of the area of one of the farms, Botany Bay, had been 'laid down', or had 'grown to lyng': the crops of oats, rye and some turnips from the fields which remained in cultivation could only be described as 'tolerable'.[75] On some of the poorer soils enclosure was not followed by any attempt at reclamation: instead, as in Breckland, large landowners took the opportunity to plant woods and plantations. Thus at Westwick Lord Petre carried out a sustained planting campaign from the 1770s into the early nineteenth century, involving more than 500 acres of land. On the Felbrigg estate William Wyndham kept a detailed forestry book which describes his planting activities in the years around 1800. In spite of the high prices of grain it is clear that most of the plantations were established on newly-enclosed heathland on the Holt-Cromer ridge.[76] Nevertheless, while the very worst soils might revert to heathland, or be used for forestry in this way, on the whole the later eighteenth and nineteenth centuries saw a significant expansion of arable in the region.

[71] Wolterton Hall Archives, WOLT 14/6.

[72] NRO, 683.

[73] All references NRO. Attlebridge 1730 (DCN 127/27); Baconsthorpe 1768 (PD 334/11 (11)); Gt Barningham 1768 (56 BCH); Lt Barningham 1739 (Accn. Mar 1972); North Barningham 1758 (Aylsham 788 (Map Tree)); Blickling 1729 (R152 c); Cawston *c.*1600 (MS 4521 Map Box E); Crostwight *c.*720 (MFRO 359/17); Felthorpe etc. 1738 (MFRO 97/3); Hackford etc. *c.*1600 (BUL 11/45, P157 C);

Hackford 1743 (MS18141, 77 X 6); Haveringland 1674 (NRO 29 DCH); Haveringland 1738 (Mf 97B); Haveringland 1777 (NRS 1403A); Horsford 1712 (MS 1028 – 88, 35B1); Horsford 1761 (MS 11696 29E2); Horstead 1699 (Private Collection); Mannington late 16th century (Acc. Walpole 19 11 70 P150 B/4); Smallburgh 1582 (Acc. 4.3.86 above P152 A).

[74] NRO, MF/RO 334/1,3.

[75] NRO, BUL 11/503 618 X 9.

(iii) *The Flegg Loams*

The Flegg region displays a pattern of development very different to those just discussed. Here parliamentary enclosure had a much greater impact than in any other region of East Anglia except Breckland. In the two Hundreds of East and West Flegg no less than 59 per cent of the total land area was enclosed by parliamentary act. Moreover, a very high proportion of the land so effected (55 per cent) consisted of open-field arable. This puts the Flegg Hundreds ninth, in percentage terms, of the 350 districts in England listed by Gonner, with an enclosure density comparable to such classic Midland counties as Northamptonshire.[77] In the neighbouring Hundreds of Tunstead and Happing the figure was less impressive, at 38 per cent, while in Blofield it was 35 per cent: but these were, nevertheless, substantial areas by East Anglian standards. Only a small number of parishes failed to have enclosure acts.[78] In some, huge areas were effected, like Acle (2646 acres) or Hickling (2323 acres), although these figures are inflated, characteristically, by the inclusion of extensive areas of low-lying common fen and marsh.

The extent of open-field enclosure in the region, while perhaps unremarkable by Midland standards, is particularly striking when compared with the adjacent districts, especially the Northern Heathlands. The arable land of Winterton for example consisted almost entirely of open fields when it was enclosed in 1828: the pre-enclosure survey records 295 numbered parcels, of which 278 were open field strips.[79] In Runham half the arable land still lay in open fields as late as 1805.[80] Here the 'particulars' compiled by the enclosure commissioners provide considerable detail about all the arable land.[81] Strips were still overwhelmingly small: 87.6 per cent were of less than 2 acres, and 62.8 per cent less than one. In this respect, however, Runham was a slightly unusual case. Map and documentary evidence usually reveals that, while little piecemeal enclosure had occurred, piecemeal *consolidation* – to create larger though still unhedged strips – was widespread. For the parish of Repps, for example, we can compare a Field Book of 1578 with a 'Book of Reference' made to accompany a lost map in c.1753.[82] In the intervening period average strip size more than doubled, rising from 2r 19p to 5r 6p. Nevertheless, very few *closes* are listed in either survey, and when the parish was enclosed in 1809 more than half the arable land still lay open.

Even when the pattern of landownership might have been expected to encourage it, piecemeal enclosure was, in general, limited in extent. Scratby, for example, had the bulk of its open fields enclosed as late as 1842, yet the land tax returns suggest that considerable polarisation of land holding had taken place here during the previous century or so. In 1695 a total land value of £173 was shared among seventeen owners, the largest holdings being assessed at £36, £34, £31, and £26. By the 1780s, however, one individual (John Ramey) owned land paying £113, the lord of the manor paid £33 and the remaining £33 10s. was shared between only five others.[83]

In contrast to other areas of East Anglia in which the enclosure of open fields came late, this

[76] NRO, WCK 21/2.

[77] Bacon, 'Enclosure in East Norfolk', pp. 15–16.

[78] Ashby with Oby, and Clippesby in West Flegg; Thrigby and Mautby in East Flegg; Tunstall in Walsham; Walcot and Waxham in Happing.

[79] NRO, C/Sca3/35 A.

[80] NRO, C/Sca2/235.

[81] NRO, BRO 90/8.

[82] Bacon, 'Enclosure in East Norfolk', p. 47; NRO, EVL 585; EVL 443.

[83] Bacon, 'Enclosure in East Norfolk', pp. 48–50.

was not a region in which foldcourses were prominent. Even in the Middle Ages they had been rare. Resistance to enclosure seems to have been the consequence of rather different factors. The land here was so fertile that it was considerably more expensive to buy or rent than anywhere else in East Anglia. Young quotes average rents of 25s. to 27s. per acre, but noted that some could fetch as much as 42s.[84] As a result, this was not an area characterised by large landed estates, but by small freeholders, minor local gentry, and absentee owners: members of the urban elites (or charities) of Norwich or Yarmouth, and large estates (like the Evans-Lombe estate, with holdings in Repps and Eccles) which were based elsewhere in East Anglia, but which owned a few scattered farms in the area. Given the high rents received for this fertile land even before enclosure, there was little incentive for such owners to enclose. This was especially true given the nature of local agrarian organisation: not only was the foldcourse absent, but so too were almost all other forms of communal organisation and control, so that farmers in the open fields were largely free to grow what they wanted, how they wanted.

If the uplands of the Flegg region were dominated by arable land lying in open fields, the low-lying marshes were, as we have seen, used as pasture grounds. The extensive areas of marsh occupying the Halvergate 'triangle' was for the most part anciently enclosed, and by the late seventeenth century only pockets of residual common land lay around their periphery, which were removed by parliamentary enclosure. The traditional bullock-fattening economy seems to have been maintained throughout the period studied here, although sporadic attempts at ploughing are recorded. Armstrong in 1787 noted that the marshes were sometimes cultivated and afforded 'greater crops of corn than any other land';[85] in 1803 a marshman reported that parts of Halvergate Marsh near Yarmouth had been so much damaged by salt water flooding in the 1780s 'that they have not since been ploughed', and that other pieces of marshland 'in this part of the district were also cultivated prior to the great Flood which was occasioned by overflowing of the Sea at Horsey'.[86] Landlords tried to prohibit ploughing through covenants in farm leases.[87] A valuation of the Dean and Chapter's lands on Fowlholm and Skeetholm Marshes in 1790 thus noted:

> These marshes lye in thirty nine pieces every one of which I viewed separately some of them I found sown with & ? can Lessee breake them up without consent of the Lessors they ought to be Covenanted against it under a penalty of five Pounds an Acre for every Acre yearly so converted into Tilth.[88]

Bacon in 1844 noted that since the commutation of the tithes, the area of arable was gradually being extended on the marsh: previously, the higher tithe charge imposed on arable had discouraged conversion. He nevertheless believed that their value as grazing grounds was such that 'the largest portion will in all probability never be touched by the plough'.[89] He was right: arable remained a relatively minor aspect of the economy of the marshes.

In the upper reaches of the river valleys, where most of the land was common and much consisted of fen grounds, enclosure had a more profound impact in the eighteenth and

[84] Young, *Suffolk*, p. 38.

[85] M. J. Armstrong, *History and Antiquities of the County of Norfolk* (1781), p. 93.

[86] NRO, EAW 2/118.

[87] See, e.g., NRO, FEL 579.

[88] NRO, DCN 52/2.

[89] R. N. Bacon, *Norfolk Agriculture*, (1844), p. 294.

nineteenth centuries. Much piecemeal enclosure, and some large scale enclosure, had occurred here since medieval times. In 1573 the lord of the manor of Clippesby reached an agreement with his principal tenants to fence off part of the low common and take it into private owner-ship;[90] while in 1614 the lord of the manor of Aldeby and his tenants agreed to enclose 'all such marshes rushe grounds and reede grounds … as nowe bee or are reputed to bee or might be used or fedd in common', something finally achieved in 1635.[91] The 1720 parliamentary enclosure of the common marsh at Stokesby (the earliest act in East Anglia) was thus following in a long tradition. Nevertheless, large areas of common marsh and fen continued to exist, especially in the valleys of the Ant and Thurne, and these were removed in the great spate of enclosure in the years around 1800 which also swept away the open fields of the adjacent 'uplands'.

Enclosure was frequently associated with improvements to drainage. Many acts ordered the erection of drainage mills and most provided for new dykes and embankments, and established Drainage Commissions to maintain them.[92] Yet enclosure often made little difference to estab-lished patterns of land use. Where commons had been used as grazing marsh, this continued to be their principal function after enclosure; and most fen grounds, whether privately owned or used as poor allotments, continued to be cut for hay and litter, sedge and reed, and turf. Indeed, in many places there seems to have been a marked increase in the extent of turf cutting following enclosure, and mid and late-nineteenth century maps show large areas of fen occupied by extensive, but shallow, 'turf ponds'.[93] Sporadic attempts were, it is true, made to convert fens into improved grazing grounds. Bacon in 1844 thus described how peat marshes in Surling-ham had been embanked, under-drained, top-dressed, and manured, and drained by mills: 'loose peat bog' had been thus turned into valuable pasture.[94] The ruined remains of drainage mills in the middle of waterlogged fens at Catfield and elsewhere are evidence of similar attempts. Most, however, met with limited success, due to compaction of the peat and increased incidence of flooding, and the areas in question were abandoned to reed and sedge in the middle and later years of the nineteenth century.[95]

(iv) *The Claylands*

The enclosure and land-use histories of the three principal clayland regions – the Central Clays, the Dissected Clays, and the Southern and Western Clays – display considerable variation. The Central Claylands were little effected by enclosure in the period studied here: maps and surveys suggest that only *c.*15 per cent of the total land remained in open fields in 1660, but that this had been reduced to less than 4 per cent by 1790, when the first enclosure acts to affect the region were passed, through the continued progress of piecemeal enclosure.[96] Parliamentary enclosure in this region was almost entirely concerned with the removal of greens and com-mons, most of which had survived significant encroachment. Following the passing of an award such areas were almost invariably put to the plough. It is important to emphasise, however, that even these acts were largely concentrated in the north of the region – in south Norfolk and the extreme north of Suffolk – and great swathes of central Suffolk were completely

90 Cornford, 'Commons of Flegg', p. 16.

91 NRO, MS 7458, 736; MS 19913 123 X 1.

92 Williamson, *Norfolk Broads*, pp. 92–9, 118–25.

93 *Ibid*, pp. 99–103.

94 Bacon, *Norfolk Agriculture*, pp. 293–4.

95 Williamson, *Norfolk Broads*, pp. 98–9.

96 Skipper, 'Wood-Pasture', *passim*.

untouched by parliamentary enclosure of any kind.[97] In short, in this large region – comprising around a fifth of the total land area of East Anglia – enclosure was of minor significance in the agrarian and landscape history of the eighteenth and nineteenth centuries.

This does not, however, mean that there were no significant changes in the way that land was used. In the late seventeenth century, as we have seen, the Central Claylands had been dominated by pasture.[98] By 1840, to judge from the tithe award maps and the tithe files, this was largely an arable region, with significant areas of permanent pasture only surviving where soils were particularly tenacious. Whereas in 1650 most farms in the area had, on average, perhaps 20 per cent or 25 per cent of their land under the plough, by 1840 70 per cent or even 75 per cent was the norm.[99]

Such evidence as there is suggests that the expansion of arable was beginning before the marked rise in cereal prices which occurred after 1760. By 1760, of the 1700 acres owned by the Adair estate in Flixton and the South Elmhams – an area comprising the heaviest soils in Suffolk – 798 acres were already in tilth.[100] Young in 1786 suggested that a major shift had occurred between the 1740s and 1780s – 'about forty years ago there was very little under tillage' – and relates the change initially to an increase in the cultivation of fodder crops, including both turnips and cabbages, in an intensification of the existing cattle-based economy.[101] However, towards the end of the century the area of arable expanded more rapidly – in Withersdale in 1758 55 per cent of the land was under the plough, but by the end of the century this figure had risen to over 75 per cent.[102] The inflated prices of the Napoleonic War years saw the demise of large-scale dairying in the area. Young, writing about north Suffolk in the second edition of his *General View* of 1803, noted that 'since the former edition of this work [1796] much larger tracts of grass have been broken up and the number of cows very much reduced'.[103] As Biddell, later in the nineteenth century, commented:

> The decrease in the number of cows commenced when the war prices of the first decade of the century remained long enough to impress the farmers of that day with the idea that the permanent price of wheat would be 100s per quarter. Pasture farming, with its herds of milch cows and butter at 9d. a pint could not stand before the temptation of £3 a coomb of wheat.[104]

Most landlords were initially reluctant to countenance large-scale conversion to arable, and leases usually forbade the ploughing up of pasture – or at least stipulated that an equal amount of arable should be put down to grass in compensation. It was generally held that this heavy land was damaged by ploughing: an estate survey of Flixton in 1750 typically stated that 'the heavy land should not be ploughed, except to clean it and lay it down'.[105] Nevertheless, by 1820 the process of arablisation was largely complete.

The development of agriculture on the Dissected Clays of central Norfolk differed in a number

[97] Turner, 'Parliamentary Enclosure'; D. Dymond, *The Norfolk Landscape* (1988).

[98] Theobald, 'Changing landscapes', pp. 10–24.

[99] Kain, *Atlas*, pp. 45, 74.

[100] ESRO, HA12/E1/1/20.

[101] A. Young, 'Minutes relating to the dairy farms of High Suffolk' *Annals of Agriculture* 27 (1786), pp. 193–224.

[102] ESRO, FC90/C1/34.

[103] Young, *Suffolk*, p. 163.

[104] H. Biddell, 'Agriculture', in *White's Suffolk Directory* (1874), p. 26.

[105] ESRO, D3/1.

of important respects. As already noted, open-field agriculture was more deeply entrenched in this region. Piecemeal enclosure appears to have made less headway by the start of our period, partly because these lighter soils were better suited to arable farming, partly perhaps because foldcourses continued to operate in some parishes. Hardly surprising, then, that parliamentary enclosure was more important here. Of the 155 parishes in the region, no less than 130 were affected by some form of parliamentary enclosure; and of these, 72 had acts which removed open fields as well as commons.[106] However, analysis of a sample of 12 awards relating to parishes in which both commons and open fields were removed suggests that common land was the main target of the enclosers. On average, only c. 25 per cent of the area enclosed comprised open-field arable, and 75 per cent commons and wastes.

Much open-field land certainly disappeared before the parliamentary enclosure period. Open arable accounted for c. 25 per cent of the area of Raveningham, and c. 36 per cent of Morley in the mid-seventeenth century: but none existed in either parish by the early nineteenth century. Raveningham did not have an enclosure award and that for Morley related mainly to 541 acres of common land, removing only residual grazing rights from small areas of enclosed arable land. In many other parishes the story was the same. Brisley, for example, had over 40 per cent of its area under open field cultivation in 1622 but was entirely enclosed by the early nineteenth century, with the exception of the commons which in this case remain open to this day. Of course, only a small minority of parishes in the region have early maps of this kind but, extrapolating from those that do, it would appear likely that at the start of our period around 50 per cent of the land in the region still lay in open fields, while 20 per cent consisted of commons and wastes, and 30 per cent was enclosed. The bulk of open-field land was thus enclosed piecemeal between c.1650 and c.1790, leaving only 7 per cent of the total area in open fields. This, together with the majority of common land, was enclosed by parliamentary acts, largely concentrated in the War years.

The enclosure of common land was almost invariably followed by ploughing, and those areas of old-enclosed pasture land scattered along the remote interfluves were also generally put to the plough, in the years around 1800. The extensive 'grazing grounds' shown on eighteenth-century maps at Wood Dalling on the Heydon estate, for example, had all been broken up by the time the tithe award maps were surveyed. The expansion of arable was less dramatic than in the Central Claylands, because a greater proportion of the land here had always been under cultivation. Nevertheless, between a quarter and a third of the total land area passed from grass to tilth during the eighteenth and early nineteenth centuries.

The enclosure history of the Southern and Western Clays is more akin to that of the Central Claylands. This was an area virtually untouched by parliamentary enclosure. A handful of parishes in the extreme west of the region – Withersfield, Great Thurlow, Great Wratting, Haverhill and Great Bradley – had acts which removed residual areas of common pasture and arable, and elsewhere some small tyes and greens were removed in this way (at East Bergholt, Polstead, Hadleigh, and Semer). But that was all. The muted impact of parliamentary enclosure was here, however, not so much due to the fact that piecemeal enclosure had been continuing

---

[106] Although 130 parishes were affected by enclosure, only 98 acts were passed, many involving land in more than one parish. See Stacey, 'parliamentary Enclosure', pp. 27–29.

throughout the previous century, but rather because most parishes had never had much open land. Yet if the *enclosure* history of this region allied it with the Central Clays, its *land use* history was more like that of the Dissected Claylands. Arable already accounted for some 45–50 per cent of land use at the start of the period, to judge from estate maps, rising to 65 per cent or more in most parishes by the time of the tithe files.

(v) *Fenland*

As described in the previous chapter, seventeenth-century reclamation of the southern peat Fens had been followed by the lowering of the ground surface and extensive flooding, and in consequence the extent of arable land was limited for much of the eighteenth century. At the end of the century, however, the area under cultivation began to expand once more. Young in 1804 described the practice of burning and paring, or *den-shiring*, in terms very similar to those used by Blith in 1658. Having stripped the surface turfs and burnt them in piles, the ashes were spread across the fields. 'Coleseed is then sown on one shallow ploughing', followed by oats. The land was then laid to grass for many years. He noted, however, that this traditional form of convertible husbandry was being dropped in favour of a more intensive course of cropping: 'the common conduct is to make this operation the preparation for successive corn crops, and perhaps in bad rotation'.[107] This was a very recent development, inspired by the high cereal prices of the War years; and Young was still able to describe the Norfolk peat fens as 'one of the richest tracts of grass in Norfolk',[108] while Faden's map of Norfolk (1797) and Hodskinson's of Suffolk (1783) denote the area as unimproved marsh. Nevertheless, arable land use continued to expand in the years around 1800, to judge from a variety of estate maps, and this process continued steadily in the first half of the nineteenth century. Drainage was improved, partly through the construction of new watercourses (notably the Eau Brink Cut in 1821) and partly as a consequence of the employment of steam pumps in place of wooden drainage mills. The Sutton St Edmund (Lincs) steam engine was erected as early as 1817, although it was not until the 1830s that they began to appear in the Norfolk and Suffolk fens, with the construction of the Magdalen Fen engine (TF 598098) in 1834, and the Brandon engine in 1836. By the 1850s steam drainage was ubiquitous. The new machines were a great improvement on windmills. Not only could they drain much larger areas (the largest could deal with 15,000 acres or more), they were also much more reliable, continuing to operate whatever the wind conditions. It should be noted that these improvements rested on the development of appropriate organisational structures: a series of parliamentary acts, beginning in 1727 with Haddenham in Cambridgeshire, established a number of Drainage Commissions consisting of locally elected landowners who were responsible for the establishment and maintenance of the drainage of compact areas of fen and marshland. They were empowered to levy taxes, borrow money, employ staff and construct drains and mills.

Equally important, however, were changes in the soil environment. In many places the continued wastage of the upper levels of the peat – resulting both from desiccation, and from the wind erosion consequent on paring, burning and ploughing – allowed the underlying clay

---

[107] Young, *Suffolk*, pp. 182–5.   [108] Young, *Norfolk*, p. 376.

to be excavated with relative ease, and spread upon the surface. Caird discussed this process in some detail in 1852. It involved

> Digging trenches into the clay, and throwing it over the surface. A trench two feet deep and two feet wide is made along the field, and the clay which is taken out of it is laid four yards over the surface on either side of the trench. The same process is repeated throughout the field, a new trench being opened eight yards apart from the last.[109]

More detail was supplied in 1858 by Sewell Read.

> The greater part of the Norfolk fens has, happily, a substratum of clay, the overlying peat varying in thickness from 2 to 20 feet. Even at the latter depth clay is raised to the surface by means of deep trenches. It often happens that the peat, by being weighted and well drained, is so compressed that in a few years the clay is nearer the surface, and consequently more accessible for a second dressing. The border lands – those fens which skirt the higher grounds – are more improved than any others, being better situated for the extensive application of clay, marl, chalk and sometimes sand. Extraordinary dressings of these earths, from one to two or even three hundred loads per acre, are applied, and a rush-growing morass has, by these means and by draining, been speedily converted into a fruitful cornfield.[110]

The clay acted not merely as a mineral manure. It also stabilised the peat, and reduced the speed at which it degraded and blew away. The cost of this operation, according to Caird, was about 35*s.* an acre but it was 'a permanent improvement, not requiring to be repeated during a lease'. The change in the Fenland landscape in the first decades of the nineteenth century was remarkable. Successive estate maps, such as those dawn up by the Hares of Stow Bardolph in 1812 and 1840, show the steady arablisation of the fens.[111] In 1836 Calthrop believed that the price of wheat had been adversely effected by the 'immense tracts of land brought into cultivation in the fens of Lincolnshire, Cambridgeshire and Norfolk'.[112] By *c.*1840, according to the tithe award maps, around 70 per cent of the peatlands were under the plough.

Landscape change in the northern silt fens, or Marshland, was less dramatic. Here, too, grazing predominated in the early and middle decades of the eighteenth century. Thomas Cox in 1700 thought that the farms of the district 'turn to more profit by grazing than ploughing', and tithe books suggest that virtually all the silt soils in the parishes of North Runcton and West Winch were under pasture in 1713.[113] The area under cultivation seems to have expanded rapidly in the later eighteenth century and by the early nineteenth, to judge from commentators like Young, arable farming was widespread on the 'more mild and temperate' soils. Here, too, arablisation proceeded apace in the early nineteenth century, and by the 1840s around 60 per cent of the land surface was in tilth.

While both fen districts thus saw a marked expansion of ploughland, it is important to emphasise that this was not, in any significant way, associated with enclosure. The bulk of Marshland had been subject to only very limited rights of commonage even in the Middle Ages,

---

[109] J. Caird, *English Agriculture in 1851* (1852), p. 181.
[110] C. S. Read, 'Recent improvements in Norfolk Farming', *JRASE* 19 (1858), pp. 267–8.
[111] Stow Hall archives, uncatalogued.

[112] Minutes of evidence taken before select committee on agricultural distress, 1833, Q. 7794.
[113] NRO, PD 332/20.

and such rights had generally been extinguished by the end of the seventeenth century. The 8000 acres of Marshland Fen and Marshland Smeeth were enclosed by an act of 1796, and a further 5000 acres of common land in Outwell, Stow Bardolph, Wimbotsham and Downham were enclosed in 1798, but few other commons of any size survived into the eighteenth century. The peat fens had also largely been enclosed in the period before 1660. In all, well over 80 per cent of the two areas were thus already held in severalty at the start of our period, leaving only residual areas of common land to be removed by parliamentary act.

(vi) *Conclusion*

The history of enclosure, reclamation, and land use change in East Anglia in the eighteenth and early nineteenth centuries is thus immensely complex: every region had its own distinctive experience. While at the start of the period there were many areas which were already largely enclosed – such as the Central Claylands – there were others which still lay largely open, and which were to remain so for another century or more. Even in regions in which large areas of open land existed in the late seventeenth century, some individual parishes were already entirely enclosed. The reasons for these marked regional and local variations are complex, and evidently the result of the interplay of many factors. Some general determinants can, however, be suggested. The most important, in regional terms, were patterns of earlier land use and agrarian organisation. Districts in which enclosures predominated by the end of the seventeenth century were those in which open field and commons had always been of limited extent (e.g., the Southern and Western Clays) and/or those in which, in early modern times, livestock production had dominated over cereal cultivation (e.g., the Central Claylands or the Fens). In the period studied here, however, it was not so much regional as local patterns which structured the history of enclosure: patterns of ownership and tenure. In all regions, small parishes in single ownership, or with only small numbers of proprietors, were enclosed earlier than larger, more populous ones with more complex structures of ownership. In sheep-corn areas, as we have seen, this distinction was often accentuated by the institution of the foldcourse.

Beckett is clearly correct in his insistence that there has been an overemphasis on parliamentary enclosure at the expense of enclosure by other means.[114] Not only was enclosure by non-parliamentary means widespread in the period before 1780; it also continued on some scale after this date. Enclosure by act was an expensive business and where landowners had some alternative in systematic engrossment they usually took it. A more important observation, however, is that enclosure made comparatively little impact on the East Anglia landscape in the course of the eighteenth century, a period in which arable yields rose steadily. In all, it is likely – drawing together the various broad estimates advanced in the course of this section – that around 66 per cent of East Anglian was already in severalty by 1700. Of the remaining open fields and commons, probably around 18 per cent were enclosed in the period of the Napoleonic Wars, mainly, but by no means exclusively by parliamentary act; and a further 1 per cent was enclosed after the end of the War. Allowing for land still technically unenclosed, no more than 14 per cent of the total land area of the two counties was thus enclosed, by whatever means, between 1700 and *c.*1790.

---

[114] Beckett, *Agricultural Revolution*, p. 39.

The above discussion also suggests that some historians have concentrated over-much on enclosure when examining landscape change in the period of the 'Agricultural Revolution'; and have too easily conflated enclosure in the legal and tenurial sense with reclamation and land-improvement. One the one hand, it is important to emphasise that vast areas of *several* heathland and rough grazing were reclaimed in the course of the eighteenth and nineteenth centuries; and on the other, that the legal enclosure of marginal land was not always followed by improvement, or at least by sustainable reclamation. In Breckland, in particular, some areas of heath were left largely as they were following enclosure and many reverted to rough grazing in the course of the nineteenth century.

The dominant theme in the agrarian history of East Anglia in this period was, nevertheless, the expansion of tillage at the expense of pasture. In the Fens, in the Central Claylands, and to some extent in the other clayland regions, the ploughing up of pasture was unquestionably the key development of the eighteenth and nineteenth centuries. In traditionally arable districts, too, cultivation expanded as heaths and sheepwalks were put to the plough. Around 40 per cent of the ground area of East Anglia had been under arable cultivation in 1700: by the 1850s, to judge from Sir John Walsham's figures, this figure had risen to around 65 per cent.[115] Enclosure was one aspect of this great change, but there were others which have perhaps received insufficient attention from historians, most importantly various practices intended to alter the structure and chemistry of the soil itself; and it is to these that we must now turn.

2. Improving the land: marling, underdraining and field rationalisation

(i) *Changing the soil: marling*

As marling was of central importance in the East Anglian agricultural revolution, it is surprising that most modern commentators have chosen to pay so little attention to it, Beckett's *The Agricultural Revolution*, for example, giving the subject a mere six lines.[116] Contemporaries, in contrast, had no doubts about its fundamental significance. The individual writing under the synonym 'N' in the *Gentleman's Magazine* in 1752, for example, put it at the head of his list of practices which typified the improved husbandry of Norfolk.[117]

Both 'marl' and 'marling' are difficult terms which have caused confusion to both contemporaries and modern historians. In essence, marling was the practice of digging large pits in order to extract an underlying subsoil, different in character from the topsoil, and spreading this on the surface. As Mathew has recently argued, the technique was not primarily intended to improve the texture of the soil but rather to counteract the natural acidity to which most soils in England, especially the more porous, are prone, due to the fact that lime is constantly leached downwards by rainwater.[118] This does not mean that marling was never employed (rightly or wrongly) to improve soil texture. At Hunstanton in 1645, for example, payments were made for carrying sand 'into some rank stiff clay places'; and again in 1653, when sand was spread on 'churlish stiffe clay places'.[119] But the main intention was unquestionably the

[115] BPP 1854, LXV, pp. 290–300.
[116] Beckett, *Agricultural Revolution*, p. 18.
[117] *Gentleman's Magazine* 12 (1752), p. 502.

[118] W. M. Mathew, 'Marling in British Agriculture: a case of partial identity', *AgHR* 41 (1993), pp. 97–110.
[119] NRO, LeStrange KA9.

neutralisation of acidity, as Marshall made clear in his *Rural Economy* of 1787.[120] Of four different kinds of Norfolk 'marl' which he tested all, he concluded, were forms of 'calcareous earth'. The samples could be divided into two main types: *chalk-marl*, which occurred in the centre and west of Norfolk; and *clay-marl*, which was found in the east.

The former material, he rightly concluded, consisted of the upper levels of the solid chalk, variously mixed with the lower levels of the overlying strata. In the west of East Anglia the chalk was generally buried by thin (3–6 metre) deposits of sandy drift. In central areas it was more deeply mantled by superficial deposits and could usually only be excavated from pits dug in the sides of the principal valleys. West of a line drawn, roughly, from Weybourne to Hoxne, then south-westwards to Stowmarket, and then in an irregular fashion to Ipswich, the chalk is more deeply buried: not merely beneath glacial drift but under thick layers of the Pleistocene Crag. Only in two main areas within the eastern half of East Anglia could it be reached with relative ease: in the valley of the Yare between Norwich and Blundall, and in the valley of the Bure between Aylsham and Coltishall. Major centres for the excavation of marl developed in the neighbourhoods of Whittlingham, Thorpe-Next-Norwich, Horstead, Wroxham, Coltishall and (to a lesser extent) at Oxnead and Lammas. Ease of transport provided by the Broadland rivers added further stimulus to the industry: the produce of these pits was, by the 1780s, widely disseminated by wherry through the north and east of Norfolk.[121] Young described how Hemsby, Langley Ludham, Thrigby and Martham received marl from the Thorpe pits, Catfield from those at Horstead, and Honing from Wroxham.[122] Marshall similarly noted how marl from pits near Norwich was brought to Woodbastwick, by water, via Yarmouth – a distance of more than forty miles – although by road the distance was little more than six.

There were other kinds of marl available in the north-east of Norfolk – in the Flegg Loam Region and the Northern Heathlands. This was the material described by Marshall as 'clay marl'. He analysed samples of this 'clay marl' from a pit at Hemsby and discovered that it was composed of only 43 per cent 'somewhat impure chalk', the rest consisting of 50 per cent clay and 7 per cent sand. This material was, in fact, the particularly calcareous clay of the North Sea drift, which occurs in substantial but disconnected blocks within the otherwise sandy drift at a depth of four metres or so beneath the surface.

Such material was absent from the claylands further to the south. Here the drift, which was deposited by earlier phases of the ice advance, contained small quantities of chalk but this was often mixed with much non-calcareous material of Jurassic origin. Young, describing the practice of 'claying' on the central Suffolk loams, noted that some of the material employed was 'so exceedingly strong and loamy, that it will not mix with the soil', while another sort was 'very tender', with an admixture of sand. The best, however, was 'strong and full of particles of chalk', and Raynbird in 1849 similarly observed that 'there is very little clay applied to the land that does not contain a large proportion of lime; and the general test as to the good quality of clay is the presence of small particles of chalk'.[123] Such material was not available throughout the claylands. In 1849 it was reported, for example, that 'there is but little marl' in the area

[120] Marshall, *Rural Economy*, II, pp. 16–27.
[121] *Ibid.*, II, p. 364.
[122] Young, *Norfolk*, pp. 402–12.

[123] W. and H. Raynbird, *On the Farming of Suffolk* (1849), p. 52; Young, *Suffolk*, pp. 186–93.

around Halesworth, while further south, around Framlingham, one of Raynbird's correspondents in the 1840s similarly reported that 'We have no quantity of marl here'.[124]

To the east, in the Sandlings region, there was neither calcareous drift nor calcareous subsoil: the glacial outwash sands and gravels contained no chalky till, and below them lay, not the chalk, but the Pleistocene Crag. In many places suitably calcareous clay might be carted in from the claylands to the west, but this was an expensive operation. In the neighbourhood of Wrentham it was reported in 1849 that 'Marling is but little done in this locality, by reason of the distance it has to be brought'.[125] In 1824 the agent of the Middleton estate wrote of the Denham Bridge farm that 'There being no clay or heavy earth to be obtained, prevent the improvement of this light soil': similarly, there was no marl or chalk on Thomas Arnold's farm in Nacton and as a result the outlook for both farms was considered bleak:

> Lands of this description have felt a greater depression than the fair mixed soil. There is a great uncertainty of crop, for want of fresh earth or clay the layers will not stand well, even for one year.[126]

Only in restricted areas of the Sandlings – principally in the vicinity of Woodbridge – was suitable material locally available. Here the underlying crag had a particularly shelly, and therefore calcareous, composition. It was used to improve the quality of the soil since at least the early eighteenth century.[127]

The availability of marl thus varied greatly from region to region; but so too did the importance and character of marling. Heavier land – especially in the Central Clays – certainly benefited from applications of calcareous subsoil, but the gains were nothing like as great as in light soil areas: the topsoil was, in general, much less leached and acidic. Marling here usually took place when pasture land was first broken up for cultivation. The Raynbirds thus reported in 1849 that

> On heavy land it [marl] is used on freshly broken-up pasture land, and mixed with farmyard manure in the formation of compost heaps. On light soils its application is of course more extended ...[128]

In 1750 on the Flixton estate marling was recommended, but only where old pastures were being ploughed.[129] The 1790 survey for the same estate recommended marling on a number of farms in the Elmhams area, but once again only in the context of the conversion of old grassland to tillage.[130] Occasionally, where the clays were well mixed with acid sands (as often in the Dissected Clayland region, or in the major valleys within the central Claylands) more routine applications might be made. Thus a Shotesham lease of 1804 stipulated that 500 loads should be laid on the farm for every year of the 14 year tenancy. But for the most part the clays were less in need of regular liming than the light sandy soils of East Anglia.

It was thus in areas of light land, and especially in areas of sandy soil, that marling was most necessary, and made the greatest impact in the eighteenth century. Marling was essential when

[124] Raynbird and Raynbird, *Suffolk*, pp. 129, 133.

[125] *Ibid.*, p. 132.

[126] ESRO, HA 93/3/155.

[127] Raynbird and Raynbird, *Suffolk*, p. 56.

[128] *Ibid.*, p. 52.

[129] ESRO, Adair D3/1.

[130] ESRO, Adair E1/5/86.

heaths and sheepwalks on such land were being converted to arable. The 'hungry dry soils' of the Itteringham heaths, according to a Blickling survey of 1756, could not be cultivated without marl.[131] Maps drawn up to accompany the improvements planned by the Walsingham estate in Stanford and Sturston in the 1770s carefully noted possible sites for digging clay and marl, indicated by such captions as 'chalk at 6 foot' and 'good clay at 4 foot', etc.[132] The central importance of marling to land reclamation schemes appears again and again in accounts and correspondence. In the 1740s William Greenway, the Hon. Thomas Barret's agent in Horsford in the Northern Heathlands, described how he had 'examined all the tenants. Muskett has hitherto carried his true quantity of marl'.[133] It is a letter written three years earlier which places this activity in the context of a reclamation scheme: 'Muskett is doing very well by the farm and he has second fenced a considerable quantity of land where most needed. Could have done more but for the want of bushes and hurdles hereabouts'.[134] These references, moreover, follow on from an earlier comment, made in a letter of 1739, in which Thomas Marsham – having inspected the Horsford property – found a 'vast tract of land' he believed to be improvable were it not for the presence of a warren, and 'especially if marl and clay be easily had'. Another letter, from Stephen Norris in 1742, noted that a certain farm here would cost £4 per acre to improve – a total cost of £1300 'even if clay and marl were to be found conveniently placed' (although even then he deemed the project 'very uncertain').[135] By 1754, however, it was reported that the tenant had marled about 50 acres with 123 score cart loads of marl.[136]

But in addition to its use in land reclamation, by the end of the century marl was being routinely applied in large and sometimes enormous quantities to *long-established* arable on the lighter land of East Anglia. Marshall reported how farmers applied anything from 20 to 100 loads per acre, followed by smaller doses after a decade or so. At the end of the eighteenth century Breckland leases often stipulated that 75 loads per acre should be applied for the first four years of a lease, fifty per acre for the next four years, and twenty five for the rest of a twelve or eighteen year lease.[137] Marling on this scale amounted to a radical alteration to the natural environment, and some contemporaries became alarmed by the side effects. Raynbird in 1849 described how

> Although marl has been found … most excellent for wheat, yet a sad mortality in the sheep has been observed whilst feeding on land that has recently been marled.[138]

Estate correspondence makes a number of references to the problem. Mr Fox of Tottington – a Walsingham tenant – sustained great losses 'by sheep warping [aborting] their lambs last year'. Mr Lincoln, a neighbouring tenant, claimed in 1836 that he had lost 200 lambs 'being warped in consequence of claying land'.[139]

Marling was not in itself an innovation of the eighteenth century. A grant of 1276, for example, refers to a 'Marlepit' at Saxthorpe in north Norfolk; marling is mentioned in a number of fourteenth-century documents relating to the Breckland; and marl pits are referred to on a

---

[131] NRO, MC3/59/252 468 X 4.
[132] NRO, WLS LXI/1, 430 X 5.
[133] Letter dated 18 Mar. 1749: Essex RO, D/DLC6/13.
[134] Letter dated 19 Dec. 1752: Essex RO, D/DL/C6/21.
[135] Essex RO, D/DL/C8/1; D/DLC9/2.
[136] Essex RO, D/DL/C22.
[137] See, for example, NRO, WLS XXIX/2/34 416 X 4.
[138] Raynbird and Raynbird, *Suffolk*, p. 118.
[139] NRO, WLS XVIII/1 478 X 9.

number of occasions in thirteenth and fourteenth-century documents in the Holkham cartulary.[140] The impression given by medieval and early post-medieval references, however, is that it was then a sporadic and occasional occurrence: it is only from the early eighteenth century that very large applications begin to appear in estate documents. Some of the most striking come from North-West Norfolk, and especially from the Holkham estate. In the period 1710–15 John Carr, fulfilling the terms of his lease, marled 240 acres of his farm in Massingham (he was allowed 8s. an acre in return by the estate, thus receiving a total of £96).[141] William Dewing of South Creake agreed to spread 5000 loads of marl on his farm in 1727; William Kent of Weasenham was allowed £70 in 1748 for carrying 5856 loads of marl; and in the same year John Elliott, of Branthill Farm in Holkham, was allowed £30 for 2000 loads.[142] Raynham leases tell a similar story. In 1714 alone, in East and West Rudham, 3700 loads of marl were spread. In 1717 John Money leased Grange Farm in West Rudham for 21 years: a farm of 460 acres, of which 90 acres were breaks. Of the latter, 30 acres were designated for annual cultivation. Money was to marl 20 acres of these at his own expense with 60 loads per acre, and receive rent reductions for marling the other ten.[143]

These examples have been quoted as evidence of the agricultural precocity of the 'Good Sands' region of North-West Norfolk. But equally early references come from the Northern Heathlands. Leases from the Rant estate refer to marl as early as 1682, when J. Noble of Thorpe Market was allowed to take 'as much as he think fit' from pits on the estate. Another Thorpe Market lease, of 1690, stipulated the application of fifty loads of marl on every acre, 'the landlord paying or allowing for the said digging, loading and spreading of the said marl'. In 1701 W. Challis was allowed 30s. for every 100 loads of marl put on the land. Large scale-marling similarly features in leases of 1705 (for a farm in Southrepps where 200 cart loads were to be spread on an area of unknown acreage) and 1709 (Thorpe Market, Roughton, and Gunton; this tenant was to be allowed 30s. per hundred loads for 600 loads used on the premises).[144]

It is, however, important to emphasise that marling is not *normally* referred to in early eighteenth-century leases. Indeed, only a small minority make any allusion to the practice. Moreover, where marling *is* mentioned, it is usually in the context of reclamation of sheepwalks and heaths, and generally involved the landlord paying, or subsidising, the tenant for his efforts. It seems that, in general, marling only figures in eighteenth-century leases where land was being reclaimed: leases were not, at this stage, concerned with regular applications to existing arable land. This does not, however, mean that such applications were not being made: merely that they were not the concern of the landowner. On the Hunstanton estate, for example, leases for farms in Great Ringstead (1782), Heacham (1782), Hunstanton (1784), Heacham (1787), Barrett Ringstead (1788), Hunstanton (1788) and Heacham (1789), Hunstanton (1791), Holme (1792), Hunstanton (1795), Heacham (1795), Ringstead (1797 and 1798), Ringstead (1798), Ringstead Hall (1800), Hunstanton, Heacham and Barrett Ringstead (1801), Hunstanton (1807), and Heacham (1817), all completely fail to mention the practice.[145] Yet marling was certainly going on here:

[140] H. Prince, 'The origins of pits and depressions in Norfolk', *Geography* 49, (1964), pp. 15–32; W. Hassall and J. Beauroy, *Lordship and Landscape in Norfolk 1250–1350* (British Academy Records of social and economic history, ns, 28, 1993), pp. 186, 210, 534, 541, 564–565, 582.

[141] Holkham Hall Archives, A/B, 1711–1715.
[142] Holkham Hall Archives, A/B 1727, 1748.
[143] Rosenheim, *Townshends of Raynham*, pp. 151–2.
[144] NRO, Gunton uncatalogued.
[145] NRO, LeStrange KA22.

the Ringstead Hall labour book for 1798 records numerous payments for marl carting, raising chalk and chalk carting, as do the farm accounts for Snettisham 1810–11, and those for Court Yard Farm in 1812.[146]

The Hunstanton series of leases is slightly unusual, however. On most East Anglian estates the status of marling appears to have changed significantly in the years around 1800. Routine marling of arable land ceased to be a matter left to the discretion of the tenant and became instead a condition of a tenancy. The surviving leases for the Heydon estate, in the Northern Heathlands, show this transformation well.[147] Marling is stipulated in leases of 1724, 1729 and 1748 in contests which suggest land reclamation. Its absence from the terms of other leases does not mean that local farmers were not marling existing arable, however, for a lease of 1758 contains a clause allowing the tenant to take marl from the estate for his own use. Unfortunately, after 1761 there is a gap in the sequence of surviving Heydon leases, until 1789: after this there are leases only for 1802, 1803, and 1804. All mention marling, and make it clear that the character of the practice had now changed. The 1802 lease for Corpusty stipulated that the tenant should marl every field on the farm in the first twelve years of the lease, at twenty-five loads an acre. The 1803 lease (for Cawston) required that 35 acres were to be treated every year, with 20 cartloads per acre; while the 1804 lease (again for Cawston) stipulated 40 acres were to be marled each year, with ten loads per acre. What had once been general practice – but left to the tenant's discretion – was now being demanded as part of the terms of a tenancy agreement.

This shift in emphasis in the years around 1800 is apparent elsewhere. Thus on the Kings Lynn Borough's Snettisham estate two eighteenth-century leases for the Red Barn Farm (one undated, one of 1786) make no reference to marling. By 1803, however, an estate survey noted of the property: 'at the rent Bunn engaged the farm he ought to have covenanted to have carried at least 40 loads of marl and clay which are on the premises per acre on the whole land'. A new lease issued by the Corporation in 1807 stipulated that 250 acres were to be clayed within seven years with at least 50 cartloads per acre.[148] The implication of all this is that lease prescriptions have to be used with considerable care when we attempt to chart the adoption of marling as a general method of land improvement: and it is the stray references, like those in the Heydon lease for 1758, which suggest that large-scale marling of existing arable first became widespread in East Anglia in the middle decades of the eighteenth century.

This is certainly the impression gained from other sources, such as the anonymous correspondent to the *Gentleman's Magazine* in 1752, already quoted. Nineteenth-century commentators likewise believed that large-scale marling had developed in the middle decades of the eighteenth century. Bacon, for example, described the transformation in yields which had been effected on a Watton Farm in the 1730s and 1740s through assiduous applications to existing arable land (6378 loads between 1732 and 1742).[149] Map evidence attests the steady expansion of marling as a routine practice. A map of 1715 shows only one marl pit – 'No Mans Pit' – situated among the open-field strips of West Field in Castle Acre. A map surveyed c.1840 shows no less than seven 'old pits' and sixteen 'new pits' within the same area, now occupied by the enclosed ground of Lodge Farm.[150]

[146] NRO, LeStrange Suppl. List Box 2.
[147] NRO, BUL 11/310.
[148] NRO, AF 234, 220, 206.

[149] Bacon, *Agriculture*, pp. 267–76.
[150] Prince, 'Pits and depressions', p. 22; Bacon, *Agriculture*, pp. 267–8.

(ii) *Changing the soil: underdraining*

If marling was the main technique by which eighteenth-century farmers improved the light, acid soils of East Anglia, then underdrainage was its equivalent in clayland regions. Drainage of heavy soils was (and is) of crucial importance because seasonal waterlogging stunts the growth of all crops and precludes the cultivation of some. It also increases the soil's acidity and renders the ground more difficult to cultivate.[151] Yet the progress of drainage in the eighteenth century has been consistently underestimated by historians, largely because of a widespread belief that drainage methods were primitive and ineffective prior to the middle decades of the nineteenth century. In the view of Chambers and Mingay, 'The problem of heavy land drainage remained unsolved until the introduction of cheap tile drainage in the 1840s leaving the high-cost and inefficient farming of heavy claylands as the most obvious weakness in the progress of eighteenth century farming';[152] while in Robert Sheil's opinion, 'Poor drainage stunted growth on heavy and poorly drained soils, but it was not until the mid nineteenth century that really effective underdrainage became available'.[153]

We will argue here a rather different case: that effective systems of field drainage were widespread in East Anglia by the end of the eighteenth century; that these were an essential pre-requisite of the large scale conversion of pasture to arable that occurred in many parts of the clays in the second half of the eighteenth century; and that they were, in fact, one of the key factors in raising yields on the heavier soils in this period.

It is not entirely clear how heavy arable land in East Anglia was drained before the eighteenth century. Ploughing in 'ridge and furrow' may have been more widespread than the evidence of surviving earthworks suggests, but narrow, impermanent ridges or 'stetches' were also employed. William Folkingham, in his *Feudographica* of 1610, recommended that while 'fat, strong and fertile grounds that be tough, stiffe, binding cold and wet' should be ploughed in broad ridges, 'cold and stiffe ground inclining to barrennesse' should be ploughed in 'stitches': a practise which, he specifically noted, was common in East Anglia.[154] Either way, the crucial development of the eighteenth century was development of underdrainage. This involves laying drains beneath the surface which remove water first downwards, beyond the root zone; and then laterally, away from the field. In the course of the nineteenth century, earthenware pipes came into general use for this purpose, but in the eighteenth century the normal method was that of 'bush' drainage. Networks of parallel trenches were cut across fields and filled with brushwood, and/or various other materials (ling, straw, or stones), and then backfilled with soil (Figure 8). The drains either emptied directly into the ditches surrounding the field, or into a larger underground drain which did so. Field drains of this kind usually lasted for between ten and fifteen years, although Young reported some at Redenhall in Norfolk which were still

[151] D. H. Robinson, *Fream's elements of Agriculture* (13th edn, 1949), pp. 36–37.

[152] J. D. Chambers and G. E. Mingay, *The Agricultural Revolution, 1750–1880* (1966), p. 65.

[153] R. S. Sheil, 'Improving soil fertility in the pre-fertiliser era', in Campbell and Overton (eds), *Land, Labour and Livestock*, p. 53.

[154] R. Silvester, 'Ridge and Furrow in Norfolk', *Norfolk Arch.* 40 (1989), pp. 286–98; R. Liddiard, 'Ridge and Furrow in Norfolk: ploughing practice and subsequent land use', (unpublished MA Dissertation, Centre of East Anglian Studies, University of East Anglia, 1997). W. Folkingham, *Feudographica* (1610), p. 48.

8. Digging bush drains in Suffolk in the 1890s: an illustration from Rider Haggard's *A Farmer's Year* (1899).

serviceable after 27 years.[155] Caird reported that in Suffolk in the 1850s the benefits from such drains were normally 'expected to last for a 14 years' lease', and went on:

> At the beginning of a new lease the land is gone over again, the direction of the drains being now made to cross the old drains obliquely, and thus to *bleed* such as still remain open. As a long fallow is regarded as a routine operation twice or thrice in the course of a short lease, so is draining looked upon as a matter of regular occurrence once every 14 or 16 years.[156]

Bush drainage is often described as a primitive practice, and one of limited value, compared with that which was effected by tiles or pipes.[157] But this is only true up to a point. Earthenware drains might last longer, but they were not necessarily any more efficient than bush drains and they were considerably more expensive to install. In the middle of the nineteenth century prominent agriculturalists could still recommend the old method in preference to the new, at least for the stiffer soils, in which such drains could be expected to last longer.[158] Indeed, the practice continued to be employed on some Norfolk and Suffolk farms up until the time of the Second World War: it was still being recommended by the Ministry of Agriculture as late as 1925.[159]

The agent for the Ashburnham estate in Suffolk described in 1830 how the tenants capped their underdrains with wheat stubble, a method which ensured that they lasted 'many years'

[155] Young, *Norfolk*, p. 392.
[156] Caird, *English Agriculture*, pp. 152–3.
[157] N. Harvey, *The industrial archaeology of farming in England and Wales* (1980), p. 72.

[158] Raynbird and Raynbird, *Suffolk*, p. 116.
[159] G. Ewart Evans, *Ask the fellows who cut the hay* (1956), p. 120; *id, Where beards wag all* (1970), p. 87; *J. Ministry of Agriculture*, Feb 1925, pp. 986–8.

although created at a fraction of the cost of those made with tiles. 'I have urged all the tenants to underdrain all the land requiring it, assuring them that they will themselves partake of the benefit and be reimbursed by the first crop'.[160]

In part, modern historians' neglect of bush drainage reflects the importance they have ascribed to the later tilepipes; and this in turn reflects the prominence of the latter method in documentary sources. The various forms of tile drainage were a matter of much discussion in the pages of the *Journal of the Royal Agricultural Society of England* in the 1840s, and the government loans scheme instituted in the 1850s generated a substantial amount of documentary evidence which has been studied in detail by A. D. M. Phillips.[161] Bush drains, in contrast, have left little documentary evidence. Drainage is only occasionally referred to in leases before the end of the eighteenth century, generally where the landlord agreed in advance an allowance for draining areas being brought into cultivation (as at Shotesham in 1774, where a tenant was allowed a guinea an acre for underdraining 16 acres of Hill Close and Lower Hall Close).[162] As with marling, landlords sometimes demanded more regular drainage during the buoyant years of the Napoleonic Wars: in 1811, for example, Thomas Carter agreed, as a condition of a lease signed for a farm near Stowmarket, to 'underdrain not less than seven or ten acres of land in each year the draining to be paid for by him the said Thomas Carter'. But such clauses remained rare, presumably because – as bush drains would not last much more than a decade and a half in usual circumstances – it was doubtless felt that they would not effect the long-term value or productivity of the land, and were therefore an improvement which was entirely to the benefit of the tenant.

It is thus sources other than leases which attest the central importance of the practice in the East Anglian claylands by the later eighteenth century. The farming journal kept by Randall Burroughes of Wymondham between 1794 and 1799 is especially informative.[163] Drainage was a winter activity, and the journal unfortunately contains no record for the winter of 1796–97, and only a very gappy one for that of 1798–99. Nevertheless, drainage activity during the other years was clearly on a grand scale. In 1794–95 four fields, covering more than 25 acres, were drained. The following year there was more work in some of these fields, a further six acres were drained, and work began on the group of fields called Bones. The latter was still continuing two years later, in the winter of 1797–98, when the Six Acre Home Close was also drained. Although drainage was sometimes associated with the breaking up of old pasture closes, most took place within existing arable fields and usually occurred during the long fallow preceding the turnip shift.

Burroughes' drains were generally spaced at intervals of 12 yards, and dug to a depth of 24 or 26 inches. They fed into main drains dug to a depth of 28 inches. These dimensions were typical – similar, for example, to those quoted by Arthur Young in his *General Views* of Norfolk and Suffolk. The drains were filled with a variety of materials. In 1794–95 alder poles, brought from 'Mr Bernard's alder carr' four miles away, were used. In 1795–96 the drains in Spikes Lane

[160] ESRO, HB4/2.

[161] A. D. M. Phillips, *The underdraining of farmland in England during the nineteenth century* (1989).

[162] NRO, FEL 417.

[163] S. Wade Martins and T. Williamson (eds), *The farming journal of Randall Burroughes (1794–1797)* (NRS, 58, 1995).

Pightle were filled with oak wood cut from nearby pollards, while at Bones in 1797–98 thorns cut from the hedges round the field were used, together with poles lopped from neighbouring ash pollards. When drains were put into the field called Wolseys, however, Burroughes intended filling them up with stones

> But unfortunately after the finishing one drain the stones that had been gathered off the lands at Bones lately clay'd had too much soil adhering to them so I was under a necessity of desisting & of looking out for some wood for the same purpose.[164]

He was thus obliged to bring faggots from Ashwellthorpe Wood, *c.*7 kilometres away, at some expense.

Whatever the materials used, the fill was usually capped with straw before backfilling, a practice which could have a knock-on effect on other aspects of agriculture and land management. Thus the agent for the Ashburnham estate described in 1830 how the wheat stubble was 'left standing in the fields of considerable length having been reaped with a sickle in that manner for the purpose'. (Interestingly, the tithe file for Earsham noted with approval that the farmers there used furze and ling for their drains, 'knowing too well the use of straw for manure to bury it in this shape'.[165])

Bush drainage was not cheap: Burroughes himself describes it as 'an expensive improvement'. In 1795 he informs us that the 514 rods of drains put into Block Close cost £9 9s. 4d. (at the standard rate of a halfpenny a yard), but added that this was for labour only, 'exclusive of materials and carriage amounting to more than equal that sum', suggesting a total cost of around £20. As three other fields were drained during the course of the same winter the total bill must have been somewhere between £50 and £100. In the following year a total of 1577½ rods of drain were laid on his Browick farm up to the beginning of March, presumably at a cost of around £23 for the labour alone: but further draining occurred in the field called Bones during March at a cost of £20, the majority of which was for raw materials. Once again, a total yearly expenditure well in excess of £50, and probably nearer £100, is indicated. The costs per acre of the improvement are more difficult to calculate, because the acreages of the fields in question are seldom stated in the journal, but later references suggest that Whinn Close covered around five acres and 384 rods of drains were laid there. This must have cost (to judge from the expenditure on other fields) around £5 10s. for labour and as much again on materials: a total expenditure, that is, of around £2 per acre, more or less the figure suggested by Phillip Pusey in his remarks following Henry Evans' article 'Norfolk Draining' of 1845.[166]

Randall Burroughes was an ardent improver, and it is possible that he drained his land more assiduously than his neighbours: but he was clearly not a trail-blazer. In 1795 he agreed to supply the drainers with their tools although 'according to custom' they should supply their own, a phrase which clearly suggests that underdraining was common practice in the area. Young described in the *General View* for Norfolk in 1804 how 'draining is well established and much done' in the area between Attleborough and Hingham, while in the *General View* for Suffolk

[164] *Ibid*, pp. 74–5.
[165] ESRO, HB4/2; PRO, IR 18/6336, 5896.
[166] Wade Martins and Williamson, *Randall Burroughes*,

pp. 27–8; H. Evans, 'Norfolk Draining', *JRASE* 4 (1845), pp. 43–4; P. Pusey, 'Remarks on the foregoing evidence' [i.e., Evans], *ibid.*, p. 44.

in 1814 he simply remarked that 'This most excellent practice is general on all the wet lands of the county; it is too well known to need a particular description'.[167]

Walter Blyth refers to underdrainage as early as 1649 [168] but, so far as the evidence goes, it first became widespread in Essex in the early eighteenth century. Eighteenth-century commentators often referred to it as the 'Essex method'. Bradley, in 1727, described the practice as 'but a late invention' on the claylands of north Essex, while in 1728 Salmon described how the 'cold and wet lands' of Hertfordshire had been 'greatly improved' by the introduction of the practice 'within twenty years' from the neighbouring areas of Essex.[169] In 1845 Henry Evans was informed that underdrainage had 'prevailed for a century and a half' in East Anglia, although Pusey in the same year suggested a shorter chronology, stating that '*for a century* it has been used generally in the large and well-farmed counties of Essex, Suffolk, and Norfolk, as well as in Hertfordshire' (our italics).[170] Documentary evidence perhaps suggests a more gradual diffusion through the eastern counties. There are scattered references to 'laying faggots', presumably in drains, in farming accounts in the first half of the eighteenth century, but when a survey was made of the Blickling estate farms in Wymondham on the south Norfolk claylands in 1750, it was noted that

> Both the tenants like all others in the woodland or dairy part of Norfolk are slovenly and don't endeavour to drain their land in a husbandlike manner – heavy strong land, but could be improved.[171]

In the *Annals of Agriculture* in 1784, Young described how at Crowfield in Suffolk, hollow draining was 'done by the farmers, but not the twentieth part' that should have been carried out.[172] Interestingly, one of the contributors to the Raynbirds' *Suffolk Agriculture* of 1849 reported:

> The statement of old farmers, who allege that sixty or seventy years ago the practice was just being introduced into the parish in which they had been brought up, and that previous to that time the system of *thorough* drainage by placing drains at regular and close intervals throughout a whole field was not practised, but merely drains put in here and there to carry water from a particular wet spot.[173]

On balance, it would seem that the practice was gradually adopted on the East Anglian clays in the period after 1760, but by the 1790s had become widely established. It continued to spread during the early years of the nineteenth century, as the tithe files from the 1830s make clear, for they frequently comment on the importance of the improvement and the widespread nature of its adoption. In the north Suffolk parishes of South Elmham All Saints and St Nicholas, for example, it was said that

> There is a great spirit of improvement pervading this part of the county and that by means

---

[167] Young, *Norfolk*, p. 392; Young, *Suffolk*, pp. 172–3.

[168] S. Wade Martins, *Farms and Fields* (1995), p. 102.

[169] R. Bradley, *A General Treatise of Husbandry and Gardening* (1727), p. 23; N. Salmon, *The History of Hertfordshire* (1728), p. 1.

[170] Evans, 'Norfolk Draining'; Pusey, 'Remarks'.

[171] NRO, MC 3/59/252 468 X 4.

[172] Young, 'High Suffolk', p. 196.

[173] Raynbird and Raynbird, *Suffolk*, p. 112.

of underdraining which is now in very general practice the produce of these heavy lands will be very much increased.[174]

Negative comments on this subject in the tithe files also occur, but their phrasing implies that the practice was becoming normal. Those made about North Lopham in Norfolk are typical:

Good and effectual underdraining is constantly necessary and this in the case of the small owners and occupiers is sometimes neglected on account of the heavy expense.[175]

By the 1840s, when bush drains were beginning to be supplemented or replaced by tile pipes, underdrainage was a standard feature of clayland husbandry, and one of the contributors to the Raynbirds' survey of Suffolk agriculture in 1849 went so far as to assert that 'At the present time nearly every piece of land in the heavy land district of this county has been drained, and many pieces several times'.[176]

The adoption of tile-pipe drainage in the middle and later decades of the nineteenth century thus represented a development of an existing practice rather than a radical new departure. Its superiority over the traditional method was never perhaps as great, in East Anglia at least, as some historians have implied; and in some districts at least its period of popularity was short. It is true that earthenware tiles were being used in parts of Suffolk in the early nineteenth century. Arthur Biddell, of Playford in Suffolk, recorded the purchase of 'One thousand draining tiles from Goodings of Tuddenham' in December 1817.[177] But they probably did not come into widespread use for several decades. In 1849 the East Suffolk Agricultural Association was offering a prize to 'the tenant (a member of this Association) who shall have spade-drained … the greatest number of rods, in proportion to his occupation'. The individual had to state, among other things, 'the materials used in draining'. Significantly, the society offered an *additional* premium to the tenant who 'shall have drained the largest breadth of land exclusively with tiles, or pipes, in proportion to the extent of wet or clay land upon his occupation'.[178] The wording suggests that tile drainage was still comparatively rare in the 1840s. The method was probably spreading more rapidly by this time, however, following the fall in the price of pipes (by as much as 70 per cent) which resulted from Thomas Scragg's introduction of mass production methods in 1846, together with the availability of government loans for drainage schemes (although the extent to which these were taken up by East Anglian estates remains unclear). In 1851 Caird described how bush drains were still in widespread use in Suffolk, but pipes were generally used for the main drains, and

In all cases where it is found desirable that the work should be permanent, pipes or tiles are used throughout, and the drains cut from three to four feet in depth.[179]

By 1858 Sewell Read was able to assert that 'Bush-draining clay soils is a very ancient practice in Norfolk, and though pipes are now mostly used, the old mode still exists'.[180]

The fact that the tile drains were more permanent, as well as being more expensive, than the

---

[174] PRO, IR 18/9736.

[175] PRO, IR 18/6069.

[176] Raynbird and Raynbird, *Suffolk*, p. 115.

[177] J. Thirsk and J. M. Imray (eds), *Suffolk farming in the*

nineteenth century (Suffolk Record Soc., 1, 1958), p. 40.

[178] Raynbird and Raynbird, *Suffolk*, pp. 49–50.

[179] Caird, *English Agriculture*, pp. 152–3.

[180] Read, 'Recent improvements', p. 270.

traditional method radically changed the status of underdraining. It moved from being an activity of practical husbandry which was of importance only to the tenant, to a permanent improvement of interest to the landlord. On the Holkham estate, tenants with farms on the heavier lands in the Dissected Clayland region in central Norfolk were generally left with the responsibility for underdraining until 1850. Not all were willing or able to carry out this task: in 1816 Blaikie reported on the lamentable condition of drainage on a Holkham farm at Tittleshall, while at Croxton Farm in Fulmondestone drainage was needed but there was no hope of improvement under the current occupier. After 1850, however, the landlord undertook drainage and charged 5 per cent interest as a surcharge on the annual rent. The importance of drainage as an item of expenditure was short-lived, however: while the sums expended rose rapidly to £1707 in 1853–54, they then fell away, and declined to a negligible amount as the agricultural depression deepened after the 1870s. James Caird concluded that only 20 per cent or less of the land that could have benefited from draining on the estate had in fact been drained by 1873.[181]

Other estates were more tardy in instigating the improvement. The first time draining appears in the records of the Flixton estate, for example, was as late as 1862, when £17 was spent at Fressingfield and £123 at Flixton Grange on underdraining, ditching, and guano.[182] When Keary prepared proposals for the Duke of Norfolk's estates in 1861, one of the main deficiencies he highlighted was the relative absence of tile drainage, noting that the tenants still relied on the traditional, cheaper methods.[183] Clearly, on the very eve of the agricultural depression, some large clayland estates were taking very little interest in the innovation, their tenants continuing to drain by the older method.

Field drainage was thus of considerable importance in East Anglia in the eighteenth and early nineteenth centuries. Bush drainage was adopted on a wide scale before the introduction of pipes, and the old method continued to predominate in many districts even during the 'high farming' period. In short, underdrainage of heavy land was a key element of the East Anglian agricultural revolution.

(iii) The rationalisation of field boundaries and removal of hedgerow timber

Field drainage in the claylands was often accompanied by other forms of land improvement, notably the alteration of field boundaries. The previous history of the Central Claylands, in particular, had created a pattern of small, often irregularly-shaped fields. While land lay under pasture this caused few problems: but when arable expanded, alterations became necessary. Small, irregular fields were inconvenient for ploughing, and the hedges shaded out the crop and took nutrients from the soil. At the same time, any large grazing grounds on the level interfluves which had escaped subdivision into smaller pasture closes were now broken up into more manageable units. This was partly because the addition of field boundaries increased the number of ditches and thus helped drainage: such ditches were particularly necessary where underdrains were being installed, because these did not work efficiently if their length was too great. But it was also because the new arable land was normally farmed under some form of

[181] S. Wade Martins, A Great Estate at Work (1980), pp. 96–7.

[182] ESRO, HA12 D/1/9/9.

[183] NRO, Smiths Gore 20.10.70 1520.

'improved' rotation, each unit of which had to be bounded by stock-proof barriers: fields of 50 acres or more were simply too large to be treated as rotational units, given the fact that even the largest clayland farms seldom extended over more than 200 acres.

Large fields and small were generally bounded by tall hedgerows which were frequently crammed with timber and pollards. Many were bordered by wide 'rows' of pollarded trees, and/or contained a more general scatter of timber and pollards. An abundance of pollards might be welcome to a small farmer operating a dairy farm, but not to an arable producer. Free-standing trees got in the way of the plough. Those in hedges, with dense and spreading heads, shaded out the crop, damaged it through water dripping from the leaves, and their extensive root systems competed for nutrients. In general the eighteenth century saw a developing antipathy towards pollarded trees. Better to plant *timber* trees in hedges, if you must have trees there at all. 'Let the axe fall with undistinguished severity on all these mutilated heads', urged Thomas Ruggles in 1796 in the *Annals of Agriculture*. By the end of the century Anthony Collet described Suffolk landlords giving their clayland tenants leave to 'take down every pollard tree that stands in the way of the plough'.[184]

Randall Burroughes of Wymondham was in the forefront of this war on the irregular, pollard-ridden, 'traditional' landscape. Every winter we find his men busy stubbing out hedges and taking down old pollards.[185] In the last two weeks of 1794, for example, Burroughes described how 'Elmer & Meadows began to through down & level an old bank in part of the pasture between little Bones & Maids Yards'; how 'at home the men were employ'd in stubbing a tree or two for firing & other odd jobs'; how 'some ash timber' was cut down; and how 'the frost continued very severe so much so that … the men employed in throwing down old hedgerows found the greatest difficulty in penetrating the ground with pick axes'. Work continued on a similar scale into the new year. In the first week of January 1795 Burroughes 'Agreed to give ninepence a rod & the firing for levelling old hedgerow in Brick Kiln Close at Suton'; while in the second week of the year he reported the levelling of 'the bank in Bertfield Close at Suton next the common' and referred in passing to wood taken from 'the bank thrown down at Little Bones'.[186] We can sometimes see how Burroughes' urge to rationalise the landscape was directed at particular areas of his estate, as in early 1796 when a field called Whinn Close was being converted from pasture to arable, and was being amalgamated with the adjacent field. In February he reported that 'The trees … at the west side of the Whinn Close were stubb'd at the rate of three pence a tree and the ground firing. A beginning also was made in stubbing the hedge between Burtfield & Whinn Close the price 6*d.* per rod & the firing … The drainers also continued making their progress in Woolseys as did Bairn & his son in levelling the hedge bank between the Burtfield & Whinn Closes'.

As well as disliking pollard trees, the agricultural improvers of the late-eighteenth and nineteenth centuries were also increasingly hostile to traditional forms of woodland management and, with rising grain prices and improvements in drainage, the heavier land which ancient woods frequently occupied could often be more profitably used as arable. It was the smaller

[184] Young, *Suffolk*, p. 57.
[185] Wade Martins and Williamson, *Randall Burroughes*, p. 29.
[186] *Ibid*, pp. 46–50.

woods and copses which were particular targets. The small copses and linear, field-edge woods shown on sixteenth and seventeenth century maps of the claylands did not disappear at quite the rate of the pollard 'rows'; but they nevertheless declined markedly in number. Thus, for example, a map of the demesne lands of the manor of Hedenham, surveyed in 1617, shows two large named areas of woodland – Hedenham Long Row, and Hedenham Wood – and a further four small woods each covering an area of three hectares or less.[187] Of these, the largest (at around three hectares) survives in the modern landscape as Round Grove but the three smaller ones had disappeared without trace by the middle of the nineteenth century.

Progressive simplification of existing field patterns, and reduction of hedgerow timber, were not restricted to the Central Clayland region, although they were certainly of the greatest importance here. The other clayland districts – the Southern and Western Clays, and the Dissected Claylands – had (as we have seen) a less 'bosky' appearance at the start of the seventeenth century, and a higher proportion of the land was under arable cultivation. Less simplification and alteration was thus required in these regions, although here too there was much felling of timber and pollards, and much realignment or removal of hedges.

3. The improvement of grassland

(i) *The poor state of pastures*

Eighteenth-century commentators were usually at pains to emphasise the poor nature of East Anglian pasture lands, particularly those in the claylands. As Young put it in 1804:

> No person can have been in Norfolk without quickly perceiving, that in this branch of rural economy the county has very little to boast. Nowhere are meadows and pastures worse managed; in all parts of the county we see them over-run with all sorts of spontaneous rubbish, bushes, briars, rushes; the water stagnant; ant-hills numerous; in a word, left in a state of nature, by men who make all sorts of exertions to render their arable land clean, rich and productive.[188]

In Suffolk, similarly, he considered that 'the management of meadows, and upland pastures ... can scarcely be worse'. Young's comments about Norfolk were echoed by Marshall in 1787: 'Admirer as I am of the arable management of this county ... I cannot refrain from condemning in full terms its grassland management'.[189] Estate surveys regularly bemoaned the poor state of the pastures. The 1750 survey for the Flixton estate, for example, described how thirty acres of the Abbey Farm was overgrown with bushes, while of another holding the reporter noted: 'I never saw so much land lay waste' or 'an estate so slovenly managed'.[190] On the claylands generally landowners made little attempt to control the activities of their tenants, and lease prescriptions were largely restricted to prohibitions on the ploughing up of old grass, 'except to clean it and lay it down'. The Tithe Files of the late 1830s frequently commented on the poor state of the region's grass. At South Elmham, for example, they noted that 'The pasture land is for the most part very indifferent'; while at Flixton there was 'an unusually large proportion

---

[187] NRO, Bedingfield 27.7.65 P150B/3.   [189] Marshall, *Rural Economy*, I, p. 314.
[188] Young, *Norfolk*, p. 370.   [190] ESRO, HA 12 D3.

of pasture – not of good quality'.[191] The meadows, sporadically, received a better press, but on the whole the picture is a gloomy one: certainly, there is little evidence for the systematic improvement of pasture grounds which John Broad has noted in parts of the Midlands.[192] This lack of interest presumably reflects the increasingly arable nature of the East Anglian economy in the eighteenth century: farmers who were busy ploughing up their pastures, and investing in arable production, simply had little interest in improving their grassland.

(ii) *The Broadland marshes*

Yet there were exceptions to all this. Young praised, in particular, the value of the Halvergate marshes to the west of Yarmouth, and these (and to some extent other areas of grazing marsh in the Flegg Loam region) do seem to have been subjected to systematic and capital-intensive schemes of improvement in the course of the eighteenth and nineteenth centuries.

The Broadland marshes, as described earlier, had been used as grazing grounds from the earliest times, but although their richness was praised by Defoe and others at the start of the eighteenth century, there remained room for improvement. In 1728, for example, the tenants of the Dean and Chapter lands in Skeetholm pointed out to their landlords the extent to which the value of the land fluctuated from year to year, for in a wet year 'the Estate for half a Year together is a Meer Puddle notwithstanding its fine Appearance in Summer'.[193] Flooding may have been an increasing problem in the late seventeenth and early eighteenth centuries due to the slow but steady changes in relative land/sea levels which continued throughout post-medieval times. Contemporaries also believed that increased tidal flows, resulting from more intensive dredging of the rivers, as well as the increased quantities of water flowing in the lower reaches of the rivers due to the reclamation of fen grounds higher up (especially in the valley of the Thurne), were increasing the threat of flooding. By 1803 one observer was able to comment that 'The marshes could not be kept dry from the water, were it not for the Engines – the water came thro' the banks every year, little or much'.[194]

The construction of drainage mills was, indeed, the principal improvement effected on these rich pastures in the course of the eighteenth and early nineteenth centuries. By ensuring that water was removed from them more quickly in winter, the quality of pasture was considerably improved: damper ground produced poorer grazing, dominated by rushes and other coarse herbage. Precisely when mills were first employed in Broadland remains unclear. In the Fenlands of west Norfolk and Suffolk they were being used for drainage in the early seventeenth century, but on Halvergate they probably appeared in the late seventeenth century. There is little firm evidence for their construction before 1700 (the earliest references is perhaps to one in Halvergate parish in 1702). The first wind pumps were small, simple, timber-built smock mills like those shown on a map of St Benet's Abbey 'with the marshes belonging to the same' surveyed in 1702, and on a survey made following the enclosure of the parish of Stokesby by parliamentary act in 1721.[195] But is was not long before brick-built tower mills began to appear. Marshall, writing in 1787, was already able to describe the standard marsh mill as 'built of brick, about

[191] PRO, IR 18/9736, 6275.
[192] J. Broad, 'Alternate husbandry and permanent pasture in the Midlands, 1650–1800', *AgHR* 28 (1980), pp. 77–89.

[193] NRO, DCN 59/15/2.
[194] NRO, EAW 2/118.
[195] NRO, Snelling 1.12.72 P150 B5; EAW 1/8; MC 351/2, 711 X 1.

twenty feet high, with sails similar to those of a corn mill, but somewhat smaller.[196] Such low mills, simple structures with 'common' sails spread with canvas, and driving a single external scoop wheel, remained the norm in Broadland well into the nineteenth century.[197]

Drainage mills spread gradually in the Broadland marshes – both on Halvergate, and in the marshes in the upper Thurne valley – in the course of the eighteenth century, although paucity of evidence makes it impossible to chart this development in any detail. All we have are a few examples of surviving structures bearing datestones (the low tower mill at Oby carries a date stone of 1753 and that on the Brograve Marshes, Hickling one of 1771) and stray references in estate papers. Thus in 1740 the accounts for the Langley estate record a payment of £50 for the construction of a mill in the Round House Marshes in Langley;[198] an undated document, probably drawn up in the mid-1760s, refers to the construction of a drainage mill in Norton; and by c.1768 another document was able to list 'The contents of ye several marshes lying in Norton belonging to W[illia]m Windham Esq w[hi]ch are drained by ye New Engine'.[199]

The construction of these early mills was usually funded jointly by groups of proprietors. Thus in June 1769 William Wyndham, the owner of the Earsham estate, reached an agreement with John Berney of Bracon Ash, John Fowle of Brome, and Dionissa his wife to erect a drainage mill. The lands in question were

> Subject to be overflowed and have been freq[uen]tly damaged by Floods and Inundations of water for want of a mill or engine and other proper works cuts, drains, dams, sluices and outlets to carry off the same.

The three parties resolved to erect a mill and associated works, paying for the work between them 'rateably and in proportion to ye number of acres w[hi]ch each of them … have or hath in the s[ai]d parcells of marshes'.[200] A similar agreement survives for the erection of a mill in the Raveningham marshes in 1778.[201]

By 1795, to judge from William Faden's map of Norfolk, there were no less than 47 drainage mills in Broadland, mostly located in the main marshland 'triangle' of Halvergate. Their numbers increased markedly thereafter, and Bryant's county map of 1824 shows no less than 73, and certainly omits a number of examples.[202] This proliferation was partly associated with parliamentary enclosure of low-lying commons. While most of the damper areas of fen ground were, at least for the time being, left in an unimproved state, those occupying areas of silt soil, which had formerly been used as common grazing marsh, were now subjected to more systematic drainage. Around two thirds of the new mills seem to have been erected as a direct consequence of enclosure acts, many of which also established Drainage Commissions for their maintenance. Mills also continued to proliferate in areas of long-enclosed marsh, however. Tunstall Marshes, for example, had long been held in severalty when Tunstall West Mill was erected some time between 1795 and 1816.

There were other changes to the marsh landscape at this time: most notably, the network of drainage dykes was steadily refined, with the straightening of old meandering channels

---

196 Marshall, *Rural Economy*, II, pp. 282–3.
197 Williamson, *Norfolk Broads*, pp. 106–122.
198 NRO, BEA 337/1–6, 438 X 7.
199 NRO, MEA 2/53, 651 X 8.
200 NRO, MEA 3/578 659 X 2.
201 NRO, KNY 27.
202 Williamson, *Norfolk Broads*, pp. 118 – 121.
203 *Ibid.*, pp. 62–71.

(inherited from the natural drainage pattern of the ancient salt marshes) and the cutting of new dykes to lead water more directly to the drainage mills. Such piecemeal improvements are evident whenever sequences of maps running from the eighteenth through the nineteenth centuries are available.[203] They are also sporadically referred to in documents relating to the management of estates on the marsh. Thus, for example, in 1825 Robert Fellowes of Shotesham was informed by his land agent:

> I have taken … view of your Halvergate Estate and I find every thing is in good order and going on in a proper manner except some small drains is wanted to be cut in the different Marshes, this will be of great use to take the water from the marshes.[204]

The erection of drainage mills and the continued refashioning of the dyke system attests a sustained interest in improving these valuable pastures during the eighteenth and nineteenth centuries, which is in marked contrast to the more general attitude to grassland in East Anglia. There was, however, one other exception to the general neglect of pasture: from the end of the eighteenth century, a number of attempts were made to introduce the practice of irrigating meadow land into the region.

(iii) *The irrigation of water meadows*

The importance of artificially irrigated or 'floated' meadows was first emphasised in the 1960s by Eric Kerridge, who went so far as to assert that much of the success of his 'Agricultural Revolution' of the seventeenth century depended on their widespread adoption. He quoted examples from the West Country, the chalklands of Wessex, and Herefordshire. Later studies by, among others, Betty and Bowie have thrown further light on the development of floating in these areas.[205] The artificial inundation of riverside meadows during the winter with continuously flowing water raised the ground temperature and stimulated an early growth of grass, so that an 'early bite' could be provided for sheep. After the flock had been moved on to summer pastures, the meadows would again be irrigated and substantial crops of hay taken in June or July. The increase in feed produced by the technique ensured that larger flocks could be kept and, as a result, more manure was available for the arable land.

There were two basic forms of irrigation. The simplest was 'catchwork' floating, in which channels were cut along the contours of the valleys side, the uppermost being fed from a leat taken off the river at a higher level, or from nearby springs. The water simply flowed down the natural slope of the valley side from one 'gutter' to the next. More expensive and more difficult to construct were 'bedwork' systems, which were used where valley floors were wide and flat and where, in consequence, water could not otherwise be induced to flow continuously, as the method required. In this system, a leat fed water into channels running along the top of parallel ridges, superficially resembling the 'ridge and furrow' of former arable fields. It flowed smoothly down the sides of these and into drains (located in the 'furrows') which returned the water to the river.

In Wessex, the irrigation of meadows on a large scale began in the seventeenth century. The

---

[204] NRO, FEL 570.
[205] J. H. Bettey, 'The development of water meadows in Dorset during the seventeenth century', *AgHR* 25 (1977),

pp. 37–43; G. G. S. Bowie, 'Water meadows in Wessex: a re-evaluation for the period 1640–1850', *AgHR* 35 (1987), pp. 151–8.

main phase of construction was over by 1750.[206] In East Anglia, in contrast, floating was not widely practised before the very end of the eighteenth century. In 1796 Kent was able to mention only a single experiment in floating, near Thetford;[207] while in 1804 Young was able to assert that the practice was 'Of very late standing in Norfolk: the experiments made are few, but they are interesting enough to promise a speedy extension'.[208] In Suffolk he similarly noted that 'Of all the improvements wanted in this county, there is none so obvious, and of such importance, as watering meadows'.

For Norfolk, Young lists five places where floating had recently been undertaken, all either in North-West Norfolk or in Breckland: at Riddlesworth, West Tofts, Lynford, Wighton, and Houghton St Giles. All appear to have been the work of noted improvers, either landowners or large tenants. Young further records, however, that at the time of writing floating was being contemplated at Heacham where 'Mr STYLEMAN has engaged Mr BROOKS to make a trial': works apparently in place by 1812, when 'ten acres of water meadow grass' were mown here.[209] In Suffolk less was achieved in this period, and writing in the second edition of the *General View* in 1803 Young lamented that

> In ten years something has been done, a little; but sorry I am to say, that the county still continues liable to just condemnation for the extreme slowness with which this improvement moves. Joshua Grigby, Esq. at Drinkstone, has watered a meadow, and is about to extend the irrigation to others.[210]

The first decade of the nineteenth century, however, saw a number of new irrigation schemes implemented, although these were again mainly in North-West Norfolk or Breckland, and again the work of prominent improvers, many of whom were tenants of the Holkham estate. Between 1803 and 1806, for example, one of the largest and most successful of the East Anglian systems was laid out on the farm of John Beck at West Lexham (the Holkham estate itself organised and paid for the work, adding £50 per year to Beck's rent in 1807 'for improvements by irrigation', a sum increased to £100 in 1808, and maintained at that level until his death in 1822).[211] The West Lexham system was designed, like several others in Norfolk, by William Smith, who later gained fame as a geologist. Its creation and operation are described in some detail in his book, *Observations on the Utility, Form and Management of Water Meadows*, published in Norwich in 1806. West Lexham lies in the valley of the river Nar, and this river – running through the south of the North-West Norfolk region – had the highest concentration of irrigated meadows in East Anglia. A large system at Castle Acre, just downstream from West Lexham, was constructed shortly after 1808 when Thomas Purdey took over the Holkham farm here, and was completed by 1810, when he was awarded a silver tea pot, basin and cream ewer at the Holkham Sheep Shearing for irrigating 30 acres (12 hectares).[212] The system survives in derelict, but archaeologically striking, condition, complete with the ruins of the three aqueducts which carried the principal carriers across the river. Although primarily a 'bedwork' system, it

206 Bowie, 'Water meadows in Wessex', pp. 154–5.

207 Kent, *Norfolk*, p. 51.

208 Young, *Norfolk*, p. 395.

209 *Ibid.*, p. 401; NRO, LeStrange, supplementary box 2. The earthworks of the system, in the form of 'bedworks' extending over an area of c.4 hectares, still survive.

210 Young, *Suffolk*, p. 196.

211 Holkham Hall archives, Audit books, A/Au 71.

212 *Norfolk Chronicle*, 30 June 1810.

featured an area of 'catchwork' fed from springs and field ditches. Bacon, writing in 1844, refers to a further area of water meadows higher up the river Nar, at Kempstone (created by 'the late General Fitzroy', who was a Holkham tenant here from 1808 until 1838 and a prominent agriculturalist):[213] and another system was created some time before 1841 at East Lexham, probably by F. W. Keppel, who bought the estate in 1806.[214] Lastly, close to the source of the Nar, at Mileham, there were two catchwork systems, 'reclaimed from a bog' in 1816 by one William Beck (probably the son of William Beck of Lexham).[215]

There was a similar, if less marked, concentration of activity in the valley of the river Stiffkey (again in North-West Norfolk) and a number of schemes were attempted in Breckland. But elsewhere there are only a few places where, to judge from the documentary and archaeological evidence (notably the 1946 RAF aerial photographs), floating seems to have been attempted, and there can be little doubt that the practice never really caught on in the area.[216] In the middle of the nineteenth century, according to Bacon, irrigation had been 'but very partially introduced' in Norfolk.[217] The same seems to have been true of Suffolk, where the practice is not even mentioned by the Raynbirds or their correspondents in 1849. Here, a less systematic survey of the archaeological evidence has been attempted, but it is clear that earthwork traces of irrigation systems are rare and, as in Norfolk, can usually be correlated with the activities of noted 'improvers' mentioned by Young and others. Thus earthworks at Drinkstone clearly represent the meadows constructed by Joshua Grigsby, mentioned by Young in 1803; while those to the south of Thetford are presumably those referred to by Kent in 1796.[218]

The chronology of the East Anglian water meadows may have been different from that of the Wessex examples, and the scale of their adoption considerably less, but their mode of management was broadly the same. They were intended both to supply an early 'bite', and to produce an increased summer hay crop. As in Wessex, floating began in late October and continued until early March. After a short drying-out period, ewes and lambs (or occasionally cattle) were put on to feed until early May. They were then taken off, the grass was watered again and allowed to grow, and a hay crop taken in mid-late June.[219] If Young's descriptions of the meadows at Houghton and Riddlesworth, or Smith's account of those at Lexham, can be believed, this amounted to a yield of around two tons per acre, comparable to those reported from irrigated meadows in Wessex, Oxfordshire, and Nottinghamshire in the same period and around double those produced by non-irrigated meadows.[220]

---

[213] Bacon, *Agriculture*, p. 91.

[214] It survived until at least 1846, when its main carriers are clearly shown on the East Lexham tithe award map, NRO, 440.

[215] Bacon, *Agriculture*, pp. 290–1.

[216] William Smith mentions three in his *Observations on the Utility, Form and Management of Water Meadows* (1806): at Taverham, by Thomas Branthwayt; at Beechamwell, by 'Mr Motteux's tenants'; and by 'Money Hill', probably at Waterden – he received a prize for watering meadows here in 1808. In addition, Bacon in 1844 mentions one 'Mr Foster', of Easton near Norwich, as one of Norfolk's limited band of irrigators. No other floated meadows seem to be referred to in published sources, and there are only a few places where the 1946 RAF aerial photographs (the earliest to provide comprehensive cover) suggest small-scale attempts at floating not mentioned in written sources, most notably in the valley of the Wensum at South Raynham.

[217] Bacon, *Agriculture*, p. 91.

[218] Kent, *Agriculture*, p. 51.

[219] Smith, *Observations*, pp. 112–16; Young, *Norfolk*, pp. 395–400.

[220] Smith, *Observations*, p. 116; Young, *Norfolk*, p. 401; P. Pusey, 'On the theory and practice of water meadows', *JRASE* 10 (1849), pp. 462–79.

The reasons for the late and limited adoption of water meadows in East Anglia are complex. One was that the East Anglian irrigation systems were, for the most part, comparatively expensive to create. The elaborate works at Castle Acre and West Lexham cost, according to Bacon, between £10 and £40 an acre.[221] In other words, the total cost of the former must have been between £300 and £1200, that of the latter between £500 and £2000. These were large sums, rather more than the figures quoted for contemporary meadows in the west of England,[222] and comparable to the amounts spent on major farm rebuilding schemes. This might not have mattered so much, were it not for the fact that – as we have argued elsewhere – the East Anglian environment was not well suited to the practice of floating.[223] The gentle gradient of most valleys not only precluded the institution of cheap 'catchwork' systems but also made the creation of successful bedworks dependent on the construction of long, elaborate leats. Without these, the fall of water would be insufficient for successful floating, and it is noteworthy that Young himself gives examples of problems with the meadows at Riddlesworth, West Tofts and Wighton apparently caused by this deficiency. As Bowie has pointed out, the sharp gradient of the Wessex valleys was the 'critical factor' in the widespread adoption of the system there and, by implication, elsewhere in the west.[224] The problem was not just the high cost of constructing very long leats. There was also the difficulty of other lands intervening 'between those to be flooded and the place where the water must be taken out of the river':[225] the greater the length of the principal carrier, fairly obviously, the more likely that it would need to cross the land of several proprietors, and also to interfere with the water supply to mills. Topography may have been important in another way. Wide flat valleys with gentle gradients tended to contain soils which were rather more peaty and acid than those found in the valleys of the west, and even when irrigated tended to produce a rather coarse herbage.

Yet topography cannot have been the only reason why water meadows remained rare in East Anglia, for moderately steep valleys can be found in certain districts, especially in parts of southern Suffolk. A more significant factor was probably the climate. In the west of England mild winters and early springs made the early forcing of grass feasible on a regular basis. In the more Continental east, however, sharp and often late frosts, sometimes continuing for long periods of time, made the early 'bite' less dependable. As Pusey noted in 1849, the practice of floating was less well suited to the drier and colder areas of the country. Even as ardent an advocate as William Smith acknowledged the problems encountered in the second year of floating at Lexham, when 'The water was applied every night, but, from the coldness of the season, produced but little effect'.[226] It is hardly surprising, then, that water meadows were only championed in East Anglia by particularly ardent improvers, during the boom years of the Napoleonic Wars.

[221] Bacon, *Agriculture*, p. 290.
[222] Bowie, 'Water meadows', p. 155.
[223] S. Wade Martins and T. Williamson, 'Floated Water Meadows in Norfolk: a misplaced innovation', *AgHR* 42 (1994), pp. 20–37.
[224] Bowie, 'Water Meadows', p. 152.
[225] Smith, *Observations*, p. 120.
[226] *Ibid.*, p. 115.

4. Changes in farm size

There was much discussion amongst eighteenth-century commentators about the relative merits of large and small farms. Nathaniel Kent went so far as to argue that it was one of the most important issues to be considered by the Board of Agriculture. He was one of a minority who felt that increases in farm size did not bring any marked benefits.[227] Similar sentiments were expressed by the agent for the Wolterton estate in 1743: 'I am of your honour's opinion that small farms laid to larger, unless they are worth the money they are let for, seldom are of any advantage to the farms they are let to'.[228] Whether or not they approved of the fact, however, all commentators believed that small farms were disappearing.[229] Modern historians have generally shared this view, although the precise chronology of this process remains contentious.[230] As Ginter has recently written, 'The argument surrounding the decline of the small landowner has grown to become one of the most important debates in agricultural history'.[231] Some historians have related the decline to specific periods and processes. Thus Sheppard has discussed the marked decline in small farmers in the post-Napoleonic war depression in Sussex, Martin the pattern of 'dislocation and change' during the years of enclosure in Warwickshire.[232]

Other studies have suggested a more gradual and general pattern of change. In Mingay's words, the growth in farm size during the eighteenth century was the 'product of a wide variety of forces', including increased demand arising from general demographic growth and industrialisation, the adoption of new capital-intensive methods, and the simple fact that large farms were more efficient.[233] Turner noted a decline in the number of landowners on new and old enclosed land alike in Buckinghamshire in the course of the eighteenth century,[234] while Allen has argued that 'By the early 19th century, most of England's farmland had passed from family farms to large scale capitalist tenants'.[235] Conversely, Howkins has emphasised the extent to which small farmers survived in large numbers into the nineteenth and, indeed, twentieth centuries.[236] The issue is an important one in the present context, because many historians have suggested that increases in farm size were associated with improvements in productivity.[237]

Much research on farm size has been based on the Land Tax returns, but there are a number of problems with this source, as Ginter has shown, and, while his views may be overly pessimistic, this source has not been employed here.[238] The brief discussion that follows is based on

---

[227] Kent, *Norfolk*, p. 129.

[228] Wolterton Hall archives, WOLT 8/24.

[229] Marshall, *Rural Economy*, I, p. 9.

[230] J. V. Beckett, 'The debate over farm size in eighteenth-century England', *Agricultural Hist.*, 68 (1983), pp. 308–25. See also D. Grigg, 'Farm size in England and Wales, from early Victorian times to the present', *AgHR* 35 (1987), pp. 179–90.

[231] D. E. Ginter, 'Measuring the decline of the small landowner', in B. A. Holderness and M. Turner (eds), *Land, labour and agriculture. Essays for Gordon Mingay* (1991), p. 27.

[232] J. A. Sheppard, 'Small farms in a Sussex Weald parish, 1800–1860', *AgHR* 40 (1992), pp. 127–41; J. M. Martin, 'The smallholder and parliamentary enclosure in

Warwickshire', *EcHR* 32 (1979), pp. 328–43.

[233] G. E. Mingay, 'The size of farms in the eighteenth century', *EcHR* 14 (1961–2), p. 484.

[234] M. Turner, 'Parliamentary enclosure and landownership change in Buckinghamshire', *EcHR* 28 (1975), pp. 565–81.

[235] Allen, *Enclosure and the Yeoman*, p. 265.

[236] A. Howkins, 'Peasants, servants and labourers: the marginal workforce in British agriculture, c.1770–1914', *AgHR* 32 (1994), pp. 49–62.

[237] R. Brenner, 'Agrarian Class Structure and economic development in pre-industrial Europe', *Past and Present* 70 (1976), pp. 30–74; Mingay, 'Size of farms'.

[238] D. E. Ginter, *A measure of wealth. The English Land Tax in historical analysis* (1992).

various stray references in tithe accounts and estate documents; on the evidence of the tithe award maps, surveyed in the late 1830s and early 1840s; and on the census of 1851, which was the first to include information about the size of farms and the numbers of men employed on them.

One problem with the kinds of broad generalisation advanced by Allen is that they take little account of local and regional variations which, in East Anglia at least, were marked by the mid-nineteenth century. In the Flegg loam region, on the claylands, and in the Fens, the 1851 census shows that small farms, largely employing only family labour, were still numerous. Indeed, in the Fens and the Flegg Loam region over 40 per cent of the holdings recorded were of under 50 acres. The average size of farm in all these regions was rather larger, although still small by modern standards. In the Fens the mean size was 110 acres; in Flegg, 104; and in the Central Claylands a mere 96, although in the southern and western clays the figure was rather higher at 113. In contrast to these regions of heavy and fertile soil were those of light, acid land in which much larger holdings were usual. In North-West Norfolk small farms of fifty acres or less were virtually unknown: the average farm size was around 420 acres, while in Breckland it was around 450. In the Sandlings and the Heathlands average farm size was lower, at 212 and 224 acres respectively, in part because many parishes included areas of more amenable soils. Generally speaking, therefore, a simple rule seems to operate: the poorer the soil, the larger the farm; and farms on the very poorest soil, like those on the Culford and Merton estates in Breckland, could cover well in excess of 1000 acres.

As most of East Anglia consists of comparatively heavy and fertile soil, it might appear at first sight that the census figures support Howkins' contention that small farmers continued to be an important element in landholding well into the nineteenth century. Yet we need to distinguish here between, on the one hand, the number of farms of different sizes; and on the other, the proportion of land farmed by units of varying size. The important point here is that even in areas like the Central Claylands many large farms, of 150, 200 or even 300 acres, existed alongside the numerous small unit of 50 acres and less. Although such farms might *numerically* be in the minority, in many parishes they nevertheless farmed the majority of the land.

A useful indicator of the extent to which land was farmed in large capital units is the proportion of any district cultivated by farms of 150 acres or more at the time of the 1851 census. In areas of poor acid soils this figure was generally high. In the Northern Heathlands and Sandlings 75 per cent of the land was farmed in such units, in North-West Norfolk 91 per cent, and in Breckland 88 per cent: indeed, the figures for the proportion farmed in units of 300 acres or more in these regions was 45 per cent, 44 per cent, 74 per cent and 72 per cent respectively. What is more striking is the fact that, to judge from the census figures, even in areas of heavy and fertile soil a high proportion of land was already being cultivated in units of 150 acres or more. In the Central Claylands the figure was 41.5 per cent, in the Southern and Western clays 52 per cent, in Flegg 53 per cent and in the Fens as much as 66 per cent. Even the amount of land cultivated in units of 300 acres or more was surprisingly high: around 10 per cent in the clayland regions, but approaching a quarter in the Fens and Flegg. Nevertheless, there was still a clear difference between the areas of poor, acid soils, where large farms had almost a monopoly of exploitation: and other regions, where their dominance was more muted.

The available evidence suggests that this pattern of variation developed, or at least intensified, during the course of the period studied here. In North-West Norfolk, for example, a 1689 survey of the farms in the open fields of Hunstanton suggests that only two held more than 100 acres: two between 50 and 99 acres; four between 20 and 49 acres; and two between 10 and 19 acres. No less than 25 were under ten acres, although some of these no doubt formed parts of holdings in adjacent parishes.[239] The average farm size was a mere 17 acres. By 1707, 'all exchanges between the tenants being set right', there were four farms with over 100 acres (although none with more than 150), four with between 50 and 99 acres, and two with between 10 and 49 acres.[240] The average size was now 99 acres. The figures are not quite as straightforward as this, for the map covers only half the parish, the 1707 survey a larger area, but some degree of consolidation is clearly suggested, and this continued during the rest of the eighteenth century. A terrier of 1819 shows that the number of farms had been halved: three held in excess of 200 acres, and two between 50 and 100 acres. The average size of farm was now over 223 acres.[241]

Figures from the neighbouring parish of Ringstead show a similar pattern of consolidation, with an estimated 22 farms in 1690 being reduced to only seven, each with over 100 acres, by 1819.[242] Similarly, small farms declined in number on the Raynham estate from the 1660s, although the reduction was much faster under 'Turnip' Townshend from the 1700s. In 1716, 31 farms commanded a rent of more than £40 and 5 more than £200. By 1735, tenants who farmed land worth more than £200 accounted for 55 per cent of the estate's total value.[243] In North-West Norfolk, at least, there is thus fairly clear evidence for a substantial increase in the average size of farm in the course of the late seventeenth and eighteenth centuries, largely achieved through the disappearance of the smallest holdings.

In other areas of light acid soil the pattern was similar. A map of the Wolterton estate in the Northern Heathlands, surveyed in 1732, shows twenty holdings: one of over 200 acres, four of between 100 and 199 acres, six between 50 and 99 acres, and nine of less than 50 acres.[244] The average size of holding was 56 acres. The next available figures are for 1809, by which time the estate had been enlarged, intermingled lands had been bought up and residual areas of open field and common enclosed.[245] There was now a total of sixteen farms. Five of these were very large (over 300 acres), five covered between 200 and 299 acres, four between 100 and 199 acres and one was of 40 acres: the average size of farm was now 236 acres.

On areas of light acid soil the trend towards larger farms seems to have continued through the nineteenth century. There are three sets of figures available for farm sizes on the Heydon estate in the Northern Heathlands: for 1780, 1840 and 1890.[246] These show a more complicated pattern, due in part to changes in the size of the estate over time:

[239] NRO, LeStrange BH1.
[240] NRO, LeStrange BH3.
[241] By this time the size of the park had also increased. NRO, LeStrange BH9.
[242] NRO, LeStrange BH8.

[243] Rosenheim, *Townshends of Raynham*, p. 147.
[244] Wolteron Hall archives, no number.
[245] NRO, S175B; estate survey by Bailey Bird.
[246] 1780, NRO, BUL 11/3 615 X 6; 1840, tithe award NRO, 500; 1890, Heydon Hall archives, uncatalogued.

Acres	1790	1840	1890
Over 300	3	1	8
200–299	6	7	5
100–199	8	6	7
50–99	2	7	7
10–49	9	3	2

In 1790, the average size of farm was 153 acres; 23.5 per cent of the land had been held in farms of 300 acres or more, while 68.5 per cent had been held by farms of 150 acres or more. A century later average size had increased to 201 acres, 52 per cent of the land was held in farms of 300 acres or more, and 80 per cent in holdings of 150 acres or more. Similarly, on the Hunstanton estate, average farm size increased from 223 acres in 1809 to 294 acres by the time of the 1839 tithe award (although this included the home farm, which embraced the extensive landscape park associated with Hunstanton Hall).

Wherever figures are available from light soils areas, the same pattern of attrition seems to be indicated. On the Somerleyton estate, on the northern fringes of the Sandlings region, a survey of 1663 can be compared with a sales catalogue of 1851.[247] Between these two dates the average size of farms virtually doubled, from 56 to 106 acres. In the former period 62 per cent of the tenanted land had been farmed in units of more than 150 acres; by the mid-nineteenth century the figure was 83 per cent. Small farms still survived – there were 14 holdings of less than 100 acres, including ten of less than 50 – but they now accounted for a far smaller proportion of the total farmed area.

The pattern of change in areas of heavier or more fertile soil is less clear, largely because (as already noted) the 1851 figures suggest wide variations from parish to parish, variations which were principally related to patterns of landownership: larger farms were more important wherever large estates had significant holdings. Such areas constituted only a comparatively small proportion of the regions concerned, yet they provide the bulk of the evidence available for studying farm size. The records of such estates, mainly on the claylands, suggest that a considerable reduction in the numbers of small holdings often occurred at an early date. As early as 1725, on an estate around Denham in mid-Suffolk, only one farm covered less than 50 acres: one covered more than 300 acres, the others – four in all – were between 50 and 300 acres.[248] On an estate in Hoxne, Denham and Wetheringsett in 1757 fifteen farms had an average size of 186 acres, and 84 per cent of the land was already farmed in units of 150 acres or more (with 44 per cent in farms of 300 acres or more).[249] On the Earsham estate, similarly, considerable consolidation of holdings had already taken place by 1770, when an estate survey recorded eighteen holdings. Some were as small as two acres, and the average size of farm was only 75 acres, but 22 per cent of the farms were 150 acres or more and these together cultivated over 60 per cent of the estate.

[247] ESRO, 194/A11/11; 749/2/165.
[248] ESRO, HB 21/280/3.
[249] ESRO, HB 21/280/2.

What is striking in this case, however, is that there was little subsequent increase in farm size. By 1810 the average farm size was still 75 acres, and the share of land cultivated by the large farms had increased only slightly, to *c.* 64 per cent. By 1864, average farm size had risen further, but was still only 110 acres, while the share of land cultivated by 150-acre farms had increased only marginally, to 69 per cent.[250] Scattered evidence from other clayland estates hints at a similar pattern – of the emergence of comparatively large holdings by the early or mid eighteenth century, but little further consolidation. Thus on the Ashburnham estate in 1772 there were 25 farms with an average size of 131 acres; 73 per cent of the estate was already farmed in holdings of more than 150 acres, and 20 per cent in holdings of more than 300 acres. But there was little subsequent change: by 1830 there were still 25 farms, the average farm size was still 131 acres, and the share of the estate farmed in units of 150 or more acres had actually declined slightly, to 68 per cent.[251] Indeed, in one case the evidence appears to suggest a fall in farm size after the late eighteenth century. On the Wyburn estate in South Elmham in 1750 farms were already fairly large, with an average area of 208 acres: 44 per cent of the land was farmed in units of 300 or more acres, over 80 per cent in farms of 150 acres or more. Ten years later the same estate, now owned by the Adairs, had increased in area and the average farm size had risen to 237 acres; 69 per cent of the land was now farmed in units of 300 or more acres, no less than 80 per cent in farms of 150 acres or more. It is difficult to compare these figures with those supplied by the tithe award maps of the late 1830s, for the estate had increased further through the purchase of additional land. Nevertheless, it is suggestive that average farm size on the estate was now rather lower, at around 100 acres.

Large estates owned only a minority of land in the claylands, however, and as already noted, the 1851 census figures suggests that areas dominated by small estates and owner-occupiers were characterised by much smaller farms. Nevertheless, these places also seem to have seen some consolidation of holdings during the eighteenth century. The parish of Stansfield in the South and Western Clays had no dominant landowner. The tithe accounts of 1766 list 16 farms with an average area of 83.3 acres, and 34 per cent of the parish was already being farmed in units of 150 acres or more.[252] A later series of accounts, for *c.* 1800, lists only nine farms, with an average area of 126.6 acres: farms covering 150 acres or more now cultivated 80 per cent of the land.[253] The 1840 tithe award map similarly lists nine farms within the parish, now with an average size of 166 acres and with 66 per cent of the land in units of 150 acres or more.[254] It is not entirely clear that these three sets of data are directly comparable but the similarity with the pattern in parishes already discussed is noteworthy. The parish of Mattishall in the Dissected Claylands of central Norfolk was likewise split amongst many small proprietors, some of whom were owner-occupiers, and some petty landlords. Figures from the tithe accounts of 1786 describe 38 holdings extending over more than two acres, with an average size of 37 acres. Of these, only one covered more than 150 acres, accounting for a mere 12 per cent of the farmed parish area. A further five held between 100 and 149 acres (42 per cent of farmed area) and three between 50 and 99 acres (16 per cent), with a further 27 farmers holding between 2 and

[250] 1770, NRO, MEA 3/2 658 X; 1810, NRO, MEA 3/6 652 X 7; 1864, NRO, MEA 3/539 658 X 8.
[251] ESRO, HA1/HB4/1.

[252] WSRO, FL627/3/18.
[253] WSRO, FL627/3/21.
[254] WSRO, T 53/1, 2.

49 acres (30 per cent), most of whom were probably part-time farmers.[255] Small farms continued to be important here into the nineteenth century, but there had nevertheless been a significant degree of consolidation. The tithe award map of 1840 shows that farms holding 150 acres now accounted for nearly a third of the farmed acreage, and that average farm size had now risen to 57 acres, although there were still 27 holdings of less than 50 acres.[256]

Changes in farm size were thus closely related to soil type: in areas of poor light land there was a more marked decline in the number (and a more substantial increase in the average size) of farms during the eighteenth and nineteenth centuries than in areas of better-quality soils. In large measure the relationship is doubtless due to the simple fact that it was harder to make a living on these poor soils: inputs of manure, marl and the rest were expensive, profit margins small, small farms increasingly uneconomic. Yet estate policy clearly played a large part in this process. Prejudice against smaller holdings was widespread among owners and administrators. A document of 1756 from the Blickling estate typically suggested that it was not worth repairing or improving the buildings on farms under 50 acres, and advocated concentrating investment on the larger farms. Dislike of small holdings was in part motivated by the costs of maintaining a multiplicity of small farm buildings, but largely due to the need to attract men with capital to farm these light lands. Of one Itteringham holding of 21 acres, for example, it was declared that the small white-walled and thatched house, and mud-walled and thatched stables and barn, were not worth repairing as the land was poor and the rent would not improve. An eleven-acre holding was said to have a bad house and to be a 'dear lot as all these small things are'.[257] The crucial role of large estates in the growth of larger farms is clear from the claylands. Here large estates were a much less prominent feature but where they did exist farms were larger than average for the district.

Although Howkins is no doubt right to remind us that small farmers continued to be numerous in many areas right through the nineteenth century, when the actual *area* cultivated by such individuals is examined a different picture emerges. Around 70 per cent of East Anglia was probably farmed in large holdings of 150 acres or more by 1850; and nearly a third in very large units, of 300 acres or more. At a conservative estimate, the figures for 1700 would have been perhaps half these, the change in the intervening period being largely due to the disappearance of the smaller holdings, those of less than 50 acres, especially in areas of light poor land.

5. The development of farm buildings

(i) *Introduction*

Farm buildings have been the subject of serious academic study for several decades.[258] Initial work, such as that by Peters, concentrated on the architectural development of the buildings. More recent research, most notably by the Royal Commission on Historical Monuments, has been more concerned with their use as evidence for agricultural history. Farm buildings are, it

[255] Gonville and Caius College MSS, Cambridge, notebook of Rev. John Smith, vicar of Mattishall, 1781–1803 (hereafter Smith notebook).

[256] NRO, 195.

[257] NRO, MC3/59/252 468 X 4.

[258] J. E. C. Peters, *The development of farm buildings in west lowland Staffordshire up to 1880* (1969); N. Harvey, *A history of farm buildings in England and Wales* (1970); P. S. Barnwell and C. Giles, *English Farmsteads 1750–1914* (1997).

has been argued, important because they can indicate 'local manifestations of national trends', and their study can allow us to assess 'the impact of new ideas, of technical advance ... and the time at which the perception of need coincided with the availability of the financial means to implement change'.[259]

East Anglia has many thousands of farm complexes which are principally composed of buildings erected before the late nineteenth century: buildings which survived with little alteration through the long years of agricultural depression, but which – with the return of prosperity, the impact of new technologies, and the general growth of farm size in the decades after 1945 – have increasingly become redundant, and subject to demolition or conversion to new uses. Nevertheless, these structures still survive in sufficient numbers to allow their study to add to our understanding of agricultural history. Systematic research in East Anglia began in the 1980s, with a programme of survey work in selected areas.

Although farm buildings display much variation, they also share common forms, and common principles of spatial organisation. The largest and, in most cases, the oldest structure is the barn, designed to provide at least one threshing floor between a pair of double doors, as well as storage space for the unthreshed crop and residual straw. Many examples erected before 1700 survive in East Anglia, especially in Suffolk. Adjacent to the barn – typically on the south side – most surviving farmsteads have one or more yards surrounded by sheds for cattle, often creating a regular 'U' or 'E' shape (depending on the number of yards defined by the rows of sheds). Occasionally, especially on the grander estate farms, the fourth side is closed, so as to create a regular courtyard plan. Most surviving examples of cattle housing are of late eighteenth or nineteenth-century date. Before this period the provision of cattle housing was more limited. Eighteenth-century barns frequently incorporated a range of loose boxes or open-fronted shelter sheds in an integral leanto on either side of a porch, often along a south wall; the yard itself was apparently often a temporary enclosure made up with hurdles every winter (Randall Burroughes in his farming journal of the 1790s describes how he divided up the 'parr yards').[260] Leases on the Heydon estate from the mid-eighteenth century often give the tenant the right to take rough timber for the construction of racks and stalls for cattle, implying rather impermanent structures.

If the housing of store cattle was slow to develop in East Anglia (as in other lowland regions) this was not so true of horses, which had long been stabled. The earliest surviving stables usually comprise an internal subdivision at one end of the barn: from the mid eighteenth century, however, separate buildings (usually with a hay loft above) became the norm. During the nineteenth century there were further changes, as it became customary to turn horses out into an adjacent yard at night, and separate hay houses became more common.

To these essential elements of the farm complex – barn, cattle housing, stables – various storage facilities might be added: granaries, cartlodges and implement sheds. While such structures did exist in the eighteenth century, they were not then a common feature and surviving examples are usually – like cattle housing – of nineteenth-century date.

[259] P. Barnwell, 'An extra dimension? Lincolnshire farm buildings as historical evidence', *AgHR* 46 (1998), p. 40; S. Wade Martins, *Historic Farm Buildings* (1991).

[260] Wade Martins and Williamson, *Randall Burroughes*, p. 42.

In theory the size, construction and distribution of East Anglian farm buildings ought to tell us a great deal about levels of past agricultural investment and productivity. Although these structures do have something to tell us about the former, their use for the latter purpose is more problematic. At first sight it might appear obvious that the capacity of barns should be related to the volume of grain being produced, and that changes in the size or numbers of barns ought, therefore, to provide some indication of changes in crop yields. Unfortunately, it is clear that barns were primarily structures for *processing* the grain crop. Although the threshed-out straw might remain in the barn until it was needed in stables, boxes and yards, the threshed grain was usually stored elsewhere and much of the unprocessed crop might be housed in thatched stacks, usually in a yard beside the barn. The extent to which this was done seems, however, to have varied from place to place and from period to period. Roger North of Rougham, writing in the 1690s, contrasted the north and west of England – where crops were normally stacked and 'the people care not for barns, but only to thresh' – with East Anglia, where stacking was less popular and the farmers 'know nothing willingly, but clapping into the barn'. The farmers, he went on, 'cease not to grumble 'till more barn-room be provided'.[261] A century later Nathaniel Kent made similar complaints; farmers were against stacking and were 'always crying out for barn space and they certainly are indulged in a greater proportion [i.e., in Norfolk] than in any other county'. In the following century Francis Blaikie criticised Holkham tenants for demanding large barns, and Thomas Coke for giving in to their demands.[262]

By the second half of the eighteenth century it is clear that only a minority of the crop was barned before threshing. On the Holkham estate the massive barn designed by Samuel Wyatt at Leicester Square farm, for example, could only house 120 acres of the crop on this 800 acre farm (half of which would have been producing cereal crops each year).[263] Randall Burroughes' farming journal makes it abundantly clear that much if not most of the crop on his clayland farm in the 1790s was stacked prior to threshing.

There is thus only an indirect relationship between barn capacity and farm productivity, and farm buildings can tell us little about changes in cereal production. They can, however, add to our knowledge of agricultural history in other ways, especially when examined in the context of the evolution of regional farming systems, landscape development, and patterns of land-ownership. The following discussion is based, in part, on a programme of survey work carried out at the Centre of East Anglian Studies in the late 1980s;[264] and in part on supplementary survey work carried out as part of an ESRC-funded research project between 1994 and 1996. Not all regions of East Anglia, largely for logistical reasons, received the same degree of attention in terms of field survey, and the fens and the Suffolk Sandlings, in particular, remain relatively unstudied. Nevertheless, the data collected and analysed here does permit the main patterns of variation to be isolated and employed as evidence in our more general enquiry.

---

[261] H. Colvin and J. Newman (eds), *Of Building: Roger North's Writings on Architecture* (1991).

[262] Wade Martins, *Great Estate*, pp. 70, 155.

[263] Young, *Norfolk*, p. 20.

[264] The Norfolk Farm Buildings Survey was based at the Centre of East Anglian Studies and was directed by the late Alan Carter and Susanna Wade Martins. More information can be found in Wade Martins, *Historic Farm Buildings*.

(ii) *North-West Norfolk*

The farm buildings in this, the traditional heartland of the 'Agricultural Revolution', display a number of features which distinguish them from those in other East Anglian regions. In part this is because it is the only district in which building stone of reasonable quality can be found: carrstone, an iron-rich sandstone; and clunch, or hard chalk. These materials, used alone, in combination, or in association with brick, make for buildings which are visually attractive but often difficult to date, not least because they have often been subjected to complex sequences of rebuilding and remodelling.

Documentary sources show that substantial farm buildings were widespread from the start of the period studied. Thus a late seventeenth-century map of the village of Ringstead shows twelve barns, two of which were provided with two threshing floors, as well as various smaller buildings, some of which may have been stables; individual farmsteads are arranged in a fairly irregular fashion.[265] A 1736 map of the nearby parish of Sedgeford similarly shows substantial barns, one with two threshing floors. Various other buildings are depicted, and the overall layouts are again scattered and irregular.[266] The 1649 parliamentary survey of the Dean and Chapter holdings here describes a brick and stone house at Westhall with, stables, barns, outhouses and yards, while at Easthall the mansion house of 'competent largeness' had barns, stables, outhouses and yards.[267] This documentary and cartographic evidence can be compared with that provided by standing buildings within these parishes. Two barns with seventeenth-century datestones survive in Ringstead (one of 1630 at Gedding's Farm (TF 706403), one of 1670 at Sedgeford Road Farm (TF 706407)) while another, at Eastend Farm (TG 709403), was probably built in *c.*1690. In Sedgeford parish there are no less than four seventeenth-century barns, one with a datestone of 1672 (TF 695363). Not only early barns, but also early granaries (that is, erected before *c.*1750) are a notable feature of this region, mostly set above open-fronted cartsheds, usually of two or three bays, although a fine example at Barrett Ringstead, of two phases (late eighteenth- and early nineteenth-century) has no less than eight bays (TF 688399).

Yet while the presence of early farm buildings is interesting, their numbers should not be exaggerated. They are largely restricted to farms in areas of fertile, calcareous soils, located in the major valleys or along the coastal strip: they are largely absent from farmsteads on the acid, drift-covered 'uplands'. Even on the calcareous soils they are outnumbered by later structures. On the Le Strange's Hunstanton estate, for example, which is largely composed of such soils, no less than 16 out of a total of 28 surviving barns date from the last decades of the eighteenth century, with a further five of early or mid-nineteenth-century origin. Only seven pre-date 1750.[268]

In part, the prominence of such comparatively recent structures is explained by the fact that this was a region of large-scale enclosure in the eighteenth and early nineteenth centuries, which often led to migration of farms out from villages, in a pattern familiar from the Midlands. A typical example is Red Brick Farm (TF 730335), centre of a 700-acre holding created after the enclosure of Snettisham in 1766. Of the buildings then erected in the centre of the newly-

---

[265] NRO, LeStrange EH8.
[266] NRO, LeStrange 1C.

[267] NRO, DCN 51/91.
[268] Wade Martins, *Historic Farm Buildings*, pp. 132–6.

enclosed fields, a huge barn with two threshing floors (and five loose boxes in lean-tos behind), and a fine eight-bay cart lodge, survive. They are built of rough squared flint blocks: only the fine Georgian farmhouse is built of the red brick which gives the farm its name. At nearby Inmere Farm (TF 708342), the layout of buildings shown on a map of 1819, which was presumably created soon after the enclosure of 1766, still survives. It consists of two barns, a six-bay cartlodge, and a stable with a granary above (the later additions are all shelter sheds, ranged around cattle yards). Shaw Farm (TF 710375), a Norwich Dean and Chapter property to the north of Sedgeford, was similarly erected on a virgin site following a parliamentary enclosure, in 1796. Here less survives: a chalk, flint and brick field barn appears to be original, but once again the E-shaped brick and tile shelter sheds and yards were constructed in the later nineteenth century.

The erection of isolated farms on virgin sites is a striking feature, but it was less important than the rebuilding of existing farm complexes, which evidently continued on a large scale throughout the later eighteenth and early nineteenth centuries. Indeed, the region includes some of the most impressive farm buildings in East Anglia, those erected by the Holkham estate. A third of the farms here were substantially rebuilt between 1780 and 1820, to include a large barn, stables and shelter sheds on either side of a U-shaped yard. Similar designs were produced, and farms built, throughout the 1820s and 1830s, although large sums were also spent on more piecemeal improvements. Between 1820 and 1842 seven farms were completely rebuilt and on many others there were major alterations.[269] Both individual buildings – especially barns – and total farmsteads were often grand, architect-designed structures, as at Leicester Square Farm, or Crompton Hall Farm, South Creake, both the work of the country-house architect Samuel Wyatt. The most famous Holkham building is, and was, the Great Barn in Holkham Park, designed by Wyatt and built in the 1790s as the setting for the Holkham 'sheep-shearings'.

The Holkham buildings are impressive, but atypical: no other estate in north west Norfolk built on such a grand scale. Indeed, estate buildings varied greatly, with the fortunes and personalities of landowners. The farms on the Walpole's Houghton estate, for example, were much less imposing affairs, to judge from the 85 illustrations contained in a survey made between 1797 and 1800 for the new owner, George James Cholmondeley, Fourth Earl of Cholmondeley. His Walpole predecessors had allowed the estate to become run down and many of the cottages appear very dilapidated.[270] The farm buildings, in contrast, appear on the whole to be in better condition – a telling indication of contemporary priorities. Not one of the farms has a planned courtyard layout, however, and none a cattle yard. The barns all have single threshing floors. A number of stables are illustrated, generally with haylofts above: some are free-standing structures, some are attached to one end of a barn or, in one case, to a house. Few other buildings are depicted. The only possible cattle accommodation takes the form of lean-tos on either side of the threshing doors of barns. This lack of provision for yarding cattle is particularly surprising. The succession of the Cholmondeleys led to some rebuilding in the first half of the nineteenth century, although never on the scale witnessed at Holkham.

To judge from surviving buildings, barn provision in North-West Norfolk was often generous

[269] Wade Martins, *Great Estate*, p. 156.

[270] D. Yaxley (ed.), *The survey of Houghton Hall estate, 1800 by Joseph Hill*, (NRS, 50, 1984).

by the nineteenth century. Many barns are very large, and many farms have more than one (usually of different dates). Two threshing floors are not uncommon; a few have three or more. Yet while substantial amounts of money were being evidently expended by most estates in the later eighteenth and early nineteenth centuries, the majority of farms continued to have a relatively unplanned layout well into the nineteenth century. A map book of 1819 shows 40 farms on the Hunstanton estate. Most still exhibited a random layout, although a few contain L or U-shaped groups (Hall and Lodge Farms, Snettisham (TF 686345 and 691348); Lodge Farm, Hunstanton (TF 685407); Courtyard Farm, and Eastend Farm, Ringstead (TF 689399 and 400729). Indeed, the majority did not develop an E-shaped plan until after the tithe award maps were surveyed in the late 1830s. Even on the Holkham estate, it was a only a minority of farms which attained a regular planned layout in this period.[271]

There was thus a phase of large-scale rebuilding in North-West Norfolk in the later eighteenth and early nineteenth centuries. Nevertheless, significant numbers of earlier buildings also survive, although there is a clear dichotomy here between the farmsteads exploiting primarily the rich calcareous soils of the valleys and coastal strip, and those on the acid soils of the interior. It is on the latter soils that survival of early structures is rare, and the phase of rebuilding in the 'Agricultural Revolution' period most striking.

(iii) *Breckland*

Breckland, like North-West Norfolk, was an area dominated by large estates, in which extensive enclosure and reclamation in the later eighteenth and early nineteenth centuries led to the creation of new farms and the wholesale rebuilding of old ones. The buildings on the Culford estate are typical. Place Farm, Ingham has a mid-eighteenth century barn, two other barns of late eighteenth-century date, together with early nineteenth-century yards and cattle housing. Culford Lodge and Neville House Farms likewise have late eighteenth-century barns and early nineteenth-century yards and shelter sheds; while Timworth Hall Farm has an early nineteenth century barn and mid-nineteenth century cattle housing. Some earlier structures do survive – Wordwell Hall boasts a fine late-medieval aisled barn alongside late eighteenth and nineteenth-century ranges – and some later ones – Home Farm, Culford and Timworth Green Farm (TL 836700 and 860691) are planned farmsteads of the 'High Farming' period. But there was clearly a peak in building activity in the late eighteenth and early nineteenth centuries, which is evident on other estates.

On the Euston estate, for example, a number of new farms were created following the enclosure of Barnham Heath. These include West Farm and East Farm, Barnham, where extensive ranges, built of red brick and flint and with black glazed pan-tiled roofs, were erected. West Farm has the most extensive set of surviving buildings, consisting of two barns (one with two threshing floors) and two sets of E-shaped yards, as well as stables and cartsheds. The farm house is an elegant structure of flint and yellow brick, clearly designed to attract the kind of farmer with capital needed to bring these extensive tracts of poor land into full cultivation. New farms were also erected following the enclosure of the heaths at Bardwell and Fakenham. Set well away from the old village centres, amidst huge rectangular fields, they boast large barns,

---

[271] Wade Martins, *Great Estate*, pp. 142–83.

ranges of cattle sheds and extensive yards. Enclosure led to the expansion of existing farm complexes as well as to the construction of entirely new ones. Bowbeck Farm in Bardwell is shown on a map of 1789 as a small group of buildings: by 1810, following enclosure, a much larger complex was established here.[272]

On the Walsingham estate, similarly, the late eighteenth and early nineteenth centuries seem to have seen the erection of many new buildings. Sadly, few of these structures – principally in the parishes of Thompson, Merton, Tottington, Stanford and Sturston – survive, due to the area's incorporation within the army's battle training area. The estate records are, however, very detailed and show that here a number of planned 'model' farms were erected in the Napoleonic War years. The few barns which survive from this phase – one at Westmere and one at Mortimer's Farm, Tottington – are very large (39 metres × 7.3 metres and 22.5 metres × 7.3 metres) and extremely well-built, of dressed flint and yellow brick with decorative lozenge-shaped ventilation panels.

The farm buildings erected in Breckland in this expansionary period did not necessarily replace flimsy or impermanent structures. Keymer's map of the parish of Tottington, for example, surveyed in 1774, prior to enclosure, shows twelve farm complexes, all with large barns and five with stables. Westmere Farm is drawn particularly clearly and included a stable with hayloft above, and a two-threshing floor barn with bullock boxes placed in a lean-to.[273] The few farm buildings which survive in the region from before *c*.1750 are in general fairly substantial structures, like the fine timber-framed barn at Rectory Farm Euston, the aisled barn at Sparrow Hall Farm Euston (TL 891793), or that at Wordwell Hall Farm (TL 828721) already mentioned. They are located in or beside pockets of the more calcareous, less marginal of the region's soils: often beside churches and associated with medieval manorial sites. They demonstrate that manorial lords, at least, could make a reasonable living from such soils. Nevertheless, the most striking feature of this area is the large-scale rebuilding of farms, and the creation of new ones. The enormous capacity of some of the barns erected in the region during the Napoleonic War period is a clear indication of the optimism of landlords: often misplaced, as subsequent experience was to show.

(iv) *The Northern Heathlands*

The Northern Heathlands was an area in which some large landed estates existed alongside smaller gentry properties, and the pattern of building here differs in a number of ways from that of the two regions just discussed. The Gunton estate, which covered about 14,000 acres around North Walsham, provides a good example of the development of buildings on the larger estates, and all surviving farms here were examined on the ground. Early barns are rare: indeed, only four of the fifty-two surviving examples could be dated to the period before *c*.1700; a further 11, to judge from cartographic and documentary evidence, were built before 1784, but the majority of these were probably erected after *c*.1760; and the rest were all built between 1784 and 1835. Many are large structures (five have a capacity of more than 1000 cubic metres) and most are constructed of brick although a few are of flint and brick, or of flint alone. Tile is the normal roofing material. A few late eighteenth-century stables survive, but the majority

---

[272] WSRO, HA513 28/16–17.   [273] NRO, WLSXVII/4.

are of early nineteenth-century date, as are most cattle houses. In spite of its acknowledged status as an improving estate, the buildings are plain and functional, substantial rather than impressive. In particular, there is no evidence for the creation of planned 'model farms', or even for the adoption of regular courtyard arrangements. Only the Aylsham Road Farm, and Thorpe Hill Farm, display clear aspirations in this direction.

The eleven farms examined on the nearby Wolterton estate are broadly similar. Here, too, eighteenth- and early nineteenth-century 'model farms' are conspicuous by their absence. In contrast to the situation at Gunton, however, most of the Wolterton barns (seven out of the ten surviving) are of eighteenth-century date, although only two (those at Hall Farm, Mannington and Church Farm, Wickmere) date from the first half of the century, and none from the period before 1700. On most of the Wolterton farms the farmhouse itself is the oldest building, generally predating the earliest of the other surviving structures by a century or more.

The accounts for the Wolterton estate, which survive from much of the eighteenth century, detail the allowances made to tenants for building and repairs.[274] Thatching, bricklaying, claying, daubing and paving were frequently listed. New barns, stables, carthouses and granaries are referred to. These records indicate sustained interest in investing in farm buildings in the middle and later decades of the eighteenth century: as does an undated early nineteenth-century memorandum of Lord Orford instructing that 'particular attention must be paid to the state of farm buildings – repairs should be made in the best and most substantial manner'.[275]

Piecemeal rebuilding was thus the order of the day: but the results could, nevertheless, be impressive. Park Farm has a fine set of buildings, including a late eighteenth-century timber-framed cart lodge with granary above, and a small barn of similar date. The other buildings, including stables and loose boxes are, typically, of nineteenth-century construction. One of the most extensive groups of buildings on the estate is at Manor Farm, Calthorpe. Stables and a horse yard are fitted into the angle of the roads, and there is a datestone of 1794 in the back corner of the horse yard. To the south is an eighteenth-century brick barn with a single threshing floor, and to the south of this an early nineteenth-century cattle yard with shelter sheds along the road. Sale particulars of the 1820s and 1830s describe some equally impressive farms in Saxthorpe; one in 1827 had

> Two spacious barns, waggon and cart lodges, granaries, cowhouse, riding horse stable, chaise house, stabling for 20 horses, slaughter shop, piggeries, off premises, two barns, stabling for 12, waggon lodge and convenient outhouses.[276]

The farm buildings on the neighbouring Blickling estate, which by the 1870s covered some 8000 acres, have much in common with those of Wolterton. Here too there appears to have been a steady policy of piecemeal rebuilding in the later eighteenth century, and few earlier buildings survive. The two-threshing-floor barn at Lodge Farm, Oulton, is dated 1730 and two mid-eighteenth-century barns survive at Green Farm, Oulton. Otherwise the farms are provided with one single-threshing-floor barn of late-eighteenth or early-nineteenth century date.

The medium-sized gentry properties in the region show a similar pattern of development to

[274] Wolterton Hall archives, WOLT 3/5/2.   [276] Wolterton Hall archives, WOLT 14/1/3.
[275] Wolterton Hall archives, WOLT 3/21/2.

these large estates, with extensive rebuilding in the decades around 1800 but little in the way of classic 'model farms' or planned courtyard arrangements. On the Heydon estate, for example, a memoranda in Erasmus Earl's notebook states that the almost unbelievable sum of £24,000 was spent on estate buildings in the 1790s.[277] Not surprisingly, few early barns survive. Of the 22 surviving farm complexes examined, 16 have barns (one farm has two): one barn of c.1700 survives at Crabgate Farm in Cawston and another was recently demolished there; two other farms have examples which probably date from the first half of the eighteenth century; but of the rest, seven appear to date from between c.1750 and 1800, and seven from the first half of the nineteenth century. All are brick-built structures. Some pre-1800 stables also survive, but few other buildings. These must have been swept away in the late eighteenth and early nineteenth centuries, for they had certainly once existed: a book of plans of the Heydon estate, surveyed between 1770 and 1790, shows that most farms consisted of a number of buildings, rather irregularly scattered around the yard, which usually included one longer building, presumably the barn.[278]

There are one or two exceptions to this general pattern of late eighteenth/early nineteenth-century piecemeal replacement, where farms of planned 'courtyard' form were erected. Most seem to be related to late eighteenth or early nineteenth-century programmes of enclosure and reclamation. The most striking example is Docking Farm, Cawston, created by the Heydon estate following the reclamation of Cawston Park in 1786 (see above, pp. 46). It was built on a virgin site: the only structure marked here on a map of 1786 was an intriguingly-named 'moveable barn' (presumably an early example of a type of structure described as a 'flying barn' in the *General Views* of Lincolnshire and Berkshire, and introduced by Nathaniel Kent to George III's farms at Windsor in 1791).[279] The building chronology of the surviving structures is hard to interpret – in particular the barn/stable block has been altered on a number of occasions – but by the early nineteenth-century the farmstead had a planned courtyard arrangement.

The development of farm buildings in the Northern Heathlands thus exhibits a degree of variation from estate to estate, yet at the same time displays much coherence. Although farm-houses are frequently early, barns and other farm buildings dating to the period before c.1770 are rare. On both large and medium-sized estates earlier structures were replaced from the later eighteenth century, either because they were impermanent structures of timber, thatch and 'mud', or because they were inadequate in other ways for the needs of husbandry. There are, however, few examples of planned, courtyard farmyards on the approved 'model' pattern.

(v) *The Flegg Loams*

The fertile Flegg Loam region was not an area dominated by large landed estates and as a consequence there is relatively little documentary evidence relating to the history of farm buildings. Their development can, however, be illustrated by the results of a systematic survey of 60 farms in the parishes of Rollesby, Hemsby, Ashby-with-Oby and Fleggburgh. The most striking features of the region are the large size of many farm complexes and the existence of

[277] NRO, MF/RO 334/1,3.

[278] NRO, MF/RO 334/1,3.

[279] Royal Archives, Nathaniel Kent's journal, pp. 170, 184, 198; G. V. Pearce, *General View of the Agriculture of*

Berkshire (1794), p. 3; T. Stone, *General View of the Agriculture of the County of Lincolnshire* (1794), pp. 107 and 228.

9. An early eighteenth-century barn at South Burlingham, Norfolk.

numerous early barns, brick-built with thatched roofs (Figure 9). Indeed, thirty of those on the farms examined were erected before c.1780, and probably around half of these before 1750. Three are certainly of pre-1700 origin: like the fine aisled barns at Hemsby and Rollesby. (Two of the finest late-medieval barns in Norfolk, at Paston and Waxham, also lie within this region, although not within the parishes surveyed.) Also noteworthy is the generous provision of barn space. Four barns have volumes of over 600 cubic metres and most of the farms which, by the time of the 1840 tithe surveys, cultivated in excess of 150 acres possessed more than one. Church Farm in Rollesby, for example, had – in addition to the early aisled building just mentioned – two substantial eighteenth-century brick barns. The neighbouring Sewell's Farm in the same parish has two large brick barns, one dated 1719 and the other of c.1750. In contrast to this wealth of pre-nineteenth century barns, early buildings of other kinds are relatively rare. Few certain examples of cattle yards constructed before 1800 were located; of the forty surviving stables, only eight were erected before 1800; and no examples of cattlesheds built before 1850 were encountered.

   Elsewhere in this region, however, some interesting evidence for innovative methods of cattle rearing was recovered. William Marshall in 1787 described the 'large expensive buildings which were used in the Blofield Union to fatten cattle for market'.[280] Up to 20 cattle were housed in

---

[280] Marshall, *Rural Economy*, II, pp. 274–6.

aisles separated by arches from a central turnip store which was entered through double doors at each end. At least two buildings of this type have been discovered to the north of the river Yare, within Blofield Union, at Upton (TG 390122) and Freethorpe (TG 411050); while two others were discovered to the south of the river, in Toft Monks (TM 418953) and Wheatacre (TM 433940). Although none of the surviving structures can be dated as early as the 1780s (that in Freethorpe bears a date of 1828), they have the same plan and proportions as those described by Marshall. They testify to the existence of a system of intensive cattle-fattening around the edge of the Halvergate marshes: such structures would have been well suited to farmers holding extensive acreages of marsh pasture but little arable land, men who would have been short of straw for littering open cattle yards and who did not need the large quantities of manure that such yards produced. Their main cash product was fat cattle which could easily be transported from here to Norwich or Yarmouth.

This was a region in which open fields survived into the nineteenth century and a few farmsteads were erected on new sites shortly after enclosure. Bloodhills Farm, Somerton, is one example: the complex includes two barns and other substantial buildings, including a carthouse or root store with a granary above, under a steeply pitched roof, which has some architectural pretensions.

(vi) *The Clayland Regions*

The buildings of the Central Claylands and the Southern and Western Clays have so much in common and differ so much from those in the regions so far discussed that they can usefully be considered together. In part the difference is one of building materials; timber framing and clay lump (large, unfired blocks of clay and straw) are more in evidence here than in other regions. But more important are characteristics of chronology. In all other districts, even the Flegg Loams, the overwhelming majority of farm buildings are of post-1780 construction, and structures surviving from before 1700 are rare. In these two clayland regions, in contrast, early buildings – especially barns – are frequently encountered. This pattern shows clearly on Figure 10, a map derived from the lists of buildings of historic and architectural interest prepared for the Department of the Environment in the 1980s. (As detailed survey work has shown, whilst this source provides only a general and incomplete picture of the total stock of early farm buildings, omissions will to a large extent be of a random nature.)

Two sample areas illustrate well the character of early buildings in the claylands. The first comprises the parishes of Ashwellthorpe, Morningthorpe, Wreningham, Hethel, Fritton and Ketteringham, on the northern edge of the Central Claylands region: a total of 19 farms. Here there is an extraordinarily high survival rate for early barns: nine out of the 22 examined (some farms had more than one) were erected before 1700 (Figure 11). Pre-nineteenth century cart lodges and stables also survive in some numbers here: three of the stables recorded pre-date 1700. The barns were often of substantial size – four had a volume in excess of 500 cubic metres. Those erected in the period after 1700 mainly date from the eighteenth rather than the nineteenth century and – unlike the earlier examples – are mostly constructed of brick.

In contrast to barns and stables, most of the other structures on these farmsteads are of early or mid-nineteenth century construction. Some are of timber, some of clay lump, but most are of brick. All cattle yards appear to be of early or mid-nineteenth century date. It is, perhaps,

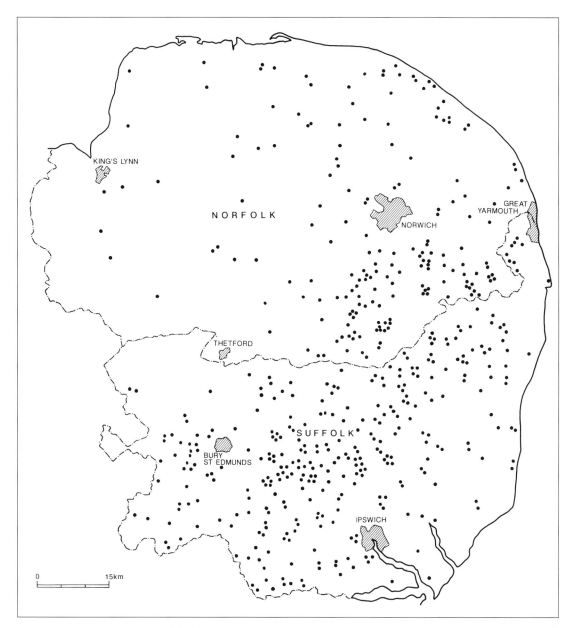

10. Farm buildings in Norfolk and Suffolk erected before 1700, as 'listed' by English Heritage.

almost superfluous to add that none of the farms in the six parishes had a planned layout, and indeed, only one farm had a regular E-plan layout at the time of the tithe surveys of the late 1830s/early 1840s.

The buildings in south Suffolk are in many ways similar, to judge from a small sample studied in the parish of Stansfield. Here, too, the tithe award map (the earliest surviving map of the parish) shows farms with a scattered arrangement of buildings: only at Windolphs Farm is a

11. A seventeenth-century timber-framed barn at Church Farm, Hethel, Norfolk.

more regular layout, a simple 'U' with barn at the back and two wings of cattle sheds, shown. The most extensive collection of buildings was that at Bayments Farm, where sales particulars from 1847 provide more details: here there were 'Two large barns, two stables, a cow house, cart and cattle sheds, large granary, piggeries and other outbuildings'.[281] The surviving buildings in the parish are generally timber-framed with wattle infill, and often weather-boarded. Large barns survive on five farms, two now converted to houses. Of these, the five-bay aisled barn with jowled wall posts at Stansfield Hall is the oldest – a probable sixteenth-century structure – whilst that at Gatesbury is of seventeenth-century date. The so-called 'tithe barn' at Glebe Farm probably dates from the mid-eighteenth century while that at Windolphs, which has two porches and threshing floors, is early nineteenth century. Two groups of early nineteenth-century stables survive: one at Cordell's Hall and one at Laurel Bank, previously Hill Farm. Both are timber-framed and have hay lofts above. There are some nineteenth-century brick cattle yards at Windolphs Farm, but no others have survived. Several farms have cart lodges, probably of eighteenth-century date. On the whole the buildings here are less substantial or durable than those in the Hethel/Morningthorpe area and the survival of early buildings is less

[281] WSRO, HD536/897/1–4.

striking, but the character and chronology of the buildings here – which seems to be fairly typical of the region – is nevertheless in marked contrast to those in the areas of light acid soil previously discussed.

Map evidence confirms that the farms in both these clayland regions were well-supplied with buildings, especially barns, from an early date; and also demonstrates that fairly extensive provision of cattle housing was being made as early as the seventeenth century, although no examples appear to survive today. One of the earliest maps to provide such information is that of a small estate in Aspall and Debenham, Suffolk, drawn in 1624. Here the farmstead comprised of an irregular group of buildings: a house and cottage, barn with a single threshing floor, two long single-storey buildings beside yards, and one building with a single door opening out into fields.[282]

Eighteenth- and nineteenth-century surveys made by the comparatively few large estates in the clayland regions provide additional information. That made in 1750 of the Adair's Flixton estate in north Suffolk, for example, describes the barns as built of 'mud and thatch', or as 'timber and clayed'. Several farms had more than one barn although only one barn had two threshing floors. 'Neat houses' for housing cattle, and dairies separate from the house, were present on most farms, as were stables, sometimes occupying one end of a barn. Few buildings were of brick, and thatch rather than tile was the usual roofing material.[283] On the Ashburnham estate in the mid-Suffolk parishes of Darmsden, Badley, Creeting and Battisford in 1830 all the farms were described as having barns and stables (a fine timber-framed stable range still survives at Badley Hall Farm). Many also had cow houses and 'detached dairies'. At Badley Hall Farm, for example, there was a 'cow house for 12 cows with loft over' and two lean-to calf pens, as well as a 'detached dairy and cheese chamber'. The majority of barns remaining on these farms vary considerably in date but some – like the two huge examples at Badley Hall – are massive structures, of fifteenth- and sixteenth-century origin.[284]

Although estate surveys attest the abundant provision of buildings, they were normally critical of their condition. The 1750 Flixton survey, for example, lamented their sorry state but added that they were 'much on a parr with the common state of repairs of other estates in that country'. Similarly, the farm buildings on the Ashburnham estate were described in 1830 as generally of a 'very inferior description, mostly being very old and having been neglected for a great many years, there are now considerable repairs wanting'. Surveys made in the 1860s and 1870s of the Duke of Norfolk's estates in south Norfolk, of the Flixton estate and of the Earsham estate, suggest that buildings were inadequate, dilapidated or both.[285] It is true that by this time, changes in agricultural practices associated with 'High Farming' had rendered older forms of building obsolete: the report on the Duke of Norfolk's estates thus described buildings 'not adapted to the present mode of farming'.[286] Nevertheless, the evidence suggests a general lack of investment in farm buildings in the claylands in the course of the eighteenth and early nineteenth centuries which is in marked contrast to the situation in the regions of light, acid soil.

---

[282] ESRO, HB79/2/1.

[283] WSRO, HA12 D3/1.

[284] ESRO, HA1 HB4/2.

[285] NRO, Smiths Gore 20.10.78, no. 225, 1520; ESRO, HA 12 D4/26; NRO, MEA 3/539).

[286] NRO, Smiths Gore 20.10.78, no. 225, 1520.

The development of farm buildings in the Dissected Claylands region of mid-Norfolk differs in many ways from that of the other clayland regions. Some early barns survive in the region – like the fine example at Manor Farm, Colton, with the date '1666' proudly displayed in decorative brickwork across the front facing the public road. But large estates held more land here than in the other clayland regions, and there was much rebuilding in the second half of the nineteenth century. Sixty-four farms on the Evans-Lombe estate, based around Bylaugh and Great Melton, were examined on the ground, and a further 29 on the Letton estate. On over half of the Evans-Lombe farms on which significant numbers of buildings survive, substantial rebuilding in a standard estate style had taken place in the later nineteenth century. Earlier barns were generally retained but few are of any great antiquity. None survives from before 1700, and the majority are brick-built structures of late eighteenth- or early nineteenth-century date. On the Letton estate the situation was broadly similar. Here the barns – generally smaller than those on the Evans-Lombe estate – had a greater chronological spread, with two surviving from the period before 1700. Of the rest, eleven were of eighteenth-century date (closer dating is difficult, because traditions of timber-framed construction were maintained with little alteration throughout this period) and five were built between 1800 and 1850. Again, there are few other buildings surviving from before c.1840. On both estates farm plans – to judge from map evidence – seem to have been universally irregular until the middle of the nineteenth century.

(vii) Conclusion

This brief account is sufficient to demonstrate the varied character of the farm buildings surviving in Norfolk and Suffolk, and in particular their varied chronology. In some regions large numbers of early buildings survive; in others, structures dating to before 1800 are rare. Yet before examining the reasons for such variations in the pattern of building, it is worth summarising what the building histories of the different regions had in common, and what this might tell us about the development of agriculture. Up until the end of the eighteenth century most East Anglian farmsteads consisted of a scatter of buildings arranged without any ordered plan. A barn, sometimes with lean-to cattle sheds and occasionally with a porch, was the main building of the farm. This usually had a single threshing floor, more rarely two. Other than this, most farms possessed a stable, sometime integral with the barn and often with a hay loft above, and some a cow house, cartlodge or open sided shed. Few granaries are depicted on maps or referred to in documents, and even fewer survive. More significantly, there is little evidence for the provision of shelter sheds for cattle before the end of the eighteenth century. The practice of in-wintering cattle was the basis of the large-scale manure production central to the new systems of 'improved' agriculture: such yards must have existed, but were presumably temporary structures divided off with hurdles and providing little shelter for the animals except in the barn lean-tos. Open-fronted shelter sheds for cattle were increasingly added to farmsteads in the period c.1790–1840, however, usually defining a yard or yards. Ideally, as agricultural theorists urged, the result should be a regular 'U' or 'E' shape, depending on the number of yards so defined. In fact, regular arrangements of any kind remained rare on East Anglian farms until well into the nineteenth century: an analysis of 400 Norfolk farmsteads depicted on the tithe award maps of c.1840 reveals that half were still of an irregular plan

(Figure 12).[287] Many nineteenth-century writers were aware of this discrepancy between theory and practice. The Raynbirds, for example, noted in 1849:

> In every village are to be seen buildings arranged in every form except that which would give economy in the manufacture of manure, or in the feeding of cattle.[288]

The fact that shelter sheds were rarely provided before the nineteenth century, and that regular layouts remained exceptional before *c.* 1840, suggests that there was only a very loose connection between husbandry practice and the physical structures of the farm. Large numbers of bullocks could clearly be over-wintered on turnips in yards, and large quantities of manure thereby produced, without either. Where regular layouts were adopted in the eighteenth century it was often for reasons which were essentially non-agricultural and non-economic: such complexes generally formed, as at Holkham, an element in the landscape of aristocratic display. Expressing wealth, taste, and the landowner's active involvement in the life of the estate, they were constructed for motives which were essentially ideological in character. It is no coincidence that the Great Barn at Holkham, one of the finest eighteenth-century farm buildings in Norfolk, was designed not only as a setting for Thomas Coke's 'sheep shearings' but also as a focal point – suitably embellished with ornamental planting – for the new southern extension to Holkham park.

In broad terms the farm buildings of East Anglia in this period display little regional variation in terms of the *kinds* of structures present on the farm: in all areas we find the same range of structures – barns, stables, cattle housing – in the same general arrangements. There are, it is true, minor variations on this theme, more detectable in the documentary evidence than in the surviving buildings themselves – the presence of 'neat houses' in parts of the Central Claylands, for example. But the most important regional variations are in the materials used to build these structures and (of central significance to our enquiry) in the chronology of the surviving building stock. Pre-1750 farm buildings – barns, for the most part – are strikingly concentrated in the claylands, in some parts of North-West Norfolk, and in the Flegg Loam region: that is, in areas of comparatively fertile soils. Elsewhere – in regions of more acid and infertile soils, characterised by large estates and by large-scale reclamation – the vast majority of farm buildings, even the barns, post-date 1780. In such areas a wave of rebuilding swept away the earlier building stock.

By the eighteenth century most East Anglian farmers were tenants and farm buildings were the landlord's responsibility. They were relatively expensive pieces of plant and both owners and agents were anxious to limit the amount spent on their erection and subsequent upkeep. Although social and ideological motivations might, as at Holkham, be an important factor in deciding what kinds of buildings a landowner erected, for the most part building activity was related to the need to attract good tenants, responsible and reliable men with capital. Where existing farm buildings were equal to this task, they would be maintained and updated as required. But where circumstances rendered them inadequate to the demands of prospective tenants, they would be updated or replaced if the necessary resources were available.

The distribution of surviving structures indicates that in areas of poor acid soils – the Northern Heathlands, Breckland, and *parts* of North-West Norfolk – those farm buildings

---

[287] Wade Martins, *Historic Farm Buildings*, p. 199.   [288] Raynbird and Raynbird, *Suffolk*, p. 60.

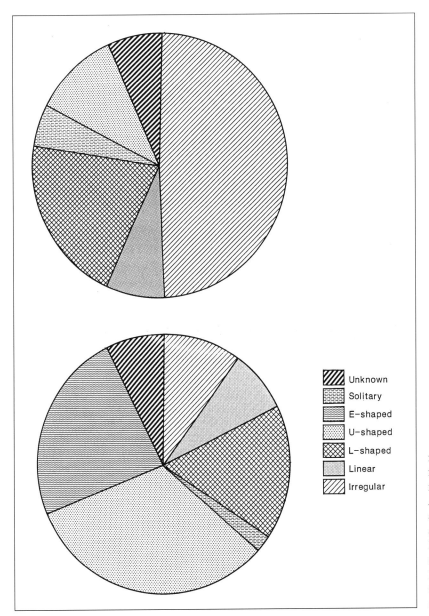

Unknown
Solitary
E-shaped
U-shaped
L-shaped
Linear
Irregular

12. The development of
farmstead layout in the
nineteenth century.
Above: farmstead layout
as depicted on the tithe
award maps of the 1840s.
Below: farmstead layout
as depicted on the First
Edition OS 25″ of the
1880s. Based on a sample
of 400 Norfolk farms.

which existed in the middle of the eighteenth century were generally unsuited to the requirements of later decades and were replaced on a large scale. They were presumably rendered
redundant in part by expanding production, as new tracts of land were brought in to
cultivation; and in part by changes in farm size – by the growth in the number of large farms
and the decline in the numbers of smaller holdings. Larger barns were now needed to process
the crop (and larger yards were needed to produce the large quantities of manure on which
the cultivation of these light lands depended). Piecemeal refurbishment and alteration of
existing structures would not have been enough to attract the men of capital needed to stock

these light land farms, and enclosure required, in many places, the wholesale relocation of farms out onto new sites.

In areas of more fertile soils, in contrast – in the Claylands, in the Flegg Loam Region, or on the more fertile and calcareous of the soils in North-West Norfolk – far greater numbers of barns, and to some extent other buildings, date to the period before *c.*1750. This is probably the consequence of several factors. Firstly, the general quality of the buildings in existence in the early eighteenth century in these regions was probably often better than in those just discussed: it is noticeable that the distribution of pre-1750 farm buildings closely mirrors that of pre-1750 domestic buildings. Better soils presumably generated sufficient wealth for the erection, before the eighteenth century, of buildings sufficiently durable to meet the requirements of later occupiers, and thus to survive in some numbers. In some regions (such as the Flegg Loams) the expansion of production in the period after *c.* 1750 was not so great as to render existing barns redundant. On the claylands, however, and most strikingly in the Central Clayland region, a massive increase in production occurred as old grassland was converted to arable. The survival of many early barns here may in part be due to the fact that, before the late eighteenth-century expansion of arable, many had been larger than required for the processing and storage of the harvest because they had served a range of other functions: some, as we have seen, certainly incorporated stables and it is possible that some sections were used for stalling milking cattle, or young calves at certain times of the year. Moreover, on all these soils (and to some extent on the Flegg loams and in parts of North-West Norfolk) landlords were able to resist the demands for more barn space, and for farm improvements more generally, because in the later eighteenth and early nineteenth centuries they had little trouble finding tenants for their farms. Farmers simply had to put up with what was available, storing an ever higher proportion of the unprocessed crop in the stackyard.

Farm buildings thus represent an approximate surrogate for more general estate investment in the agricultural revolution period. That investment was lowest where soils were most fertile. Investment was greatest in areas of the poorest soils, where marginal land was being brought into cultivation and where there was the greatest need for – but also the greatest difficulty in attracting – good tenants.

CHAPTER III

The Development of Farming Practice, c. 1700–1830

1. The development of crop rotations

(i) Introduction

There is general agreement among historians that there was a substantial increase in arable yields in England in general, and in East Anglia in particular, during the course of the eighteenth century. The traditional view attributed this principally to the widespread adoption of 'improved' rotations combining, in a regular sequence, courses of cereals, turnips and artificial grasses (clover and nonsuch).[1] The central importance of cropping was emphasised by contemporary improvers. In Arthur Young's words:

> If I were called on to name one peculiar circumstance, which has done more honour to the husbandry of Norfolk than any other to be thought of, I should, without hesitation, instance this of the rotation of cropping.[2]

The most famous form of 'improved' rotation in the eighteenth century was the so-called 'Norfolk four-course', a recurrent four-year cycle of wheat, turnips, barley, clover/grasses, which was varied on occasions by the extension of the grass 'ley' to two or three years. In such a system, according to the nineteenth-century agricultural writer Low, 'in each year, one half of the farm is under exhausting, one half under restorative, crops'.[3] Young and others repeatedly emphasised the fundamental importance of the cardinal rule, that the farmer should never take two consecutive courses of cereal crops.

The main benefit of the new systems was that they enhanced the levels of soil nitrogen, which are steadily depleted by cropping.[4] In 'traditional' rotations, nitrogen was returned to the ploughsoil principally during a regular year-long fallow, in the form of dung from the animals grazed on the land, and from the weed growth ploughed into the soil at the end of the year. The new systems of cropping eliminated long fallows by substituting courses of legumes, principally clover, and roots, principally turnips. The former were able to fix atmospheric nitrogen directly in the soil; the latter increased the amount of stock being kept through the winter, the amount of dung produced, and thus the amount of nitrogen (and other minerals) returned to the soil.[5]

Historians traditionally posed a rather simple dichotomy between medieval and early-modern agriculture, featuring two years of grain crop followed by a year-long fallow, and these

---

[1] For instance, Sheil, 'Soil fertility'; Overton, 'Determinants', pp. 284–5; G. P. H. Chorley, 'The Agricultural Revolution in northern Europe, 1750–1880: nitrogen, legumes and crop production', *EcHR* 34 (1981), pp. 71–93.

[2] Young, *Norfolk*, p. 193.

[3] D. Low, *Practical Agriculture* (1838), p. 205.

[4] See, especially, Sheil, 'Soil fertility' and Chorley, 'Agricultural Revolution'.

[5] Sheil, 'Soil fertility', pp. 74–5.

'improved' rotations of the eighteenth century. Recent research has suggested a more complex picture.[6] Legumes had already become a standard feature of agriculture in some parts of England (including areas of East Anglia) in the medieval period. In particular, Bruce Campbell has demonstrated that in north-east Norfolk, where closely-regulated field systems were absent and lordship relatively weak, nitrogen-fixing fodder crops were being cultivated by the thirteenth century as part of an innovative agricultural system which featured the assiduous application of manures of diverse kinds, and the virtual elimination of year-long fallows.[7] These were important developments, if limited geographically, but the sixteenth and seventeenth centuries saw further changes: a shift from peas and vetches to clover, a more effective nitrogen-fixer. By the middle of the seventeenth century 'artificial' grasses – both clover and nonsuch – were being widely integrated into arable rotations, sometimes in the form of long leys of five, six or more years – that is, in a form of up-and-down or 'convertible' husbandry. As a result of these developments the frequency of fallowing was, in many areas of England, considerably reduced.[8] Turnips, which had been grown as a garden crop since the sixteenth century, only began to appear in field rotations during the later seventeenth century. During the eighteenth century the cultivation of these two crops in regular rotations ensured a steady rise in yields.[9]

The four-course rotation brought a number of other benefits which have received rather less attention from recent writers. During the latter half of the traditional fallow year fields were systematically ploughed and harrowed in order to prevent the seeding and germination of weeds. Indeed, although modern writers emphasise the role of the fallow year in maintaining fertility, its importance for weed control may have been of equal importance to farmers, especially tenants holding on a short lease. The four-course provided an alternative method of cleansing land, but to explain how it did so it is necessary to describe the structure of the 'improved' farming year by looking at the sequence of cropping within an individual field.

Wheat was sown in September or October, and harvested in August or September the following year.[10] The stubbles were then grazed by stock into the winter, and then 'summer-tilled' – repeatedly ploughed and harrowed to eliminate weeds (as in the old year-long fallow) and to provide the fine seed-bed necessary for turnips. These were planted around mid-summer, either drilled or dibbled in regular rows, allowing for repeated hoeing during the summer and autumn. This benefited the plants but also provided a more general measure of weed control, which would have been impossible with more closely-growing plants, sown broadcast. As the plants grew they further suppressed weeds, their dense foliage shading and out-competing them. The turnips were ready for consumption by livestock in late Autumn. They were either 'pulled' and taken back to yards to be fed to livestock, or were eaten off in the field. Either way, the fields were free of the crop by February or March. Barley was sown around April, and under-sown with clover or other 'artificial' grasses. The barley was harvested in August or September but the 'seeds' continued to grow through the stubbles into the following year. The following summer the grass or clover would be cut for hay and grazed by livestock. On thin, light soils the grass might be left for a second year, on the very worst soils for a third. In late summer

---

[6] Campbell and Overton, 'A new perspective', pp. 54–66.

[7] Campbell, 'Agricultural Progress'.

[8] Campbell and Overton, 'A new perspective', pp. 58–60.

[9] *Ibid.*, pp. 60–1.

[10] See, in particular, Wade Martins and Williamson, *Randall Burroughes*, pp. 12–18.

the field was ploughed and harrowed again, ready to receive the wheat seed, and thus the whole cycle began again.

Historians like Ernle associated the adoption of such clover- and turnip-based rotations with the activities of great aristocratic improvers like 'Turnip' Townshend in the 1730s and 1740s.[11] But in the 1960s and 1970s a number of scholars drew attention to the evidence for the widespread cultivation of turnips, in East Anglia and elsewhere, by the 1680s. They formed an element in Eric Kerridge's 'Agricultural Revolution of the seventeenth century'.[12] Both this view, however, and to some extent the traditional chronology, have more recently come under attack (and especially in so far as they relate to East Anglia) from Bruce Campbell and Mark Overton.[13] The latter, using the evidence of probate inventories, has questioned both the extent to which turnips formed a key feature of arable rotations in the seventeenth century, and also the accepted reasons for their initial cultivation. In a review of the evidence for the long-term development of agriculture in Norfolk, from *c.*1250 to *c.*1850, Campbell and Overton emphasised the remarkable stability of cropping up to the mid-eighteenth century. 'Some new crops were introduced and some established crops rose or declined in relative importance but, on the whole, farmers in early modern Norfolk grew the same crops, in much the same proportions, as their forebears'.[14] The new crops were being cultivated in the fields of Norfolk and Suffolk by the end of the seventeenth century, but only in fairly small proportions. Moreover, turnips were originally grown, not as part of a system designed to improve arable yields, but as an extra source of fodder by farmers in East Anglia's main cattle-rearing and (to a lesser extent) dairying districts. In the principal arable areas, in contrast, the crop was of minor importance before the second half of the eighteenth century. Even in their livestock-rearing heartlands, turnips were not a major crop before *c.*1750. Indeed, Mark Overton has calculated – from the evidence of probate inventories – that in the period from 1660 to 1739 no more than 3 per cent of the cropped acreage in Norfolk was devoted to clover, and only 8 per cent to turnips.[15] The cultivation of these crops was thus simply not on a sufficient scale to have made any real impact on the amount of livestock kept, and thus on the amount of manure available in the first half of the eighteenth century. In so far as yields per acre rose in this period, Overton believes, the cause must be sought elsewhere. Moreover, even when present in the fields in the period before *c.*1750, turnips and clover were not being combined in the ways most beneficial to fertility: 'In the early eighteenth century few farmers seem to have been employing anything resembling a fully-fledged Norfolk four-course'. Indeed, it has even been suggested that 'one of the earliest' examples of a four-course rotation in East Anglia comes as late as 1787–94.[16]

The precise chronology with which the 'improved' rotations were adopted in East Anglia is, therefore, of crucial importance. Yet before we explore this issue further we must first clarify some terms and concepts. Many writers have emphasised the crucial importance of the 'Norfolk four-course'. But even a cursory examination of eighteenth- and nineteenth-century sources reveals that there were a number of ways in which turnips and clover could be incorporated in rotations. The four-course was not necessarily the ideal form of 'improved' husbandry on

[11] Riches, *Agricultural Revolution*, pp. 81–92.

[12] E. Kerridge, 'Turnip husbandry in High Suffolk', *EcHR* 8 (1956), pp. 390–2.

[13] Campbell and Overton, 'A new perspective'.

[14] *Ibid*, p. 55.

[15] Overton, 'Determinants', p. 312.

[16] *Ibid*, pp. 313–4.

all soils. Low, writing in 1838, described it as the basis of 'nearly all the most approved rotations', but added, as qualification, '*on the lighter soils and inferior clays of this country*'. Bacon, writing specifically about Norfolk in 1844, emphasised that it was pre-eminently a light land system, which enabled 'the farmers to keep the thin-skinned and poor lands in cultivation'.[17] Eighteenth- and early nineteenth-century commentators like Kent and Young describe a number of other turnip-based rotations. Of particular importance was a five-course rotation, the 'Flegg five-shift'. This violated Young's cardinal rule, by allowing the farmer to take two consecutive crops of corn, *viz*:

> Wheat → barley → turnips → barley → clover/grasses.

More widely distributed was a related rotation, the 'East Norfolk six-shift', which, while still having a barley crop directly after wheat, added a further clover or grass crop:

> Wheat → barley → turnips → barley → clover/grasses → clover/grasses.

Numerous variations on these essential forms were widely distributed on the better soils of East Anglia, especially in the Central Claylands and on the Flegg Loams.[18]

A wide range of documentary evidence makes it clear that the development of rotations varied widely, not only in character but also in chronology. For this reason, and others, the discussion that follows will once again be framed within an explicitly regional framework.

(ii) *Breckland, North-West Norfolk, and the Northern Heathlands*

As already noted, Mark Overton has cast doubt on North-West Norfolk's traditional role as cradle of the Agricultural Revolution, arguing that turnips were first grown as a field crop in East Anglia's cattle-farming areas and were only later adopted in arable rotations in traditional sheep-corn husbandry areas. This suggestion was largely made on the evidence of probate inventories, although it was supported by the only really detailed evidence for early eighteenth-century cropping practices within a sheep-corn area yet found: a tithe book for the parish of Hunstanton in North-West Norfolk, covering the years 1705–1711, the information in which can be related to a slightly earlier parish map.[19]

Hunstanton parish is characterised by the fairly fertile soils of the *Newmarket 2* and *Hunstanton Associations*. It includes only very limited areas of the kind of poor sandy soils characteristic of the upland interior of the region. The tithe book shows that about half the land at any one time was under a grain crop, of which barley was by far the most important, covering about a third of the farmed acreage (*c.*358 acres). Barley was particularly prominent on the Hunstanton soils: on the Newmarket soils further inland wheat (71 acres in all) was more important. Rye was less significant, and almost entirely restricted to the Newmarket soils (19 acres), and a mere 7 acres of oats was grown, making a total cereal acreage in any one year of around 450 acres. The rotations employed, while superficially chaotic, fall into a small number of basic types. The most common – employed on some 60 per cent of the land – consisted of a basic sequence of wheat → barley → peas → barley, followed by a fallow or,

[17] Low, *Practical Agriculture*, p. 265; Bacon, *Agriculture*, p. 30.

[18] Young, *Norfolk*, pp. 193–208.
[19] NRO, LeStrange KA9, BHC 7.

more usually, by one or two years of rotational clover/grass, and then a fallow. Rye was occasionally substituted for wheat. Most of the other rotations involved sequences of barley, grass and fallow with courses of peas, vetches or buckwheat intruded or substituted at intervals. Often two successive crops of barley were taken. As Overton has pointed out, turnips were not well represented in the fields of Hunstanton. An average of only nine acres of the crop was grown, always in closes beside the farms in the village: around 0.8 per cent of the total cropped acreage of the parish.

Hunstanton is not the only parish in North-West Norfolk in which turnips do not seem to have been cultivated on any scale in the late seventeenth and early eighteenth centuries. In Barsham, for example, tithe accounts covering the period 1671–1735 make no mention of the crop before 1701, and only twice thereafter. When turnips are mentioned, the implication is, as at Hunstanton, they were being grown in small closes, rather than as a normal part of the field rotations. Thus in 1713 the accounts record payments from one farmer for 'ye Tith of his *patch of peas and turnips*'. As late as 1735, when the incumbent drew up a list of the tithable crops growing in his parish, he failed to make any mention of turnips, although rye, maslin, barley, oats, peas, buckwheat, clover, and grass were all recorded.[20]

At first sight, then, the evidence suggests that turnips came late to North-West Norfolk. Yet closer inspection suggests a more varied picture. On the Raynham estate turnips were being widely cultivated as a field crop by the first decade of the eighteenth century.[21] A series of letters from 1661 to 1686 make no mention of turnips; but the next run of estate correspondence, from 1706, shows that they were by then a well-established part of the farming regime. On 16 February, for example, Lord Townshend's agent informed him: 'As I remember your L[or]dship intended the new enclosure called Girdhill, which is next the new pond, for turneps', but added that he considered that 'ye close by the wind mill more fitt for turnips this yeare'. Both turnips and clover begin to be referred to in Raynham leases in the 1710s and 1720s.[22] Often large acreages are specified, up to a fifth of the total area of the farm for each crop. By the 1730s, covenants were beginning to state that turnips were 'not to be accounted a crop' in the prescribed sequence of husbandry. The terms of the leases imply that the tenants were allowed to insert a course of turnips among two or even three years of grain crops, before laying the land down to clover for two years.

Raynham was not unique in all this. Turnips were being grown 'in very considerable quantities' at Houghton as early as 1673, and the correspondence of John Wrott, agent for the Walpoles, suggests that their husbandry was on a large scale by the beginning of the eighteenth century.[23] On 3 March 1701, for example, Wrott complained that 'wee have had a very tedious winter for Bullocks and Sheep in Turnips, that they are nothing so forward as they used to be other years'. On 14 March he commented: 'As to the ploughing concerned this yeare, it will be thus: wee shall sow about 40 acres of Turnips, & about 70 acres of Barley, which is more than we used to sow, and shall therefore sow the lesser quantity of oates, not above 12 or 14 acres of oates …'. On 28 March Wrott reported that he had sold 'five score of the weathers in

---

[20] NRO, PD 117/35.
[21] Saunders, 'Estate management at Raynham', pp. 41–2.

[22] *Ibid.*, p. 63.
[23] Plumb, 'Sir Robert Walpole and Norfolk Husbandry', pp. 86–9.

Turnops' to Norwich butchers.[24] Surviving accounts from other estates in North-West Norfolk present a similar picture. Turnips were being cultivated as a field crop on the Holkham estate by 1710, while on the Hunstanton estate's Downs Farm in Barret Ringstead turnips featured in the rotations in almost every field during the period 1715–19, although the rotations were irregular by later standards.[25] In contrast, the rotations on three farms in west Norfolk between 1734 and 1751 were described by a correspondent to the *Gentleman's Magazine* in 1752: not only were turnips here a standard feature of cropping, but a strict Norfolk four-course rotation was already being followed.[26]

The probate inventories used by Overton, and the tithe books from Hunstanton and Barsham, thus give us only part of the story. The evidence suggests that there was a marked dichotomy in cultivation practices in North-West Norfolk which mirrored the distinction in the structure of the landscape, between the calcareous soils of the coastal strip and the principal valleys – the landscape of large villages and unenclosed open-fields – and the enclosed lands of the acid uplands – an emptier countryside of depopulated villages and large estates. In the first half of the century the cultivation of turnips was limited in the former area but widespread in the latter: here they were perhaps adopted in an attempt to expand livestock production and to diversify into bullock fattening at a time of low cereal prices, within an area in which there was a shortage of good-quality pastures and, in particular, meadowland.

In Breckland, too, turnips seem to have been grown as a normal field crop in some places from an early date, as at Shropham in 1681, while in 1723 they were said to have been grown in the common fields of Thetford 'for 25 years past'.[27] A lease for an enclosed farm in Thompson in the Breckland in 1720 stated that after two years of grain crops the land was to be sown with turnips 'fed on the land'.[28] By 1738 leases for the Livermere estate were stipulating that the tenant was not to grow two crops in succession 'except for turnips', without a fallow, terms repeated in a number of mid-century leases for the area.[29] By the 1780s, certainly, improved rotations featuring turnips were widespread: in 1788, for example, nearly 500 acres of turnips were growing in the parish of Tottington.[30]

Turnips were also being widely cultivated in the Northern Heathland district by the start of the eighteenth century. As early as 1666 a lease for a farm in Horsham St Faiths bound the tenant to leave twenty acres sown with the crop (hoed twice).[31] A tithe account for Thorpe St Andrew lists the crops growing on six farms in 1706. Of these, five were growing turnips in quantities ranging from 6 per cent to 34 per cent of their cropped acreage. In all, turnips accounted for some 13 per cent of the total acreage under crops.[32] By 1729 Erasmus Earle, the owner of the Heydon estate, was comparing the prices fetched by his grass-fed and turnip-fed cattle;[33] while in 1723 a lease for a farm at Felbrigg included the following clause:

And whereas 'tis said in the old lease that not above 3 crops of corn shall be sown before the land is lay'd down with clover or non such and that he may sow turnip seed between any of

[24] *Ibid*, pp. 87–8.
[25] NRO, LeStrange OA3.
[26] Parker, *Coke of Norfolk*, pp. 10–11; *Gentleman's Magazine* 12 (1752), p. 501.
[27] NRO, Petre Box 9/1.
[28] NRO, WLS XIX/27/2.

[29] ESRO, HA 93/3/286.
[30] NRO, WLS XXVII/23 415 X 5.
[31] NRO, MSS 16.023.
[32] NRO, PD 228/51 (W).
[33] NRO, NRS 10360.

the three crops of corn. Now the meaning is that he may have liberty to sow one crop of turnips besides three crops of corn before it is laid down as aforesaid.[34]

The earliest surviving lease from the Heydon estate, from 1724, similarly instructed the tenant of Beer House Farm 'Not to sow more than four crops whereof one is turnips, before laying down to three years olland'.[35]

The Home Farm accounts of the Wolterton estate, which run for a few years from 1738, make it clear that 'dutch sedge', turnips, clover and nonsuch were all being widely grown.[36] The field book entitled 'About the Management of our Farm' provides more detail, listing the crops grown on 29 fields from 1737 to 1742.[37] The rotations vary widely. In some fields convertible husbandry with leys of four or five years, and often quite short cropping spells, was practiced and turnips were absent. More usual – practised on some 30 per cent of the fields – were rotations which alternated only one or two years 'olland' or grass ley with two or three cereal courses. Yet most common of all – practised in 55 per cent of arable fields – were rotations featuring fairly regular courses of both seeds and turnips: variations on the four-course, the five-shift, and the six-shift rotations described earlier. Moreover, by this date such improved rotations were apparently being demanded on *all* the cultivated land of the tenanted farms. By the 1740s the normal stipulation was not to grow cereals for more than two or three years before laying down to turnips or grass. Nevertheless, while *in general* turnips seem to have been incorporated into field rotations in this region in the first decades of the century, once again there are places where this does not seem to have occurred. Tithe accounts covering the years 1732–1737 for Hempstead near Holt, for example – a parish of particularly light and acid soils – make no mention of the crop.[38]

The evidence thus suggests a diverse picture. Sometimes whole parishes in these acid soil districts failed to cultivate turnips on any scale in the early eighteenth century, while neighbouring ones grew them with enthusiasm. In some places, as on the Wolterton estate in the late 1730s, turnips might be cultivated in some fields of a farm, but not in others. To understand this pattern it is helpful to think not so much in terms of the diffusion of the *idea* of turnip cultivation – from enlightened to unenlightened farmer – but rather in terms of the factors which discouraged or limited the crop's successful cultivation.

The first limiting factor in these districts was an institutional one: the nature of field systems. The crucial factor here was not open-field agriculture *per se*, but the existence of a *foldcourse*, in which the manorial flocks had a right to range freely over the arable during the fallow season. Under such an arrangement – particularly characteristic of Breckland and North-West Norfolk, but also a feature of some parishes in the Northern Heathlands – the cultivation of turnips was difficult. All the references in the estate correspondence from Houghton and Raynham are to turnips in *closes*, and it is worth noting that in the Raynham leases from the 1720s and 1730s different conditions were applied to the enclosed land and the unenclosed breaks, with the cultivation of turnips being stipulated on the former but not on the latter. Similarly, at Hunstanton in 1705–9 the only turnips grown were in closes hard by the village. The relative absence

[34] NRO, WKC 5/95/3.
[35] NRO, BUL 310 617 X 4.
[36] Wolterton Hall archives, WOLT 3/5/1.
[37] Wolterton Hall archives, WOLT 8/7.
[38] NRO, NRS 20993 69 X 3.

of turnips from the fields of early eighteenth-century Hunstanton, Barsham, or Hempstead was probably not, therefore, the consequence of 'ignorance' on the part of the farmers, but of the survival here of particular institutional arrangements, inherited from the medieval period.

In the 1720s the lord of the manor of Thetford still retained rights of foldcourse in Magdalen Field, a right usually exercised by his tenant with 650 ewes and 350 wethers.[39] The foldcourse operated from 14 September to 3 May. Witnesses to a dispute in 1724 claimed that some occupiers of the field had been sowing turnips for 25 years, and that the shepherds had kept the sheep off them, treating them as if they were growing corn, 'until last year when the sheep ate up the defendants' turnips'. The question before the court was whether turnips should indeed be treated as corn, and the sheep kept off them as of right. A similar dispute is recorded in an undated early eighteenth-century document from Ashill. The lords of the manor here had rights of foldcourse across the common fields but had to keep their sheep off the corn. Sometimes, it was claimed, farmers deliberately planted crops in positions that prevented the sheep moving through the fields, 'By which means the sheeps' feed hath been and still is nearly precarious'. The lord of the manor asserted that the farmers should not be permitted to enclose any more land or sow

> turnipps or clover which in this parish are become a great improvement and infact Sir Henry Bedingfield descendants and his daughter who lived near the said parish and were well acquainted with the customs of the said manor did for more than 40 years ackuiesse and no way oppose the landowners inclosing and sowing the said new enclosures with turnips.[40]

Environmental factors also contributed to the slow progress of turnip cultivation in acid soil areas. Turnips do not thrive in acid conditions: they are liable to fail completely on sour land and are prone to attack by finger-and-toe disease.[41] This almost certainly explains why some mid-century records show the crop being regularly grown in some fields on a farm (presumably those of less acidic soil) but not in others. Only as intensive routine marling became widespread did it become possible to cultivate the crop more widely.[42] Contemporaries frequently linked marling with the cultivation of turnips as the two cornerstones of the new husbandry. Even on Flegg, according to Marshall, farmers had been unable to grow turnips before large-scale marling had begun.[43] The gradual decline in the cultivation of rye on these light soils in the course of the eighteenth century was also, in all probability, in large part a consequence of the same change in basic soil chemistry.

(iii) *The Sandlings and the Flegg Loams*

In both these regions cattle were generally of equal or even greater importance than sheep, and the cultivation of turnips as animal feed seems to have begun early. The crop is frequently mentioned in probate inventories from the Sandlings from the 1680s, and in a variety of other documents. Turnips were being cultivated at Herringfleet as early as 1662, at Benacre by 1665, and by 1674 a note in the manor custumal of Theberton suggests that they were a

---

[39] NRO, Petre Box 9/1–4.   *Agriculture*, p. 232.
[40] NRO, Petre Box 17/1.   [42] Robinson, *Fream's Agriculture*, p. 31.
[41] Hanley, *Practical Farming*, p. 138; Robinson, *Fream's*   [43] Marshall, *Rural Economy*, II, p. 106.

common crop: 'If any crop of turnips shall be drawn to sell or to feed fat cattle, tithe in kind'.[44] The wording implies that the crop was often *not* drawn, but rather eaten off in the fields, presumably by sheep: certainly, sheep as well as cattle were being fed on the crop at Glemham in 1726.[45] A farmer in Tunstall had fifty acres of 'somerland' sown with turnips in 1712;[46] the tithe on turnips contributed more than that on clover, and more than the rental of glebe, to the vicar's income at Glemham in 1716;[47] and by 1722 Defoe was able to comment on the abundance of the crop in the area around Woodbridge:

> This part of England is remarkable for being the first where the feeding and fattening of cattle, both sheep as well as black cattle, with turnips, was first practiced in England, which is made a very great part of the improvement of their land to this day.[48]

In the 1720s, 1730s and 1740s turnips feature prominently in estate accounts. In 1723 the agent of the Glemham estate complained that 'turnips grow short and hay is bad'; in 1739 he noted that 'The turnips are almost done ... for we have had a very great rot of them'.[49] Estate accounts and other sources show that new rotations were widely adopted by the end of the century: at Hill Farm, Rushmere for example, turnips accounted for between 17 per cent and 25 per cent of the arable area between 1806 and 1809, with clover varying from 8 per cent to 17 per cent.[50]

There is, unfortunately, rather less evidence from the Flegg Loam region, largely because this was not an area dominated by large landed estates. Probate inventories show, as Holderness has pointed out, that turnips were widely cultivated here from the 1680s.[51] Tithe accounts for Smallburgh, covering the years 1725–1759, certainly contain numerous references to the crop: although the source does not allow us to calculate the actual acreage sown, it was clearly extensive.[52] By the 1760s, according to Young, most farmers here were following the Flegg five-shift – that is, a sequence of wheat → barley → turnips → barley → clover.[53] In 1804 this was still the usual rotation in this region, although on the slightly poorer soils it was customary to extend the clover shift to two or even three years, as on a farm at Tunstead in the 1780s.[54]

(iv) *The Claylands*

In the late seventeenth and early eighteenth century land use in the East Anglian claylands fell into three broad categories: permanent pasture, convertible land, and permanent arable, some of it still lying in open fields. A map and cropping account for Green Farm, Finningham (1681–87) illustrates well how enclosed land might be managed.[55] Of the eight arable fields, which occupied around 40 per cent of the farm's area, three were either laid down to grass, or broken up, in the period covered by the account. At any one time around a third of the arable land was under rotational grass, the ley generally having a length of six or seven years. Such a

[44] Burrell, 'Sandlings', p. 57; ESRO, FAA 3/9.

[45] ESRO, HA 49/4/14.

[46] Burrell, 'Sandlings', p. 60.

[47] ESRO, HA 49/4/4.

[48] Defoe, *Tour*, pp. 86–7.

[49] ESRO, HA 49/4/14.

[50] ESRO, HA 2/A2/1/23.

[51] B. A. Holderness, 'The origins of High Farming', in Holderness and Turner (eds), *Land, labour and agriculture*, pp. 234–6.

[52] NRO, PD 189/31.

[53] A. Young, *The farmer's tour through the East of England* (4 vols, 1771), II, pp. 85, 137.

[54] Young, *Norfolk*, pp. 198–200; NRO, MC 37/159 482 X 5.

[55] ESRO, HB 405/C2/1.

distinction between arable and rotational grass on the one hand, and permanent grass, is referred to in many leases. But the distinction was not clear cut, and land could move from one sector to another, as tenants ploughed up worn-out grassland, or as arable was laid down: hence the stipulation in many leases that the tenant was not to convert to tillage 'any more land than is already so'.

In the seventeenth and early eighteenth century many rotations resembled those employed in the middle ages. A lease of 1708, for the Elwes estate in Stoke by Clare in Suffolk, stipulated that the arable was to be fallowed every third year 'in a husbandlike manner, according to the customs of the country', except for newly broken up land, from which three consecutive crops of corn could be taken.[56] A survey of farms on the Long Melford Estate, covering the years 1754–58, simply divides the land into three columns – 'summertilth', 'crop', and 'crop'.[57] The precise course of cropping varied. At Finningham in the 1680s the standard rotation was fallow, winter corn (wheat), barley; but elsewhere barley might follow the fallow, and oats or beans were often taken as the second or 'aftercrop'.[58] In different districts rye and peas might be important crops, and tithe accounts also mention the cultivation, albeit in much smaller quantities, of buckwheat, tares, hemp, and coleseed. The use of clover seems to have varied from place to place but was mainly employed for long leys on convertible land.

Turnips are mentioned as a field crop as early as 1624 at Framlingham and Saxtead.[59] By the end of the seventeenth century they were widely established. At Cavendish in 1683, for example, a note in the glebe terrier stated that 'if any of the said fields or closes be at any time seeded or sown with turnip seed' then the tithe was to be assessed at 2 shillings per acre.[60] In c.1685 Nathaniel Bisbie, rector of Long Melford, described in his memoranda book how many of his parishioners 'convert their arable … into Clover grass; and often sow their fallows with Turnips for the depasturing their sheep and cattle …'[61]

During a tithe dispute at Flixton in 1790, it was asserted that 'In regard to turnips, it is stated in some of the terriers since the year 1723 that the vicar was entitled to the tithe of the turnips'.[62] Mr Lincoln of Dickleburgh, who died in 1702, was described in his will as a turnip seedsman.[63] Nevertheless, although widely established, turnips were not usually grown in very large quantities. Thus in the 1680s and 1690s at Walsham le Willows, most farmers seem to have had between three and seven acres of the crop, while as late as 1724 at Withersdale only around four acres of one 94 acre farm was so planted.[64]

During the course of the eighteenth century, three developments transformed the practice of clayland husbandry. The first was the increasing intrusion of turnips into rotations, and a concomitant reduction in the frequency of bare fallows. The second was the gradual disappearance of convertible husbandry: artificial grasses were now generally employed in shorter shifts, lasting only one, two or three years. The third, which we have already discussed in the previous chapter, was the steady reduction in the area under permanent pasture. These developments, however, and especially the first, occurred at differing rates in different clayland districts.

[56] WSRO, HA 517/D7.
[57] Long Melford Hall archives, no number.
[58] ESRO, HB 405/C2/1.
[59] ESRO, JC 1/25/1, 166.
[60] WSRO, FL 540/3/13.
[61] WSRO, FL 509/3/15, 526.
[62] ESRO, E1/3/8.
[63] NRO, INV 71/93.
[64] WSRO, FL 646/3/6–13; ESRO, FC 92/63/1.

The best evidence for the development of clayland rotations comes from Shotesham in Norfolk, where a tithe account, embracing the whole parish, runs from 1724 into the late 1740s.[65] The parish lies towards the northern edge of the Central Claylands region, and comprises two principal soil types. The eastern and central sections of the parish – or rather, two parishes, Shotesham St Mary and Shotesham All Saints – are occupied by the comparatively freely-draining soils of the *Burlingham Association*; the higher ground, towards the south and the east, comprises tenacious clays of the *Beccles Association*.

The proportion of turnips being grown in the parish at the start of this period varied from farm to farm, and indeed from field to field. Edward Ollyets's farm, for example, had an average of 19 per cent of its cropped acreage under turnips by the late 1720s, but some farmers were growing few or none. Nevertheless the average was already fairly high, at around 12 per cent of the total cropped acreage. The most important crop in the parish at this time was barley, which accounted for 34 per cent of the arable area. Wheat was less significant, at *c.*17 per cent. Nonsuch and clover together accounted for around 19 per cent of the cropped area. The remainder comprised oats (*c.*3 per cent), peas (*c.*2 per cent), and beans (*c.*2 per cent), together with small quantities of buckwheat, vetches, rye, coleseed, and hemp. Bare fallows were already comparatively rare, accounting for only 12 per cent of the acreage. There are, it must be said, many ambiguities and difficulties in interpreting and using this source, but these figures are approximately correct.

The rotations practised in the 1720s display much variation. In some fields – probably those on the heavier lands – turnips are rare or absent. As agricultural writers in the eighteenth and nineteenth century made clear, turnips were difficult to cultivate on heavy land. This was partly because in stiffer soil it was hard to obtain the fine seed-bed required by the young plant, and partly because waterlogging encouraged the crop's principal pest, Club Root or Finger-and-Toe disease (*Plasmodiophora brassicae*). In addition, on stiff land it was often impossible to feed the crop off in the field, yet also difficult to draw it for removal to farm yards.[66] Fields in which turnips were rarely or never grown normally had rotations which featured wheat, barley, and clover, with summerleys (i.e., fallows) frequently preceding wheat and with occasional courses of oats, beans or peas. Long leys of clover were fairly common. Other fields, mainly, it would seem, on the lighter valley soils, had rotations which did feature turnip courses, often returning with much greater frequency than in the conventional 'improved' rotations. Some farmers grew two or even three consecutive courses of the crop. Barley was the main cereal crop, and two successive courses were common, and even three not unknown. Rotations were irregular in other ways: in some fields, both turnips and fallows occur; often two courses of barley were interrupted by a course of wheat. Nevertheless, some plots of land in Shotesham were already displaying one of the classic 'improved' rotations, of wheat → turnips → barley → clover, or wheat → barley → turnips → barley → clover, in the 1720s. One of the earliest examples comes from the strips of one of the remaining open fields of the parish, Great Hall Field.

In the quarter-century following *c.*1730 there were four main developments in the pattern of cropping at Shotesham. The first was a steady reduction in the proportion of year-long fallows or 'summerleys': by the late 1740s these accounted for no more than *c.*4 per cent of the arable

[65] NRO, FEL 480 553 X.   [66] Robinson, *Fream's Agriculture*, p. 332.

acreage. The second was a significant rise in the area under turnips, from *c.*12 per cent to 16 per cent of the cropped acreage. While the frequency of turnip courses declined on the lighter land, the crop began to appear in some of the fields from which it had formerly been absent, displacing not only year-long fallows but also clover, which declined from *c.*18 per cent to *c.*15 per cent of total cropped area. The third development was a change in the proportions of the various 'none four-course' crops cultivated in the parish. The area sown with oats increased significantly, from *c.*3 per cent to 6.7 per cent, and the amount of peas grown remained fairly constant at *c.*2 per cent; but there was a reduction in the acreages of the various 'minority' crops – buckwheat, hemp, etc. The fourth development was the gradual regularisation of rotations. By 1750 most farmers had abandoned the practice of growing successive crops of barley or turnips, and more and more were following rotations which approximated to some form of 'improved' model, although smaller owners often maintained chaotic rotations and turnips were still absent from many fields on the heavier land: here the use of bare fallows and long pasture leys persisted.

The early adoption of turnips and clover can be paralleled in other south Norfolk clayland parishes. At Kirstead and Langhale in Norfolk in 1742, for example, the crops at the Hall Farm consisted of 31 per cent wheat, 31 per cent barley, 16 per cent turnips, 16 per cent clover, with oats at 2.5 per cent and peas at 3.5 per cent. Six years later, on 'Mr Rayners Farm' in the same parish, 29.6 per cent of the cropped acreage was under wheat, 30.4 per cent barley, 21.6 per cent turnips, and 18.4 per cent clover.[67] By 1783 at Mattishall, the rector estimated that farmers grew the following proportions of crops: 22 per cent turnips, 30 per cent barley and oats, 26 per cent clover, nonsuch or peas; and 22 per cent wheat. Analysis of the tithe accounts for the parish suggests that various forms of 'improved' rotation were employed in more than 80 per cent of the fields.[68]

Nevertheless, farm accounts and tithe documents suggest a considerable degree of variation, and on some clayland farms the adoption of improved rotations was much slower. In many places we find rotations featuring both bare fallows *and* courses of turnips, as on a farm at Framlingham between 1760 and 1766, or on one at Parham in the same period.[69] More commonly we find clayland farmers following improved rotations in some fields but not in others. A good series of cropping accounts survives for a farm in Redgrave and Wortham for the years 1753–1775.[70] Thirteen fields are described. In the period 1754–58, turnips appear – with clover – in the rotations in four fields, from which bare fallows had been eliminated. In the others, turnips were absent and full-year fallows recurred every second or third year, with the exception of two closes in which two- or three-year clover leys seem to have taken their place. In the last five years of the record, three fields had been put down to pasture so that the contents of only ten are listed. Turnips were now being grown in six of the fields, in moderately regular rotations, and while in the others bare fallows were still being employed, these now occurred with rather less frequency, no more than every third or fourth year, and often less. Similar contrasts between the rotations followed in different fields on the same farm are apparent elsewhere. At Earl

[67] NRO, PD 300/14.
[68] Gonville and Caius College archives, Cambridge, Smith notebook.
[69] ESRO, GB1/13c/1.
[70] ESRO, HD 79/AD4/1/2.

Stonham, ten of the 26 fields (46.5 out of 126 acres) farmed by William Godwin between 1788 and 1792 had rotations featuring bare fallows and no turnips; while at Hill Farm, Rushmere six out of 24 fields were still being regularly fallowed in the period 1806–1809.[71]

On a few clayland farms turnips appear to have been shunned altogether, as on Thomas Burlingham's 29-acre farm at Framlingham between 1760 and 1765, or on a farm in Dallinghoo – of 42 acres in seven fields – during the same period.[72] Things had changed little in this parish half a century later, to judge from a cropping account for a different farm, running from 1808 to 1813: summerleys were recorded fifteen times in the eighteen fields covered by the account. Turnips were completely absent.[73] No turnips were grown on any of seven farms at Henley, Suffolk during 1787 and 1788, nor on the 74-acre Home Farm at Hasketon, 74 acres of arable land, in the years 1797, 1798, and 1801.[74] More strikingly, not one of the seven fields detailed in a cropping account for a farm at Wetherden, running from 1797 to as late as *1842*, contained turnips. Instead the fields were fallowed every fifth year, with courses of clover sometimes (although not always) interspersed with wheat, barley and oats.[75] At Brandeston in 1821 no root crops of any kind were being cultivated in the fields of seven farms, totaling 335 acres; while at Burstall between 1820 and 1830 turnips (or swedes) were only recorded six times in the farm's eighteen fields, occupying on average only around 3 per cent of the total cropped acreage.[76] At Whatfield, as late as the 1830s, long fallows were still being used on most of the fields on the glebe farm.[77]

The tithe files of the 1830s likewise show that the take-up of turnips was patchy in some parts of the claylands. Over the claylands as a whole – that is, the regions we have defined as the Central Claylands, the Dissected Clays and the Southern and Western Clays – root crops appear to have occupied an average of *c.* 15 per cent of the sown acreage, but for some parishes the figure was less, below 10 per cent and even below 5 per cent. Overall, bare year-long fallows accounted for *c.* 10 per cent of the arable acreage, but for parishes in which turnip cultivation was on a small scale, the figure could rise to 15 or even 20 per cent.[78] Yet if the spread of turnips on the clays was somewhat erratic, that of clover was much more even. Throughout the eighteenth century it was increasingly adopted as a regular feature of rotations, so that, while fallows might be retained, they became much less frequent. By the 1780s few farms had fallows every third year. Instead, the period of cropping was lengthened by intruding a clover course. Fallow → wheat → barley → clover → wheat was one common rotation; fallow → barley → clover → wheat another, often with a course of beans intruded between the fallow and the barley.

We should not, however, see the persistence of 'backward' rotations, eschewing turnips and utilising bare fallows, as reflecting the ignorance of local farmers. Instead it was a rational response to the tenacious quality of much of the clayland soil. As Young emphasised in 1794, the strong clay loams were 'Much too wet for turnips, though some are found on it'. The soil 'dries into impenetrable clods, and moistens into mud', although it could be 'vastly improved by hollow drainage'.[79] Young may have been optimistic here: on the more level or slightly

[71] ESRO, HD 305/1; HA 2/A2/1/23.
[72] ESRO, GB1/13c/1.
[73] ESRO, HB 10/427/437.
[74] ESRO, HA 93/3/235; HA 24 50/19/3.26.
[75] ESRO, HA 87 C2/2; C1/1/5.

[76] ESRO, HA 10 50/18/14.4.1; ESRO, HD 422/1.
[77] WSRO, FB 76/11/9.
[78] Kain, *Atlas*, pp. 54, 79.
[79] Young, *Suffolk*, p. 48.

concave interfluves in the Central Claylands there was insufficient gradient for bush drains to work well, while elsewhere – where the clays were more mixed with sandy deposits – the soils were insufficiently stiff to hold the 'arch' of the drain. In such contexts efficient drainage had to wait until the advent of earthenware pipes: thus at Claydon Hall near Ipswich in 1851 the agent noted that the land needed to be drained but 'probably as the soil is loose, tiles may be required'.[80] The substitution of new kinds of root crop, more resistant to the diseases (especially 'finger-and-toe') associated with waterlogged soils, also helped. Raynbird, writing in 1849 about problems previously experienced in implementing a true four-course rotation on the Suffolk clays, noted how

> Thorough drainage has obviated all these difficulties. The introduction of Swedes has done much; but mangold-wurzel has entirely overcome them.[81]

Nevertheless, on some soils, even when underdrains had been installed, it proved difficult to cultivate roots successfully, and we find some fields – and some farms – where turnip cultivation was adopted sparingly, or not at all, well into the nineteenth century. It is, perhaps, worth noting that some of the highest cereal yields recorded in East Anglia in the Tithe Files were in the very parishes in which turnips were of limited importance. Evidently, in spite of what some modern historians might assert, the turnip was not the *sine qua non* of improved yields.

(v) *The spread of the four-course*

Turnips and clover were thus an integral part of arable rotations in many regions of East Anglia by the early years of the eighteenth century, but the more widespread cultivation of the former crop was apparently held back by limiting factors of both an institutional and an environmental character: the continued existence, in many arable districts, of foldcourses; poor drainage; and soil acidity. The new rotations spread to almost all areas in the century after 1750, as these limiting factors were steadily removed by the progress of enclosure, by intensive marling and by the widespread adoption of underdrainage. Only in parts of the claylands did the tenacious nature of the soils continue to preclude the cultivation of the crop on a significant scale.

The late eighteenth and early nineteenth centuries witnessed not only the widespread adoption of turnip-based rotations, but also changes in their character. In the middle decades of the century these rotations took a range of forms which were probably well-adapted to local soil conditions, and perhaps developed out of earlier patterns of cropping. While the 'Norfolk four-course' is attested in some areas from as early as the 1730s, the 'Flegg five-shift' was also widely employed, and elsewhere rotations were irregular, often featuring (for example) three consecutive cereal courses. In the course of the century rotations in all areas gradually became more regular. Thus on the Hunstanton estate the rather irregular 'improved' courses employed at Barrett Ringstead in the 1730s had disappeared by the 1780s: leases now stipulated regular rotations, a six-year variant on the Flegg shift.[82] At Earsham, field books for the years 1773 – 1779 reveal a variety of rotations: by 1811 estate leases were insisting on the four-course.[83] At Heydon the extended cropping sequences of the 1730s and 1740s were still in evidence in the

---

[80] ESRO, HA 93/3/676.

[81] Raynbird and Raynbird, *Suffolk*, p. 98.

[82] NRO, LeStrange KA 22.

[83] NRO, MEA 3/633.

1780s, but by the 1830s, when cropping books survive for short periods for farms in Corpusty, the four-course rotation had become standard.[84] Cropping accounts for a farm in Gunthorpe, covering the years 1782–1796, show that at the start of this period a strict four or five-course 'improved' rotation was followed in only a few fields, but by the end of the period it had been adopted in the majority.[85] There are many other examples.

In the same period the four-course and its variants gradually triumphed over other forms of *regular* rotation. Young's *Tour* of 1771, for example, suggests that the Flegg five-course, with three cereal crops in every five years, was well-established in the Northern Heathlands between Holt and Aylsham. Yet by 1804 he does not mention it here: it had apparently been displaced by the six-shift version of the four-course (with an extended grass course), something confirmed by documentary sources from the area.[86] Bacon, writing in the 1840s, noted that even in 1804 it had been common in the west of Norfolk for farmers to take two consecutive crops of corn before turnips: but the four-course had now been adopted on much of the land here, as it had by the same period (according to the Raynbirds) on all the better arable land in Suffolk.[87]

The triumph of the four-course should not be exaggerated: on the better soils, and in places where owner-occupiers and absentee landowners dominated (notably the claylands and Flegg) the more intensive five-shift continued to be widely employed, and in some places courses remained highly irregular. None of the fields in Henham Park, recorded in an account of 1804–9, exhibited the kind of rotation approved of by Young.[88] Sequences recorded over the four years in question included barley → clover → turnips → barley; turnips → barley → turnips → barley; and barley → turnips → wheat → brank. Similarly, at Hill Farm, Rushmere, only three of the 24 fields displayed a regular four-course in the period 1806–1809.[89] The contents of twelve fields on the glebe farm at Kettlestone are described in a cropping account covering the years 1801–1805. Few of the fields were cropped under a regular four-course rotation. In some, rather bizarre and antiquated sequences were adopted: barley → vetches → oats → turnips → turnips, for example, or barley → clover → barley → vetches → turnips.[90] Nevertheless, it is clear that such erratic courses of cropping were becoming exceptional by the early nineteenth century: the four-course was dominant in most places, and especially on the lighter and less fertile soils.

It is often assumed that the four-course was inherently superior to other forms of turnip- and clover-based rotation, but there is no real evidence for this. The irregular rotations practised at Kettlestone between 1801 and 1805 produced perfectly acceptable yields, well up to the averages for farms in this area given by Young.[91] The regular five-shift rotation practised in Flegg produced the best annual yields recorded by early commentators, albeit on particularly fertile soils. Moreover, this rotation provided three cropped years in five, rather than two in four, as was the case with the four-course: and it is worth noting, in passing, how single-year yield figures can be a misleading indicator of overall land productivity. In any one year the yields from a farm employing the Flegg rotation could be up to 20 per cent below those on a

[84] NRO, BUL 11/498.
[85] NRO, MC 37/159 482 X 5.
[86] Young, *Farmer's Tour*, II, p. 156; Young, *Norfolk*, pp. 200–1.
[87] Raynbird and Raynbird, *Suffolk*, pp. 58–9.

[88] ESRO, HA 11/C9/25/1.
[89] ESRO, HA 2/A2/1/23.
[90] NRO, PD 610/22.
[91] NRO, PD 610/22.

four-course farm: and yet the farm's productivity per acre, measured over several years, would still be higher.

In fact, in particularly fertile areas like Flegg or the Central Claylands, the strict four-course system could be positively counterproductive. Barley, in particular, makes rapid early growth and when cultivated on particularly rich and fertile soils is likely to lodge. Moreover, the richness of the soil can adversely affect the malting quality. By growing barley after wheat, and by more generally increasing the frequency of grain crops in the rotation – in other words, by farming under a system like the 'Flegg five-shift' – these problems can be overcome. In more general terms it is worth noting that fertile loams, like those in Flegg and in much of the Claylands, could simply stand a more intensive course of cropping than the poor thin soils of Breckland, the Sandlings, or North-West Norfolk.

In addition, the character of local tenurial structures may have been an important influence on the character of rotations. In these areas of fertile soil many farmers were owner-occupiers or (more usually) tenants of absentee landlords, and thus had more freedom of action than those farming in areas of light and acid soils. This suggests that the increasing regularity of rotations in the later eighteenth century was driven not so much by careful consideration of the agrarian advantages as perceived by the cultivators, but rather by the policy of estates. Writing of north-east Norfolk in the 1790s, Kent described how:

> The landlord generally wishes to fix the management and course of cropping under a six-course shift [Wheat → Barley → Turnips → Barley/oats → clover → clover] but the occupiers will often endeavour to contract it to a five-course shift

by dropping one clover year.[92] The difference was, presumably, between landowners wishing to maintain the long-term fertility of land, and tenants with more immediate economic horizons. The four-course would presumably have been seen in a similar light, since (in Low's words) 'In this course ... each exhausting crop alternates with a restorative one'.[93] Estate correspondence sometimes reveals conflicts between tenants and landowners over the precise form of cropping to be followed. At Croxton on the Petre estate in 1817, for example, Mr Sewell's lease permitted a five-course shift, with three-fifths of the farm under cereals at any one time. The agent warned that such a course of cropping was unsuited to such light soils. In 1819 Sewell was still, nevertheless, 'continuing to crop in a way injurious to the estate'.[94] He was not alone. In 1816 the tenant of Folly Farm in Thetford was likewise triple-cropping and 'running out the lands', and the agent wanted to evict him.

It was in the landlord's interest to enforce more regular and balanced cropping patterns, and in the later eighteenth century – as prices rose, and as competition for farms increased – it became easier to achieve this. The landowner's enthusiasm for the four-course may also, however, reflect the power of fashion in this age of faddish improvement, and the strong advocacy of vociferous improvers like Arthur Young. It is also arguable that enthusiasm for a rigidly regular, four-course rotation fitted easily into a broader world view shared by the landed

[92] Kent, *Norfolk*, p. 32   [94] NRO, Petre 17 Box 1.
[93] Low, *Practical Agriculture*, p. 205.

elite: a liking for symmetry and regularity which was manifested in the symmetrical facades of their houses, and in other aspects of what Deetz has described as the 'Georgian Order'.[95]

2. Husbandry: tools and techniques

So far as the evidence goes, there were only limited improvements in the tools and techniques of arable husbandry in East Anglia during much of the eighteenth century. As Young explained in 1804, 'For more than half a century, the implements of Norfolk remained without alteration or addition'; although he added that 'of late years many great improvements' had been introduced.[96] Perhaps the most important concerned ploughing and the preparation of the seed-bed. During the second half of the eighteenth century wheeled ploughs, with many of their parts made of iron, were widely adopted. Ploughs made entirely of wrought iron appeared in Suffolk by 1770; but most continued to be constructed of wood and iron. Ploughshares continued to be made of wrought iron until 1785, when Robert Ransome of Ipswich first obtained a patent for making 'shares of cast iron', and in 1803 he obtained a patent for a new method of hardening such shares. In the Raynbirds' words,

> Before the time referred to, cast-iron shares, although occasionally used in some districts, were found to wear away too fast from the under side. When the first edge was worn off the share became too thick to cut the ground properly, and its tendency when so worn was to 'lose its hold on its work', and to pass over weeds without cutting them ... The improvement alluded to is that of case-hardening the under side the thickness of one sixteenth to one-eighth of an inch, which is in effect like a layer of steel underneath the share.[97]

Soon after this, ploughs were developed in Suffolk which had much of their body constructed of cast iron, and by the 1820s ploughs constructed entirely of cast iron were in widespread use across East Anglia. At the same time, there was a proliferation of different kinds of ploughs, all more durable and efficient, and for the most part lighter, than their predecessors, capable of ploughing even the heaviest clays with only two horses.[98] Such developments may have had some impact on labour productivity, but whether they made much difference to the level of *yields* is unclear. They may have encouraged a more thorough preparation of the seed bed – as did the development in this period of better harrows and rollers – although to judge from the evidence of leases, repeated ploughings and harrowings (especially on the heavier lands) were already routine at the start of our period.

More important, perhaps, were changes in methods of sowing. Mechanised seed drills were already available by the 1780s: William Goodwin was using one at Earl Soham from 1787. 'It does as much in an hour as one man with two dibbles in a day', he believed, and claimed that he had saved 12 combs of seed by drilling rather than broadcasting his oats and barley. He had also heard that the resulting crop might be heavier. 'The Rev. H. Close of Norwich had 400 bushels of barley for 9 sown on 10 acres of land'. In May 1788 he was recommending that the rows should be 6 inches apart, because such a spacing produced the 'largest cropping of wheat

[95] J. Deetz, *In small things forgotten: the archaeology of early American life* (1977).

[96] Young, *Norfolk*, p. 52.

[97] Raynbird and Raynbird, *Suffolk*, p. 198.

[98] *Ibid*, pp. 193–225.

and barley and the fewest weeds'.[99] The accounts of the Home Farm at Heydon for the 1790s include a 'drill roll' and a 'drill machine', but there are few other references.[100] Marshall commented that drilling was 'entirely unpractised' in Norfolk in the 1780s, while Arthur Young noted that only a handful of the more progressive farmers were drilling their cereals by 1804.[101] Cooke's seed drill was sometimes listed in the Michaelmas sale advertisements from 1800: this piece of equipment, invented around 1780, was 'suited to light dry soils and flat culture'. Its great advantage was that it could easily be 'transformed into a cultivator, horse-hoe, scarifier, or grubber, and by substituting a corn rake, stubble rake, or quitch rake for the beam of coulters or hoes it would rake corn stubbles, or clean land or root weeds'.[102] Raynbird stated in 1849 that 'Suffolk men practised the custom of hiring out drills as early as 1804 and introduced the system (of hiring) into other districts of England'.[103] On the whole, however, the use of seed drills seems to have been limited before the 1830s.

Still more significant was the change, in the later eighteenth century, from broadcast sowing to dibbling – that is, the placing of seeds in individual holes made with a stick. An undated appendix to later editions of Kirby's *Suffolk Traveller*, probably written in the early 1790s, stated that dibbling of wheat was practised with 'great intelligence and success, but nowhere will it become common practice'.[104] By the turn of the century, however, dibbling was widespread, although broadcast sowing still had its adherents.[105] Dibbling allowed for sowing in rows, which facilitated weeding and prevented crowding, but it was more time-consuming and labour-intensive. It remained the favoured method of sowing well into the mid-nineteenth century, resisting the spread of drilling which – according to some farmers – wasted seed. Nevertheless, some favoured the newer method. Dibbling wheat and drilling barley was a frequent compromise.[106] In 1846 Raynbird wrote that dibbling was still widely practised in the eastern counties, a man dibbling on average half an acre of wheat a day, providing work for three droppers, costing altogether between 7s. 6d. and 8s. an acre.[107] How far the change from broadcast sowing to dibbling effected cereal yields is unclear, although common sense would suggest that a more even distribution of plants would encourage better growth.

Of equal interest are changes in harvest tools and techniques. The efficiency of harvest tools increased in the first half of the nineteenth century, with the gradual adoption of cast steel, which gave a more durable edge, and which therefore required less sharpening in the field. But of more significance, perhaps, were changes in methods. Throughout the eighteenth century barley had been mown (with a sickle or reaping hook) but wheat reaped (with a scythe).[108] Reaping left a higher stubble which was then, according to Marshall, eaten down and trampled by cattle, who would be fed turnips in the field. It would then be harrowed ('halmed') and

[99] ESRO, HD 365/1.

[100] NRO, MF/RO 334

[101] Marshall, *Rural Economy*, I, p.167; Young, *Norfolk*, pp. 33–6

[102] H. Raynbird, *Rham's Dictionary of Farming* (rev. edn, 1853), p. 431.

[103] *ibid.*

[104] Appendix to J. Kirby, *The Suffolk Traveller* (nd, but *c.*1795), p. 10.

[105] Mr Sam Bircham of Booton Hall described to John

Leeds a field near Reepham which had been broadcast sown and produced over 19 coombs per acre 'as proof that sowing wheat is *sometimes* an advantage': NRO, 27.6.74 Adcock.

[106] NRO, MS4363.

[107] H. Raynbird, 'On Measure Work', *JRASE* 7 (1846), pp. 129.

[108] Wade Martins and Williamson, *Randall Burroughes*, p. 50.

taken back to the yards for use as litter.[109] Randall Burroughes' journal suggests that this was the normal practice around Wymondham in Norfolk in the 1780s. One respondent to Bacon's questionnaire of 1843 claimed to have mowed his wheat since 1799,[110] but in the 1820s John Leeds of Billingford in Norfolk still usually mowed his barley and oats and reaped his wheat. In 1825 he did try mowing: 'a slovenly way in my opinion although in this instance very essential in order to get the land clean'.[111] As late as 1837 Richard Girling was still reaping his wheat but mowing his barley in Kessingland in the Sandlings, but the following year noted that 'many people are mowing their wheat this year'. By 1846 Raynbird was able to report that in Suffolk 'mowing wheat is a practice coming into use in preference to reaping'. It was a much faster method: a man could mow about an acre a day, but only reap between a third and half an acre.[112]

Although they were available from the 1780s, very few threshing machines initially found their way into East Anglia. Young described several on Norfolk farms in 1804, some of which were manufactured by Mr Wigful of Lynn, who had taken out a patent in 1795 for a large stationary design that was marketed at over £100. A public notice in the *Norfolk Chronicle* in 1804 announced that one was to be erected by 'J. Ball on the farms of Mr Gee, near Norwich and Thomas Sepping at Whitehall near Syderstone where there will be demonstrations of them at work'. None, however, appear in sale dispersal sale notices until 1811, when several were offered for sale across Norfolk. These must have been of the portable variety, developed by the Suffolk firms of Ransome's and Garrett's and costing between £30 and £40 each. One on a farm at Thompson was advertised in 1813 as capable of 'clearing from the straw 20 to 40 coombs of corn in 12 hours by the power of two to four horses'. (This compares with one at Rudham, inspected by Young in 1804, which was powered by four horses and threshed 40 combs of wheat, 50 combs of barley or 60 combs of oats or peas in eight hours.[113]) In Suffolk, similarly, there is little evidence for the use of threshing machines on any scale during the first decade of the nineteenth century, although by 1813 they were said to be 'spreading', mainly as a result of improvements in their design made by Mr Asbey of Blyburgh, who had erected over a dozen in the previous few years.[114]

All the threshing machines described by Young were worked by horses, although a steam engine for 'agricultural purposes' was being erected at Heydon in 1804: as well as working the threshing machine it ground flour and cut straw.[115] Steam engines did not, however, come into general use before the arrival of the railways, and the consequent fall in the price of coal, in the 1840s and 1850s. It would appear from Young's description that the gearing to be turned by the horses was housed. However, only one roundhouse of possible eighteenth-century date survives in Norfolk, at Plumstead near Norwich. It has a diameter of no less the 40 feet. According to Young, some of these early engines were powered by as many as eight horses and a large building would certainly have been needed. A number of early nineteenth-century examples survive, or are known to have been built, like that at Sussex Farm, Burnham Sutton

[109] Marshall, *Rural Economy*, I, p. 220.
[110] NRO, MF/RO 10.
[111] NRO, 27.6.74 Adcock.
[112] Raynbird, 'Measure Work', p. 126.
[113] Young, *Norfolk*, p. 65.
[114] Young, *Suffolk*, p. 34.
[115] Young, *Norfolk*, p. 73.

(owned by the Blyths, a progressive owner-occupier farming family); and on the two Holkham properties of West Lexham Farm and Wheycurd Farm, Wighton.

Scattered references suggest that the use of threshing machines increased very gradually during the 1810s and 1820s when, for the most part, local agriculture was in a state of post-war depression. Thus, from the Hunstanton estate records, we learn of a contract thresher used at Ringstead between 1810 and 1817.[116] In 1820 Arthur Biddell at Hill Farm, Playford, near Ipswich, was threshing tares by machine.[117] John Leeds had one at Billingford in 1826, and the following year he was threshing wheat 'both with our machine and one belonging to Hindries at 1s. per 6 c[oo]mbs. Doing the work very well tho' only two horse power'.[118] References to the use of threshing machines increase through the 1830s and 1840s. In February 1832 Samuel Gross of Alderton noted how he 'began threshing my clover seed with the machine at Hollesby', and referred to machine threshing of wheat on a number of subsequent occasions. In February 1841 he recorded: 'My new threshing machine came from Mr Motum's of Dallingho'. But he failed to install one at his other farm, at Alderton, where he threshed wheat by flail.[119] Richard Girling was still threshing at least part of his crop by hand as late as 1846 (although over the subsequent few years he too seems to have gone over almost completely to machine threshing).[120] In 1845 however, there was still no threshing machine at the Home farm at Flixton.[121]

Machine threshing thus seems to have made relatively little impact in East Anglia for at least the first two decades of the nineteenth century. The main reason for this was probably the local abundance of labour, which provided little incentive for the farmer to invest in expensive machinery. In part, too, it reflected *landowners'* hostility to any practice likely to contribute to unemployment. Thus a lease for a Snettisham farm on the Hunstanton estate in 1817 specifically stipulated that the corn grown in the final year of the tenancy was to be placed in the stackyard and barn and there thrashed 'by men with hand flails'.[122] Hand threshing provided work in the winter when there was less employment available, and it is hardly surprising that the new machines aroused strong opposition from the workforce. There was a particularly serious outbreak of machine breaking in 1822, but it was the Swing riots of 1830 which really displayed the extent of local opposition to mechanisation. From the middle of November, for nearly two months, arson and machine breaking affected over 150 Norfolk parishes. In an attempt to stem the troubles, North Walsham magistrates printed a notice urging farmers to dismantle their threshing machines (and increase wages), advice endorsed by a committee of magistrates set up in Norwich for the preservation of the peace.[123] Many landowners would have sympathised. As a memorandum of 1830 from the Middleton estate put it:

> But admitting that by machinery the farmer saves 10 per cent *surely*, with a population *much on the increase* and generally *speaking* willing to work *and obey orders* if fairly treated, it is if not incumbent highly necessary that both Landlord and Tenant should go hand in *hand* in reverting to Manual Labour in every case compatible therewith.[124]

[116] LeStrange Supplementary List, box 2.

[117] ESRO, HA2/B2 no.3/1c.

[118] NRO, 27.6.74 Adcock.

[119] In 1833, however, he noted his 'new threshing machine' at Alderton and in 1841 he bought yet another machine from 'Mr Motum of Dallingho': ESRO, S1/8/3.2.

[120] ESRO, JA1/59.

[121] ESRO, D1/6.

[122] NRO, LeStrange supplementary list, box 18.

[123] E. J. Hobsbawn and G Rudé, *Captain Swing* (1970), p. 156.

[124] ESRO, HA93/3/214.

It is not surprising, then, to find the agent of the Earsham estate, J. J. Margitson, writing in 1835 to Sir W. Dalling that:

> Chambers has made several applications to me for permission to use a threshing machine. He says they are in very general use in the neighbourhood and as there are no men unemployed he hopes to be allowed to use one occasionally. I told him I could give no permission without your consent.[125]

Threshing by machine was not necessarily much cheaper than threshing by hand. This was particularly true of barley. According to Raynbird in the 1840s, when the cost of hiring a machine was taken into account, there was no real difference in the price, both methods amounting to about £40 for 20 quarters.[126] This in itself was a powerful disincentive to mechanise. The main benefit of the mechanical method was in fact its *speed*, which allowed a farmer to take advantage of sudden swings in the grain market. Whilst 152 combs of wheat took Richard Girling four days to thrash with a three-horse engine in 1847, 13 loads of barley took two men 35½ days.[127] Some farmers also thought that malting barley was bruised by machine threshing, and many of Bacon's correspondents in the 1840s thus flailed their barley while using a machine for wheat.

3. Livestock husbandry

(i) *Introduction*

Agricultural history, especially that of the eighteenth century, has traditionally been written from the point of view of the cereal farmer: it has rightly been said that 'Livestock farming occupies a subordinate position in most accounts of agricultural development in pre-industrial England'.[128]

The increased numbers of livestock resulting from the adoption of new crops and rotations in the eighteenth century have been discussed almost entirely in terms of cereal production. Animals have been considered primarily as manure producers, rather than marketable commodities in their own right. Yet even in an increasingly arable district like East Anglia, livestock production remained an important source of the farmer's wealth. Even in 1787 Marshall was able to assert that the 'affluent fortunes' made by Norfolk farmers came not from cereal growing but through dealing in stock: 'through a superior skill in the purchase of stock, secondly by a full supply of money'.[129] In periods in which grain prices were low, especially the first half of the eighteenth century, animal husbandry was – needless to say – of even greater significance.

---

[125] NRO, MEA3/205.

[126] Raynbird, 'Measure Work', p. 137.

[127] ESRO, JA 1/59. Similarly, Manfred Bidell noted the costs and organisation of the work force when he hired one in 1860: 155 combs of barley and 104 of wheat were thrashed. This involved two men on the stack, two untieing sheafs, two stacking the straw, one putting corn into sacks, two bagging the corn and three boys to help. On top of this the board of the machine operators and coal and water for the machine needed to be supplied. The total cost was £12 18*s*. and the work took three days. ESRO, HA 2/B5/1.

[128] R. Trow Smith, *A history of British livestock husbandry 1700–1900* (1959). For a recent study of the East Anglian evidence, see B. M. S. Campbell and M. Overton, 'Norfolk Livestock Farming 1250–1740', *J. Historical Geography* 18 (1992), pp. 377–96.

[129] Marshall, *Rural Economy*, I, p. 345.

In 1723, when most arable farmers were faring badly in the region, the agent at Glemham on the Sandlings was able to describe how 'Butter and cheese sell so well that make dairy farms enquired after'.[130]

The heavier soils of south Norfolk and mid-Suffolk – especially the Central Claylands region – were traditionally areas which specialised in dairying and bullock-fattening. The areas of lighter soils, especially North-West Norfolk and Breckland, in contrast, were areas of sheep ranching. This general distinction, remarked upon by commentators in the seventeenth century, was still largely in place in the mid-nineteenth, to judge from the evidence of Walsham's 1854 agricultural statistics, in spite of the fact that arable had replaced grass over vast areas of the claylands.[131] Yet we would be well advised not to overemphasise this dichotomy. Not only did some areas have a tradition of involvement in both, such as the Suffolk Sandlings, few farmers in any region kept exclusively either one animal, or the other.

(ii) *Livestock husbandry: cattle*

Although the claylands were the main areas of dairy farming, cows made an important contribution to the local economy wherever extensive areas of good-quality grazing could be found. This was especially the case in the Northern Heathlands, where extensive valley-floor meadows existed; and in the Flegg Loam and Sandlings regions, where there were extensive grazing marshes. In the latter regions dairies continued to make a major contribution to the farming economy into the nineteenth century. Thus a valuation of Brookes Farm, Nacton, of 1805 lists 50 wethers, 28 crones and 1 ram, but also 6 Scots bullocks, 1 heifer and 2 bullocks, 11 milking cows, a two-year-old heifer and a one-year-old bull.[132] Richard Girling, who farmed at Henham and later at Kessingland in the middle of the century, similarly kept a large flock of sheep, but cattle were also an important part of his enterprise at both his farms. He noted the price of butter in his diary every week.[133]

But it was not dairying, but bullock-fattening, which most interested eighteenth- and nineteenth-century commentators, and which made an ever-increasing contribution to the East Anglian economy. Marshall, writing in 1787, described Norfolk as primarily a fattening rather than a breeding county, and the same appears to have been true of Suffolk, although 'home-breds' always played some part in the livestock enterprise (like the 'ten homebreds' taken 'from the grazing ground and put ... on turnips' mentioned in the memorandum book for Parsonage Farm, Felbrigg in 1803).[134] Such animals were either the progeny of dairy cows, or 'running calves', allowed to remain with their mothers for at least a year, by which time they were fat enough for market. By the eighteenth century there were two distinct cattle breeds in East Anglia. The 'Norfolk' was a horned beef-producing animal, condemned by Arthur Young as 'possessing no qualities sufficient to make it an object of particular attention'.[135] It was regarded more favourably by Marshall, who described it as a 'small, hardy thriving race, fattening as freely and finishing as highly at three years old as cattle in general do at four or five'.[136] In

---

[130] ESRO, HA49/4/14.

[131] S. Wade Martins, 'Agriculture in the mid 19th century', in Wade Martins (ed.), *Historical Atlas*, pp. 128–9; D. Dymond, 'Agriculture in 1854', in D. Dymond and E. Martin (eds), *An Historical Atlas of Suffolk* (1988), pp. 102–3.

[132] ESRO, HA93/3/147.

[133] ESRO, JA 1/59.

[134] NRO, WKS 5/233.

[135] Young, *Norfolk*, p. 445.

[136] Marshall, *Rural Economy*, I, p. 323.

contrast, the Suffolk polled (hornless) dairy cows were universally praised as good milk producers and so it is perhaps unsurprising that, in an age of experiment in animal breeding, efforts were made to cross the two, to produce a dual-purpose animal. Mr Reeves of Wighton began crossing in the 1780s and in 1810 he showed his 'Red Polls' at the Holkham 'sheep shearings'. By 1847 the Norfolk and Suffolk Red Poll was recognised as a breed in its own right.[137]

The majority of animals fattened in East Anglia, however, were not homebreds but store cattle brought into the region by drovers from the far north and west. Most came from Scotland, although a smaller proportion originated in Ireland. Most were four years old, according to Marshall, although 'many are probably much older'.[138] Once purchased, the animals would usually be kept for one winter. Where adequate summer grazing was available – especially on the marshes of eastern Norfolk and the Sandlings – younger stock, two or three years old, might be bought, summered on grass and kept for at least two winters on turnips before being sold. They were cheaper to buy, but more expensive to feed. The advantage of this approach was that although there was less profit from the animals themselves, the farmer obtained two season's manure. 'If we consider the advantage which succeeding crops owe to it in consequence of the great quantity of manure … we shall be satisfied of the great advantage'.[139] Lastly, lean stock could be bought in September and kept for one winter and the following summer before being sold.

The actual process of buying and selling stock is described in some detail by Marshall. The animals were either purchased from neighbouring farmers or at the various livestock fairs held in the region. The first Scottish drovers arrived in East Anglia in early September, selling first in Harleston (south Norfolk) and then at Woolpit (Suffolk) and at Setchey, near Kings Lynn. On the 17th of October they moved on to Horsham St Faiths near Norwich and this, the largest of the fairs, lasted from two to three weeks. The final fairs were at Hempton Green, near Fakenham in Norfolk, and at Hoxne in Suffolk. Every week during the season cattle were also sold at Norwich market. All business was concluded by Christmas.

Most farmers seem to have purchased from a variety of sources. In 1794 Randall Burroughes recorded how he visited several fairs and Norwich market before finally purchasing a group of steers (for £7 10*s.* each) to add to the 26 he already possessed.[140] Thirty years later, John Leeds of Billingford described how he bought six 'very clever and what's more very dear heifers from Mr Campbell according to order' as well as visiting St Faith's Fair where he bought '20 little heifers at £7 a head considered well bought'.[141]

Once the animals were ready for sale the farmer had several options open to him. He could sell locally, as was generally the case with Randall Burroughes; or to a more distant market, usually London. Marshall reckoned that between two-thirds and three-quarters of Norfolk bullocks were taken by drovers to London.[142] Smithfield was the main market, with droves setting out from Horsham St Faiths once or twice a week: they took a week to cover the 112 miles, travelling Sunday to Sunday for the Monday market. The drovers took them as far as

---

[137] D. Low, *Domesticated Animalas of the British Isles* (London, 1842), p. 322.

[138] *Ibid.*, p. 340.

[139] *Ibid.*, p. 226.

[140] Wade Martins and Williamson, *Randall Burroughes*, p. 43.

[141] NRO, 27.6.74 Adcock.

[142] Marshall, *Rural Economy*, p. 345.

Mile End, where they were met by the salesmen.[143] At Henham in the autumn of 1792 eighty Scots store cattle were bought and the following spring 19 were sold at Smithfield. Details of the transaction are given for one group of twelve. The cost of droving was £3 16s., and of selling £1 5s. 6d., producing a total profit of £50.[144] Randall Burroughes took four bullocks to Tasburgh to meet the drovers on Monday, 17 April 1796 and on the 25 April he received an account for their sale the preceding day. Selling at Smithfield was always a risky business, however. Burroughes cleared £75 15s. by this sale, but he had hoped to make £80: 'the market was reported to be very much overstocked and had they not been well fattened would have returned a very bad account indeed as was the case with my brother's which were sold at a smaller price than would have been required to buy them as stock for grazing'.[145] Nevertheless, the return in this case was greater than when he sold locally, at 5 shillings per animal after costs.[146] In the 1780s and 1790s it seems that the average purchase price of stock for fattening was about £7, while the average selling price £18, probably after eighteen months (two winters and one summer).

The buying in of drove cattle, the fattening of these (and of a smaller proportion of home breds), and selling on when fat either locally, or in London, were thus the key features of cattle husbandry by the 1790s. This was also, in essence, the system still in operation fifty years later, to judge from Bacon's account of 1844.[147] So far as the evidence goes, this system was already well-established by the start of the eighteenth century. Indeed, the numbers of northern cattle brought into the region had been rising steadily during the previous century,[148] and by the 1660s there are numerous references in probate inventories to 'Scottish', 'northern' and 'Welsh' steers.[149] In 1665, for example, Mr Aldrich of Eaton died possessed of 20 Irish and 20 Scots steers, purchased at St Faiths Fair, which were no doubt fed in part on the 20 acres of turnips that he grew that year.[150] There are numerous other documentary references. An account for the manor of Colverston in the Breckland for 1680, for example, lists the purchase of, *inter alia*, seven York bullocks and six Scotch heifers.[151] Moreover, many animals were already ending their days in London. Defoe in 1722 described how the herds of black cattle, mostly Scots runts, fed on the Halvergate Marshes were so great that the farmers 'not only supply the city of Norwich, the town of Yarmouth, and the county adjacent, but send great quantities of them weekly in all the winter season to London'. In the same year the agent at Glemham in the Suffolk Sandlings reported to his employer 'six beasts are upon the road for London this week', while in 1741 he wrote, 'Mr Denny desires to know whether your Scots are to be killed at home or sent to London. There will be more made of them in London than he can give you by 10s. to 15s. a beast'.[152]

The overall organisation of beef production thus changed little in East Anglia from the late

---

[143] *Ibid*, p. 353.

[144] ESRO, HA 11 C6/28.

[145] Wade Martins and Williamson, *Randall Burroughes*, pp. 80–1.

[146] John Leeds of Billingford was not so lucky. In February, 1824 he sent 'the little heifers and a Devon cow' to Smithfield, 'for the first and last on our own act, being sold very badly': NRO, Adcock 27.6.74. Richard Girling complained in 1849 that meat prices were very low at

Smithfield, 'some bullocks not clearing what they cost lean': ESRO, JA1/59.

[147] Bacon, *Agriculture*, p. 300.

[148] Holderness, 'East Anglia and the Fens', pp. 234–6.

[149] Overton and Campbell, 'Norfolk livestock farming', p. 385.

[150] NRO, DCN 59/12/1.

[151] NRO, KNY 575.

[152] ESRO, HA49/4/14.

seventeenth century until the mid-nineteenth. Such a system depended on an abundant source of fodder, especially in those areas of light heathy land where there was comparatively little good-quality pasture or meadow. It is in this context that we should see the early and widespread adoption of turnips in Norfolk and Suffolk: numerous references attest their use for fattening stores. In 1726, for example, Erasmus Earle of Heydon in the Northern Heathlands wrote in his memoranda book that he 'put 33 bullocks to turnips', and noted that most of the crop produced on the home farm was used for cattle, rather than sheep. In 1729 he compared the prices fetched by his grass and turnip fed cattle (in fact they all made about £5 each).[153] In 1723 John Wace of Carbroke on the edge of Breckland put two three-year old heifers, three steers, twelve year-olds and ten two-year olds on the common: but he grew 80 acres of turnips for winter feed (Wace kept 39 cows and, in 1734, sold 98 ferkins of butter in Watton market).[154]

Marshall emphasised the importance of turnips as a winter feed for cattle, 'a practice which has long distinguished it [Norfolk] from the husbandry of other counties'. Cattle were either fed in the fields; in yards; or in stalls. Cattle did well in the fields if the weather was good, but in poor weather they were better off indoors. Nevertheless, in some areas they were kept out in the fields even during the winter, as Young observed in the claylands of High Suffolk in the 1780s.

Although there is little evidence for the overwintering of cattle in yards in either the structures or layouts of surviving farm complexes, it is clear from documentary sources that this was common practice. As early as 1648 payments were made for 'Filling and carrying of 15 loads of muck out of the Hall yards' at Hunstanton.[155] Well into the eighteenth century cattle housing was rudimentary: barns frequently incorporated a range of open-fronted shelter sheds in an integral lean-to, often along a south wall, and the yard itself was often a temporary enclosure made up with hurdles every winter.[156] By the late eighteenth century, yards with proper shelter sheds on either side were becoming common, but these usually enclosed a single, open area. From this time, there was an increasing tendency to divide yards up, in order to allow for individual feeding: a necessary practice because, in Reed's words, 'In a community of a dozen a few will be tyrants so the rest must be slaves'.[157]

The farming journal kept by Randall Burroughes of Wymondham in the 1790s provides much information about stock management in yards.[158] In October 1794 he bought 26 Scots bullocks to fatten, in addition to his home bred stock which comprised five steers, a cow and a running calf, and four milch cows, 'on grass during day, in straw yards at night till I can buy some turnips for them'. In December 1795 he described how he:

Took the lot of 10 bullocks into the yards for grazing with the four turnip binns and the following day the lot of 14 into the north yard, the later were fed with turnips in the 2 cow houses, the doors of which that communicated with that yard having been previously removed so as to allow free ingress and egress. The house at the west side was divided by a partition so as to separate four stalls for three cows and one bullock; the only one with horns. The quantity of turnips at Browick being reduced to about five and a half acres I was fearful

153 NRO, NRS 10360.
154 NRO, BAR 22.
155 NRO, LeStrange KA9.
156 See above p. 82.
157 Read, 'Recent Improvements', p. 295.
158 Wade Martins and Williamson, *Randall Burroughes*.

lest by feeding them as hitherto on the pastures in the day time and shutting the cattle on nights only into the yard, the feed might be finished long before the stover might be made into manure, but on this charge the consumption of straw was so great from the moisture of the weather that I found it necessary in the course of the week to send for three loads from Sutton.

Generally, Burroughes' stock were kept out in the fields during the day except in very inclement weather. In the summer the cattle were grazed either on grass leys or the local commons.

Stall-feeding was practised from an early date. A mid-seventeenth century terrier for Long Melford, for example, lists a 'stable with hayhouse for stabling and feeding cattle and such uses',[159] while in 1709 there is a reference to 'a house to fat bullocks in and for straw' in a lease for a farm at Felbrigg.[160] As we have seen, by the 1780s some cattle, particularly in Blofield hundred in the Flegg Loam region, were being kept in covered sheds. Stall feeding was more labour-intensive than feeding in yards, but produced better manure. As the agent of the Hare estate put it in 1819: 'warm [shelter] sheds were particularly valuable to cattle and greatly assist in raising manure'.[161]

While turnips continued to be the main cattle fodder, carrots and cabbages were also used in some districts by the end of the eighteenth century. Cabbages were especially important in the Central Claylands region. Six thousand were set on the Home Farm at Earsham in 1793 and in the following year gangs were paid for hoeing both turnips and cabbages.[162] In the first three decades of the nineteenth century, on heavier lands in particular, mangold-wurzel were adopted on a large scale. Oil cake, a by-product of the rape and linseed oil extraction industries, was also coming into widespread use by this time. It was first introduced onto British farms as a manure, ground up and applied directly to the fields (3300 rape cakes were purchased for the home farm at Holkham as early as 1732).[163] Marshall described a farmer at Plumstead who had spent £800 during the previous 20 years spreading ground rape cake over 100 acres of land at a rate of a ton over every three acres.[164] However, by the 1760s cake was being used as fodder by, amongst others, Mr Carr of Massingham.[165] Its high protein content made it a good animal feed, as well as improving the quality of the manure. Nevertheless, roots – together with the hay from leys and meadows, and the grazing of pastures – remained the principal food for East Anglian cattle until well into the nineteenth century.

So far we have emphasised the essential stability in cattle husbandry in East Anglian in the course of the eighteenth century. But two major changes also need to be stressed. The first is the decline of large-scale dairying within the Central Clayland region. Inventories and tithe accounts attest to its importance here in the sixteenth, seventeenth and early eighteenth centuries. By the end of the eighteenth century, however, as we have seen, rising grain prices led to the ploughing up of pasture and the decline of the dairies. Nevertheless, this was a gradual process on the heaviest clays, especially on level plateau to the south of Bungay in Suffolk. At Flixton in the 1790s, to judge from a detailed description of six farms drawn up as a consequence

[159] WSRO, FL509 3/15.
[160] NRO, WKC5/95/1.
[161] NRO, Hare MS5411.
[162] NRO, MEA3/13.

[163] Holkham Hall archives, MS 1067, bundle 23.
[164] Marshall, *Rural Economy*, I, p. 165.
[165] Young, *Farmer's Tour*, II, p. 2.
[166] ESRO, HA12/B1/2.

of a tithe dispute, dairies were still making an important contribution to the economy.[166] Between a half and a third of the area of all the farms described was still under grass, and cows were the most important livestock kept. On Gowers farm there were 23 calves and 23 cows producing 3005 gallons of milk, while the 25 cows owned by Mr Clark produced 7500 gallons. By the 1840s, however, even the High Suffolk dairies had largely gone, and the majority of the land was in tillage.

The second important change was the marked increase in the numbers of bullocks kept in light soil, traditional sheep-corn regions such as Breckland and North-West Norfolk. To judge from the evidence of probate inventories, this began on a significant scale in the later seventeenth and early eighteenth centuries, presumably reflecting agricultural diversification in the face of recession. But it continued to grow in importance as turnip cultivation became widespread and as grass leys replaced the rough permanent pastures of the open heaths. By the end of the century there were only a few light-land farms without bullocks. The Coldham diaries, for example, describe how bullocks were brought in the autumn to the yards at the home farm in Anmer in the 1780s, and were put out to grass again in April.[167] Even in Breckland – archetypical sheep country – most farms kept some cattle. The Duke of Grafton described in 1786 how, on his Euston farm, 'Besides the turnips allotted to the flock ... about 60 or 70 acres more are grown annually for the fattening of Scotch beasts and for the cows at particular times'.[168] At West Stow Hall, similarly, 48 grazing cattle and 5 cows were being kept in 1840.[169] As new farms were created following enclosure of the open fields and commons in this region, they were invariably provided with shelter sheds and yards for fattening bullocks.

(iii) Livestock husbandry: Sheep

Sheep had long been of considerable importance in East Anglian agriculture, not only for the meat and wool they provided, but also for the manure which they produced, vital for maintaining fertility on the lighter soils. The critical development in flock management in the course of the eighteenth century was the replacement of extensive grazing, over open heaths, by feeding on improved grassland, sown grass leys, or turnips within hedged enclosures. Turnips were usually fed directly, rather than pulled: as early as 1720 a lease for an enclosed farm at Thompson in Breckland stipulated that the tenant should, after two years of grain crops, sow the land with turnips which would be 'fed on the land'. In this situation, the sheep would be hurdled tightly together: in September 1780 William Marshall helped set out a sheep fold for 600 sheep which measured no more than 44 square statute rods (about a quarter of an acre).[170]

Yet although there were significant changes in methods of production, sheep maintained their importance in light land districts.[171] In the 1790s large flocks (from 400 to over 1000 animals) were common on farms in North-West Norfolk and this continued to be the case well into the nineteenth century with, for example, 800 being sold in Ringstead from the late LeStrange-Styleman's flock in 1819, and a further 800 in Hunstanton in 1825. The largest flocks

---

[167] NRO, MC40/125.

[168] Duke of Grafton, 'Account of a flock of sheep', Annals of Agriculture 7 (1786), pp. 1–15.

[169] Paine, Culford, p. 33.

[170] NRO, WLS XIX/27/2 411 X 5; Marshall, Rural Economy, II, p. 1.

[171] For what follows, P. Wade-Martins. Black Faces (1993), passim.

of sheep, however, were those kept in Breckland. This remained an area largely devoted to sheep ranching, and 1000 sheep were regularly sold each year at Wretham in the late eighteenth century.

Large flocks were necessary to keep the thinner, poorer land in cultivation. Cattle dung never replaced manure from sheep, in part because light land produced insufficient quantities of the wheat straw necessary for efficient yarding. Following the enclosure of Tottington in the Norfolk Breckland in 1774, the farms still contained between 50 and 130 acres of sheep walk. Leases stipulated that flocks of not less than 500 sheep were to be kept, and hurdles were to be put up to protect the new hedges when they were fed in the fields.[172] When the Culford estate farms were enclosed in 1800, the new leases stated that tenants were to keep 'as large a flock of sheep as has usually been kept'.[173] Tenants were not always happy to accept such conditions. In 1821, soon after the enclosure of Thompson, it was reported how one tenant did not see the need to keep 500 sheep 'now that the heath is enclosed. He is happy to keep as large a flock as the farm will bear but objects to being bound to any specific quantity'.[174] A report on Tottington, made shortly before enclosure, stated that the 'principal improvement of the light lands depends on a due quantity of sheep being kept to fold upon them'.[175] In the Sandlings, too, the extent to which arable could expand at the expense of permanent pasture was limited by the need to keep the large flocks on which the fertility of the poor soils depended. Of Bryants Farm near Ipswich, for example, the agent noted in 1809 that 'The heath enclosures' were to be 'kept in layer which will enable the tenant to keep more sheep for the improvement of the enclosed lands'. At Denham Bridge, Ipswich

> The absence of heath prevents the most being made of the arable, which is extremely light, poor and uncertain land. The more sheep an occupation can keep the better as the land is more adapted to them than corn. If 50–100 acres of heath could be added to this farm, I would consider it very desirable.[176]

Arable rotations in the Sandlings frequently featured long grass leys to provide the required feed: a lease of 1803 for a farm in Nacton, for example, laid down a six-course shift for 100 acres of the land. Under this system a sixth of the land was under turnips, a sixth under barley or oats and the rest was layer.[177]

But as well as being muck-spreaders, in the more infertile heathlands sheep often remained the principal source of farmers' income: as we have seen, in the wake of the Napoleonic Wars many Breckland farmers retrenched their arable operations and turned the worst of their land back to grass. In 1828 the tenant of Ingham Farm, who kept 1000 Southdown sheep on his 1100 acres, described to a Royal Commission how the Breckland soil was dry and sandy, 'the produce of which in corn is very precarious, amounting in dry seasons to little or nothing. The occupiers therefore depend almost entirely upon their flocks of sheep for their income'.[178] Estate accounts bear this out: in 1827 the Culford estate produced 4790 lambs and 22,587 lbs of wool.[179] Indeed,

[172] NRO, WLS XXVII/19 415 X 5.
[173] S. Wade Martins, 'From Black-Face to White-Face. An aspect of the Agricultural Revolution in Norfolk', *AgHR* 41 (1993).
[174] NRO, WLS XVII/16/12 415 X 5.

[175] NRO, WLS XVII/19 415 x 5.
[176] ESRO, HA12/3/155.
[177] ESRO, HA93/3/208.
[178] BPP, 1828, VIII, 544.
[179] Paine, *Culford*, p. 54.

the tithe files suggest that in the 1830s in many Breckland parishes much of the arable acreage was devoted to fodder crops, not only turnips and clover but also buckwheat, cabbage, carrots, lucerne, mangolds, oats, parsnips, rape, rye, sanfoin, swedes, and tares. Breckland tenants were frequently unable to pay their rent until after the sheep sales: in 1835 one Merton tenant, Mr Fox, complained that 'the late bad years had reduced his capital' and that 'in all probability he will pay when he sells his lambs'. The agent reported that another tenant 'cannot pay any money until after April when he will have three score fat sheep to sell. Within two months he will pay £150 and the remaining £100 when he sells his wool in June'.[180] The same was true in the Sandlings: in 1805 the 872-acre Purdis Farm was described as 'more calculated to be a stock farm than arable and because there had been no proper covenants in the last lease it had been ploughed too much'.[181]

Both areas were noted for their breeding flocks, to judge from sales notices in the local newspapers: one, for 1808, describes the flock of 800 Norfolk ewes sold from Nathaniel Gross' farm at Sutton Hoo, 'That well-known and really valuable flock, esteemed by the best judges to be of the first repute for breeding stock'.[182] Breckland remained the source of much of the fattening stock for Norfolk and Suffolk, with young lambs being sold at Bury St Edmunds and at Ipswich fair 'where 100,000 are usually sent by the farmers of the open country'.[183]

In contrast to the Sandlings and Breckland, in the Northern Heathlands sheep were of less importance in the local economy, because more cattle had always been kept there. In addition, farm sales notices and other sources suggest that – at least by the later eighteenth century – large-scale breeding was of limited significance. Stores were bought in for winter fattening on turnips, a practice recorded as early as the 1680s in the shepherd's accounts from Horsham St Faiths.[184] Most were purchased at Cawston fair, which was held at the end of August and described by Marshall as 'the greatest "sheep show" in the county'.[185]

The management of sheep in eighteenth and nineteenth-century East Anglia did not involve the kind of long-distance droving which characterised cattle husbandry. Most of the fat stock were bred locally, although they were occasionally brought in from further afield (in 1750 the Wolterton estate purchased 50 'Scotch sheep'). Moreover, not only was wool marketed locally, but so too were most of the carcasses. Only sporadically are there references to more distant selling, as on the Wolterton estate in 1743, when 168 sheep were driven to Mile End for sale at Smithfield.[186]

Just as cattle were present in large numbers in traditional sheep-farming areas of eighteenth-century East Anglia, so too were sheep a feature of many heavy land farms. There were numerous farmers like Mr Darby of Tivetshall in south Norfolk who left 20 cows, one bull, 77 old sheep and 52 lambs when he died in 1722; or Mr Pratt of the same parish, who left 38 sheep in 1723.[187] The Mattishall tithe accounts from the 1790s list no less than 800 sheep and 200 ewes in the parish, and 60 sheep were kept on the Home Farm at Earsham in 1789 (27 stone of mutton fat for tallow and 12 sheep skins were also sold that year).[188] Sheep – mostly stores –

180 NRO, WLS LXVIII/1 478 X 9.
181 ESRO, HA93/3/147.
182 Wade Martins, *Black Faces*, p. 42.
183 NRO, WLS XXIX/2/19 416 x 4.
184 NRO, NRS 16023.

185 Marshall, *Rural Economy*, II, p. 323.
186 Wolterton Hall archives, WOLT 3/5/1.
187 NRO, NCC 75A/16; NCC 75B/88.
188 NRO, MEA 3/13.

were being kept on most of the Flixton farms mentioned in the tithe dispute records of 1790 (no less than 221 were kept in Flixton Park).[189] Between 1794 and 1797 there were normally about 100 sheep on Randall Burroughes' Wymondham farm.[190] During the winter his lean stock (about half the flock) were kept on the stubbles while those being fattened were fed on turnips. Various entries in his diary indicate that the heavy lands did pose problems for the sheep farmer. In December 1794 for example he described how 'the wetness of the land did not permit me to hurdle [the sheep] upon Stalworthy's turnips'.[191] After the turnips were finished in April the animals were usually put on to grass, sometimes in the same field as the bullocks.

By and large, the distinction between – on the one hand – North-West Norfolk, Breckland, and the Sandlings, regions in which breeding flocks were central to the economy; and – on the other – the Northern Heathlands, Flegg, and the heavy soil areas, in which sheep were less important than cattle (which were generally brought in as stores), seems to have been maintained throughout the period studied here. The main changes were, as we have seen, the steady reduction in the area under permanent grass, the subdivision of open fields and heathlands, and the increasing dependence on turnips as a primary foodstuff. These changes in landscape and farming had in turn a knock-on effect on the types of sheep kept in East Anglia. The native breed, the black-faced Norfolk Horn, was a slow maturing, leggy animal which could 'breed and thrive upon open heath and barren sheep walks, where nine tenths of the breeds in the kingdom would starve'.[192] Gradually, however, interest in faster-maturing breeds increased, starting on the farms of the gentry and larger tenants, particularly on the Holkham estate. The first breed to attract the attention of Thomas William Coke was Bakewell's New Leicester. Coke bought his first ram in 1787 and was soon advising his tenants to cross it with the Norfolk in order to improve the character of the carcass.[193] By 1800 Leicesters were being bred by at least two of Coke's tenants, as well as by Lord William Bentinck near Lynn, by Oylett Woodhouse at Sedgeford and by Thomas Masters of Gaywood Hall, all in the west of Norfolk.[194] More popular was the Southdown, a breed much praised by Arthur Young. There were a few small flocks of this breed in Norfolk by 1790. Coke bought his first Southdowns in 1792, and in 1806 sold all his Leicesters. They were valued both as pure stock and also for crossing. Some huge flocks were soon being kept, especially in Breckland and North-West Norfolk. A flock of nearly 2000, including 581 lambs, was sold at West Tofts in Breckland in 1823.[195] Lord Walsingham kept a flock of prize Southdown ewes and tups and was selling to Germany by the 1860s.[196]

Pure-bred sheep were very much the preserve of the large-scale gentleman farmer. Smaller producers could only afford to buy an improved ram (usually Southdown after c.1805) and use it to upgrade their own stock. Rising from nothing in the 1790s, by the 1840s half-breds had

[189] ESRO, HA 12/B1/2.

[190] Wade Martins and Williamson, *Randall Burroughes*.

[191] *Ibid*, pp. 47–8.

[192] Marshall, *Rural Economy*, I, p. 365.

[193] Wade Martins, *Black Faces*, p. 22.

[194] *Ibid*, p. 27.

[195] *Ibid*, p. 24. Enclosure, and the new modes of flock management, had (so many contemporaries believed) other effects on East Anglian sheep. Better feeds meant that lambs fattened more quickly, in 1–2 years rather than

2–3. But this, claimed the wool merchant, James Fison of Thetford, also meant a decline in wool quality. Needless to say the connection between better feeding and a deterioration in the standard of fleeces was fiercely denied by the wool producers.

[196] In the 1875 Smithfield Southdown show the first prize for a ram went to 'Sandringham' and the second to 'Merton', both bred by Lord Walsingham: NRO, WLS XVII/2/14 410 x 9.

[197] Wade Martins, *Black Faces*, p. 25

come to dominate the flocks of the main sheep-keeping regions, to judge from the evidence of farm dispersal notices.[197] Indeed, the more enthusiastic 'improvers' in areas *not* normally associated with breeding seem to have been swept along by this fever for improved stock. In Autumn of 1797, only three years after Coke had introduced the breed at Holkham, Randall Burroughes of Wymondham decided to buy a breeding flock and put a Southdown ram with the ewes.[198] Burroughes was not an isolated pioneer. The sale of stock from the Home farm at Earsham in 1810 included 40 lambs, 63 ewes, 30 wethers and two tups whilst in a similar sale in 1829 53 Norfolk ewes, 20 Norfolk lambs and 2 tups were offered.[199]

By the 1860s the Southdown-Norfolk cross had become known as the Suffolk and was the most popular breed in East Anglia. Norfolk Horns, on the other hand, were fast becoming a rare breed, with a few surviving in the Suffolk Sandlings, from which breeders wanting fresh blood for their flocks could obtain a ram. Thus, in the space of only half a century after 1790, the type of sheep in East Anglia changed almost completely, to a fast-maturing breed which responded well to the new methods of husbandry. Over the same period, interest in the keeping of breeding flocks also increased and between 1820 and 1840, according to Bacon, Norfolk changed from being a net importer of store lambs to an exporter.[200]

(iv) Conclusion

The management of livestock in East Anglia in the course of the eighteenth and early nineteenth centuries thus exhibits elements of both continuity and change. The most dramatic development was the collapse of clayland dairying; but otherwise, the management of cattle changed only gradually. The complex system of buying, fattening and selling cattle which had developed by the end of the seventeenth century was maintained with few changes into the nineteenth; so too, with only minor alterations, were the broad regional biases in livestock husbandry – with sheep remaining of prime importance in the light acid soil areas, and cattle on both the heavier clay soils and those lighter soil areas (like the Sandlings or the Northern Heathlands) where there were extensive reserves of valley-floor or coastal grazing marsh. There is, however, much evidence that these distinctions became less marked over time, as the spread of turnip cultivation allowed larger numbers of cattle to be kept in traditional sheep-farming areas.

It is the changes in the methods of husbandry, and especially in the kinds of breeds kept by farmers, in the two hundred years after 1660 which are more striking. In 1660 most sheep had been grazed on open pastures and heaths, and folded on arable land: by the 1820s the heaths had been much reduced and in some regions had disappeared altogether. Sheep were now usually fed on turnips and grass leys, and the breeds of sheep changed accordingly, from pure Norfolks to Leicester and Southdown crosses. Although for the most part grazing marshes and valley 'lows' remained as permanent pasture, grazed by cattle, overall the proportion of cows and bullocks kept in this way dwindled as the clayland pastures and the peat fens fell to the plough: by the 1830s the majority of cattle were being kept on grass leys and wintered in yards and stalls where they were fed on turnips. By this time, oil cake was coming into widespread use for feeding both cattle and sheep.

---

[198] Wade Martins and Williamson, *Randall Burroughes*, pp. 92–3.

[199] NRO, MEA 3/544,546, 658 X 8.
[200] Bacon, *Agriculture*, p. 303.

Animal husbandry did not, therefore, play a secondary role in East Anglian farming during the eighteenth and early nineteenth centuries. Not only was arable farming completely dependent upon the manure that livestock produced, but in addition both cattle and sheep provided an important cash crop for farmers, especially in areas like Breckland where arable farming was always precarious.

CHAPTER IV

High Farming, *c.*1830–1870

The middle decades of the nineteenth century saw a revolution in farming which was arguably more profound than anything which had occurred in the previous century. In East Anglia at least, Thompson's sharp distinction between the first and second Agricultural Revolutions – between 'Agricultural Revolution' and 'High Farming' – seems to be amply justified.

'High Farming' is a difficult phrase to define, but one which was certainly well understood by the readers of the *Journal of the Royal Agricultural Society of England* from its inception in 1839. The term was already in wide currency in the previous decade, for the reporters for the tithe files, compiled from 1837, were specifically asked to note whether a parish 'was high or low farmed so as to affect materially the quantity of produce'. Thus the Norfolk parish of Sloley was said in 1837 to be farmed highly; the very light lands of Stanford could not be made to produce corn without high farming; while in Mattishall the lack of leases was said to prevent high farming, for 'The tenants are in moderate circumstances and not of that capital to use an extensive or speculative husbandry'.[1] Such replies give some indication of what contemporaries meant by High Farming: it was a high input–high output system suited to larger farms where tenants had secure leases and access to large amounts of capital, and was in particular a feature of the poorer soils.

The mid-century writer Pusey was quite specific about the practices which distinguished High Farming from earlier phases of the 'Agricultural Revolution': the increased use of oil cake as fodder, which allowed livestock to be fattened more quickly and also enriched their manure; the employment of 'artificial' fertilisers (a phrase used to encompass not only manufactured substances which aided crop growth, but also organic materials imported from beyond the farm); and the adoption of tile under-drainage, which allowed intensive methods of cereal production on the heaviest soils.[2] Other writers emphasised other factors, including improvements to farm buildings and the greater use of machinery.

High Farming thus involved many elements, but these can, for convenience, be divided into two broad groups: those which involved the farmer's working capital and those which required the fixed capital of the landlord.

1. The elements of High Farming: the role of the farmer

(i) *Oil cake*

As we have seen, oil cake was first introduced to East Anglian farms as a manure. Arthur Young and John Bannister repeated the story that the discovery of its value as an animal feed occurred

---

[1] PRO, IR 18/6249, 6275, 6084.

[2] P. Pusey, 'On the progress of agricultural knowledge over the past four years', *JRASE* 3 (1843), p. 205.

accidentally when young bullocks, turned out upon fallow which had been spread with broken cake, ate it with enthusiasm.[3] Its high protein content made it a good animal feed as well as increasing the value of the resultant manure, and the growth in its popularity is shown in its rising price, from £3 to £6 10s. a ton in the course of the eighteenth century.[4] At the end of the eighteenth century, according to Young, oil cake was most widely used in the Flegg Loam region, although the practice was 'by no means general' there. It was also sporadically used in other bullock-fattening regions. Thus Mr Pitts of Thorpe Abbots (in the Central Clayland region) told Young that cake was a cheaper food than bean meal. 'He gives meal with turnips, but with cake only cut hay'.[5] Similarly, across the Waveney in north Suffolk 'a few farmers have finished on cake and other articles of food'.[6]

The basic principles of the feeding system on which High Farming was based were thus in place by 1800, and a scatter of references suggest that cake was being utilised on an increasing scale in the first decades of the new century: as, for example, at Courtyard Farm, Ringstead, where in 1812 two women were employed to break up two tons of oil cake.[7] But it was only after the Napoleonic Wars, and in particular after the post-war slump, that its use became widespread. Mr Wright, in his evidence to the Commission on Agriculture in 1833, stated that feeding cake had increased steadily as agricultural fortunes improved after 1827, and in consequence farmers were 'never as well stocked as now'.[8] It is true that even in the 1840s some large farmers remained sceptical about the new method of feeding. In reply to Bacon's 1843 questionnaire, the progressive Mr Overman at Weasenham replied that he used no oil cake at all, whilst Mr Burgis of Docking wrote that 'the expense is too great to pay a return on capital laid out; the only advantage is the land is left in a high state of cultivation for the ensuing crops'.[9] Nevertheless, there can be little doubt that while in the following decades roots – turnips, mangold wurzels or swedes – continued to be the principal fodder, the use of cake increased inexorably. Indeed, by 1858 C. S. Read criticised the reliance of Norfolk farmer on the substance: 'no matter how dear it may be, he will have it … it is questionable if it be good economy to use it so extensively, especially when beans, wheat and other grain are so low'.[10] By the middle decades of the nineteenth century some farmers were using vast amounts. Mr Gedney, who farmed 330 acres at Harleston, bought 15–20 tons a year, whilst Mr Everitt at South Creake and Mr Gayford at Croxton, farming 700 and 1400 acres respectively, bought between 20 and 30 tons per year.[11] The high farmer *par excellence*, John Hudson of Castle Acre, was buying 150–200 tons a year for his 1500-acre Holkham estate farm. His activities were described in the *JRASE* in 1869. Over the previous thirty years he had spent between £2500 and £3000 *per annum* on cake, which allowed him to winter between 100 and 140 steers, rather than the 10 bullocks which were kept on the few turnips the farm produced in 1822. Each animal was fed between 10 and 12 pounds of linseed cake a day, whilst his fattening lambs received 'an allowance' of cake.[12]

---

[3] Young, *Farmer's Tour*, II, p. 2; J. Bannister, 'On the origins of feeding oxen with oil cake', in A. Hunter (ed.), *Georgical Essays*, V (1793), p. 343.

[4] Trow-Smith, *Livestock Husbandry*, p. 82.

[5] Young, *Norfolk*, p. 447.

[6] Young, *Suffolk*, p. 208.

[7] NRO, LeStrange, supplementary, box 2.

[8] BPP 1833, V, QQ. 2277–8;. 2231.

[9] NRO, MF/RO 10.

[10] Read, 'Recent Improvements', p. 287.

[11] NRO, MF/RO 11.

[12] J. M. Jenkins, 'Lodge Farm, Castle Acre, Norfolk', *JRASE*, sec. ser., 5 (1869), pp. 461, 470.

These were unusual quantities, however. More normal was Richard Girling of Kessingland, who fed his cattle both beet and oil cake (4 pounds each per day) in the 1840s;[13] or Manfred Biddell at Grundisburgh, who grew cabbages, turnips and beet for his cattle in the 1850s, but who also bought linseed and American nut cake.[14] His sheep were also fed on cake, between half a pound and a pound per day. He was not unusual in this: by the 1850s sheep were frequently fed on cake. Samuel Gross of Alderton fed the nine bullocks over-wintering in each of his yards in the late 1830s on turnips, but his sheep were fed with oil cake.[15] On the Euston Hall estate in 1850, similarly, the tenants generally gave the sheep between a quarter and half a pound of cake per day (the bullocks received 7 pounds each).[16]

The use of cake in East Anglia seems to have followed the national pattern, documented by Thompson, of an increase from 24,000 tons in 1825 to 160,000 in 1870.[17] According to Bacon, the quantity of linseed and rape cake imported through Yarmouth rose from 3884 tons in 1839 to 7452 tons in 1843.[18] In all, no less than 25,366 tons was brought into Norfolk alone at this time.[19] Philip Roe has calculated from Norfolk directories that whilst there were 24 suppliers of cattle feed in 1858, the number had more than doubled to 54 by 1875. By this date few farms were more than 10 miles from a cake dealer.[20] The Royal Commission on Agriculture of 1896 provided figures for the expenditure on livestock feed for two large farms in Suffolk, one of 590 acres on 'mixed soil', the other of 230 acres on 'heavy' land. Between 1839 and 1867 the feed bill doubled and became the largest item of expenditure on both farms.[21]

Although the increasing use of cake in the middle decades of the century owed something to its declining cost (in part the result of the spread of railways) and to the introduction of the tenant's right to unexhausted improvements, it principally reflects an increasing emphasis on the production of meat on what were, primarily, arable rather than grassland farms. Increased meat prices – due to the growth of affluent urban markets as industrialisation proceeded – coupled with improvements in transport, provided the incentives to produce good fat stock for the market. The London-Lowestoft line was opened in June 1847 and by the following May Richard Girling was sending cattle to Smithfield by train. The cost of transport and selling was £1 per animal.[22] Previously the walk to London had taken several days and the loss of weight per animal was estimated by Hudson at 28 pounds.[23] An interest in livestock production amongst heavy land farmers was understandably increased by the fact that prices of meat rose faster than those for wheat in the 1850s and 1860s.[24] When William Keary compiled a report on the Adair estate in 1873 he urged the erection of new cattle sheds and feeding yards on the grounds that 'without stock in these days no farmer can pay his rent'.[25] Nevertheless, East Anglia remained primarily a grain growing region where farmers fed cake to stock to enhance soil fertility. At Combs model farm in central Suffolk, for example, the amount of manure

[13] ESRO, JA 1/59.

[14] ESRO, HA 2/B5/1.

[15] ESRO, S1/8/3.2.

[16] Caird, *English Agriculture*, p. 161.

[17] Thompson, 'Second Agricultural Revolution', pp. 73–4.

[18] Bacon, *Agriculture*, p. 115.

[19] *Ibid.*

[20] Roe, *Norfolk Agriculture*, pp. 61–2.

[21] E. L. Jones, *Agriculture and the Industrial Revolution* (1974), p. 201

[22] ESRO, JA 1/59.

[23] Caird, *English Agriculture*, p. 170.

[24] J. Caird, 'General View of British Agriculture', *JRASE*, sec. ser., 4 (1868), pp. 273–332.

[25] ESRO, HA 12/D3/7.

produced by the cattle from a given amount of feed was carefully calculated and entered in the ledgers, while as late as 1874 Manfred Biddell, writing in the introduction to *White's Suffolk Directory*, could state that 'stall feeding with liberal allowances of linseed cake, and summer grazing of sheep on tares' were the main source of fertility in the county.

It is difficult to ascertain the extent to which the increased use of cake actually raised stocking levels on East Anglian farms in the course of the nineteenth century. Bacon and many contemporaries believed that there had been a 'vast increase',[26] but the stocking densities given by Sir John Walsham in 1854 do not appear to have been much higher than those which can be calculated for various places in the eighteenth century.[27] The 1867 crop returns show some increase, however, presumably reflecting the effects of the new modes of farming, although it is noteworthy that this was principally in the numbers of sheep rather than cattle: in Norfolk, the numbers of the former had grown from 643,864 to 776,333 (i.e., an increase of around 20 per cent) but those for cattle only rose from 102,944 to 103,273 (i.e., an increase of less than 0.003 per cent).[28] The same sources suggest that the area of arable continued to expand in East Anglia, increasing from *c.*65 per cent to *c.*69 per cent. As with the spread of root crops in the previous period, the real significance of oil cake may have been that it allowed stocking levels to be maintained as the proportion of grassland was further reduced.

(ii) *Fertilisers*

Artificial feed thus increased the quantity and quality of manure: but equally important as an element in High Farming was the use of artificial fertilisers. By the 1830s the value of bone dust, particularly when applied to the turnip crop, was becoming appreciated and the value of imports in England as a whole rose from £78,000 in 1832 to £254,000 in 1837.[29] It soon became apparent, however, that bone dust was ineffective on alkaline soils: only on acidic soils could the calcium phosphate be released. As a result of John Bennett Lawes' experiments between 1837 and 1842 it was discovered that this reaction could be effected by treating the bone with sulphuric acid in order to produce superphosphates. At the same time it was realised that mineral phosphates could be used in this process instead of bone. In 1842 Lawes was able to patent his method of producing superphosphates, and thus initiated the British fertiliser industry. Bacon's report of 1844 contains details of various trials carried out by his correspondents using such products, as well as nitrate of soda, potash, and saltpetre. Moreover, as well as artificial – in the sense of manufactured – manures, the High Farming period also saw the large-scale importation of guano from South America. This reached significant levels in the late 1830s: by the 1850s guano was extensively used on the lighter soils of East Anglia. Caird in 1852 described how, on the Euston Hall estate in Breckland, the fields were treated with guano (2 cwt per acre), rape dust, or bones prior to the sowing of turnips, 'the dung being reserved for the wheat crop'.[30] In 1858, however, Read described how in West Norfolk guano was applied alone to wheat, but normally in combination with superphosphate to barley: its price was rising at this time and so it was not normally employed on the turnip crop.[31]

---

[26] Bacon, *Agriculture*, p. 111.
[27] See below pp. 171–3.
[28] BPP 1854, LXV, pp. 290–300; BPP 1867, LXXI, p. 125.

[29] R. Brigden, *Victorian Farms* (1986), p. 188.
[30] Caird, *English Agriculture*, p. 160.
[31] Read, 'Recent Improvements', p. 277.

The pros and cons of the various new fertilisers were discussed in the *JRASE* from the time of its foundation, and during the years 1855–60 over 20 per cent of papers published were on this subject.[32] C. S. Read, among others, was sceptical about many of the new products. In most cases the farmer was out of his depth when it came to judging which was the best buy. His only sensible course was to avail himself of the free analysis service provided by the Royal Agricultural Society for its members. The days when the greatest compliment that could be paid to a farmer was that he was a 'practical man' had passed. 'Our practical ignorance cannot be bliss unless it is pleasant to buy things at double their value and loose good crops into the bargain'.[33]

Once again, the extent to and rate at which the new practices were adopted, especially by the smaller farmers, remains unclear. By 1858, according to Read, the use of fertilisers was ubiquitous and had created a veritable revolution in farming in East Anglia over the previous 15 years.[34] But it was in the areas of the lightest soils that their use was greatest, and above all in North-West Norfolk: there was no other area 'in which such an amount of the necessities of life are raised by artificial manure'. So great were the applications of artificial fertilisers 'that the crop was half bought before it was reaped',[35] and not infrequently the 'manure agent's little bill is more than the landlord's rent'.[36] On a national scale Thompson has calculated that the value of superphosphates used by farmers rose from nil in 1840 to £1,440,000 in the period 1864–67 and to £4,080,000 in the period 1877–81, and there is little reason to doubt that East Anglia saw a proportionate increase. The number of suppliers of artificial manures in Norfolk alone rose from 24 to 71 between 1858 and 1875.[37]

As more, and richer, farmyard manure became available due to the widespread use of oil cake; and as farmers increasingly employed artificial fertilisers; there was growing opposition to the restrictions imposed by the four-course rotation. After all, as Read pointed out, what was the point of all these improvements if they did not allow for the growing of more corn?[38] The answers given by farmers to Bacon's questionnaire show that the four-course system was still generally regarded as sacrosanct in the early 1840s. By 1858, however, C. S. Read could write that it was 'going out of favour in its native county', with many farmers in light land areas slotting in a crop of oats after the wheat course. There was less reliance on root crops to the extent that several Holkham farmers in the 1860s were growing two corn crops in succession with the aid of artificial fertilisers and leaving out the root course altogether.[39] Nevertheless, the established system was remarkably resilient: by 1869 John Hudson had returned to a more traditional four-course system, considering it 'better adapted to west Norfolk land'.[40] The field books for the Biddell farms around Playford on the edge of the east Suffolk Sandlings, which run from 1807 to 1870, suggest that there was little change in cropping over this long period,

---

[32] N. Goddard, 'Information and innovation in early-Victorian farming systems', in Holderness and Turner (eds), *Land, labour and agriculture*, pp. 165–90.

[33] Read, 'Recent Improvements', p. 278.

[34] *Ibid*, p. 278.

[35] *Ibid*, p. 269.

[36] *Ibid*, p. 276.

[37] Roe, *Norfolk Agriculture*, pp. 61–2. The use of bone meal declined with the introduction of superphosphates,

but some farmers treated bones with acid themselves to create fertilisers. In 1856 Mr Palmer of Eastmere Farm, Stanford, asked the Walsingham estate for a manure house in which to dissolve bones to make artificial manures: NRO, WLS LX/12.

[38] Read, 'Recent Improvements', p. 284.

[39] Wade Martins, *Great Estate*, p. 121.

[40] Jenkins, 'Lodge Farm'.

in spite of the fact that oil cake and artificial fertilisers were being used in some quantities here. Only occasionally were two crops of cereals taken consecutively, usually oats or rye after wheat.[41] The modifications to cropping made possible by the use of artificial manures were discussed in an article in the *JRASE* in 1860. It concluded, 'on light soils adapted to sheep, it will be generally expedient to follow the main features of the four-course system'.

(iii) *Mechanisation*

As we have seen, there had been a steady improvement in basic farm equipment during the later eighteenth and early nineteenth centuries, with new forms of plough, drill and handtools being developed and disseminated. By 1840 East Anglia was home to some of the leading firms of agricultural engineers in Britain, for instance Ransomes, Garretts, Smyth and Burrells. Interest in farm equipment was strong in the 1840s: the county reports by Bacon for Norfolk, and the Raynbirds for Suffolk, each devoted over 50 pages to the subject.

The first three decades of the century had seen a gradual increase in the number of threshing machines in use in the region, and by 1843, to judge from Bacon's questionnaire, they had become common in Norfolk, particularly on the large farms in the west of the county where 'sometimes are seen two and almost always one machine fixed to the barn doors'. On the smaller farms of the east, portable machines owned by contractors were more usual.[42] Horses, rather than steam engines, still generally supplied the motive power: horse gins seldom survive on East Anglian farms, although an impressive example of c.1840 was recently discovered at Cross Farm, North Creake. Bacon in 1843 noted, however, that steam was being used by a few farmers. Mr Hudson's steam engine at Castle Acre worked both threshing and crushing machinery: it was a large engine and Bacon was doubtful as to whether it would be worth installing on any but the most extensive farms. Another had been erected at Rudham, but there was insufficient work to keep it busy.[43] In Suffolk the use of both portable and fixed machines was increasing at this time. Of the three surviving round houses known from Suffolk, two date from this decade: one, in the outbuildings of Coston Hall, Little Cornard, is dated 1844, while that at Grange Farm, Hengrave bears the date 1849 (this may have fallen victim to a late bout of arson, for the stone states that it was burnt in 1849, but rebuilt by the owner, Sir T. R. Gage, bt, in the same year). According to Loudon portable engines were 'very common' in Suffolk by the 1830s:

> It is not unusual in that county for an industrious labourer who may have saved £30 or £40 to own one, which is moved from place to place on two wheels ...[44]

This may have been an exaggeration, but by the 1850s, certainly, opposition to threshing machines was fading, in part no doubt because rural population growth slackened and unemployment became less of a perceived problem. (The rate of increase in rural East Anglia declined to about 5 per cent between 1831 and 1841, and was to continue falling: after 1851, the population of most villages ceased to rise.) By 1858 machines were widely used, according to C. S. Read, so

[41] ESRO, HA 2/B3.
[42] Bacon, *Agriculture*, p. 356.
[43] *Ibid*, pp. 372–3.

[44] Raynbird and Raynbird, *Suffolk*, p. 197, quoting J. C. Loudon, *Encyclopedia of Agriculture* (1831).

that in Norfolk there were 'nearly as many as there are parishes'.[45] Hand threshing was still, however, sometimes used on the small farms of the east, where labour was more plentiful.[46]

Another important invention of the High Farming period was the reaping machine, an innovation of the 1850s. Two American machines, the McCormick and the Hussey, were shown at the Great Exhibition in 1851 and were quickly taken up by British farmers. A few of Hussey's machines found their way into Norfolk in the 1850s and some of McCormick's by 1857. They 'won golden opinions last harvest and the makers have in consequence received extensive orders from our county'.[47] The spread of the reaper was apparently faster than that of the thresher, presumably because it reduced the need for man-power at a season when it was in short supply.[48]

Various other technological developments, less dramatic but important nevertheless, characterised the High Farming period. The change from sickle and reaping hook to scythe, which we have already described, was complete by 1850; the period saw the universal adoption of the seed drill and the complete replacement of wooden ploughs by iron ones. By 1858 Read could write that drilling was almost universal in Norfolk: a variety of drills, which dropped both manure and water with the seed, were in use.[49]

The increasing use of machinery is everywhere apparent. When John Hudson died in 1869 and his stock sold, the sale catalogue listed 30 ploughs and harrows, as well as a variety of scarifiers, cultivators and rollers, a reaping machine and a threshing drum powered by a nine horse-powered portable steam engine.[50] This was an exceptional collection, but even on small farms equipment proliferated. Two inventories for Brooke's Farm, Nacton – one made in 1805, the other in 1859 – make the point well.[51] Other than ploughs, harness, wagons, carts and hand implements such as spades, the only piece of machinery mentioned in the earlier inventory is a 'chaff sieve and engine'. By 1859 the farm machinery included a five horse power threshing machine, three dressing machines, two oil cake crushers and a chaff cutter.

(iv) *Rationalisation of field boundaries*

Inputs like oil cake, fertilisers, stock and equipment were not the only forms of investment made by tenants in this period. So far as the evidence goes, it was they rather than landlords who were principally responsible for the alteration of boundaries and the removal of excess timber, which continued in clayland regions right through the nineteenth century. True, some of the more dramatic examples of rationalisation were associated with large estates, and in particular with their home farms, as on the Tollemache estate in the 1850s, where the field pattern of the Suffolk parish of Helmingham was extensively altered. But, according to the Raynbirds and others, the process was continued in a slower and more piecemeal fashion, with the permission but without the financial assistance of landlords, on innumerable clayland farms. In this context, it is instructive to compare the pattern of boundaries shown on Tithe Award

[45] Read, 'Recent Improvements', p. 280.

[46] *Ibid.*

[47] *Ibid.*, p. 281.

[48] Collins calculated that the additional demand for labour at harvest in arable counties could be as high as 70 or 80 per cent. E. J. T. Collins, 'Harvest technology and labour supply, 1790–1870', *EcHR* 22 (1969), pp. 453–73.

[49] Read, 'Recent Improvements', p. 281.

[50] Wade Martins, *Great Estate*, p. 116.

[51] ESRO, HA 93/3/147, 151.

13. Field boundaries in the parishes of Burston, Gissing, Shelfhanger, Winfarthing, and (part of) Diss in *c.*1840.
Source: tithe award maps.

maps of the late 1830s/early 1840s (Figure 13) with those shown on the first edition Ordnance Survey 6″ sheets of the 1880s (Figure 14); and also to compare the latter with the landscape depicted on the 2½″ maps of the 1950s (Figure 15). The scale of change between 1840 and 1880 was greater than that which occurred between 1880 and *c.*1950. In the 1880s Augustus Jessop, vicar of Scarning in the heart of the Dissected Clays region, bemoaned the changed appearance of the countryside:

The small fields that used to be so picturesque and wasteful are gone or are going; the tall

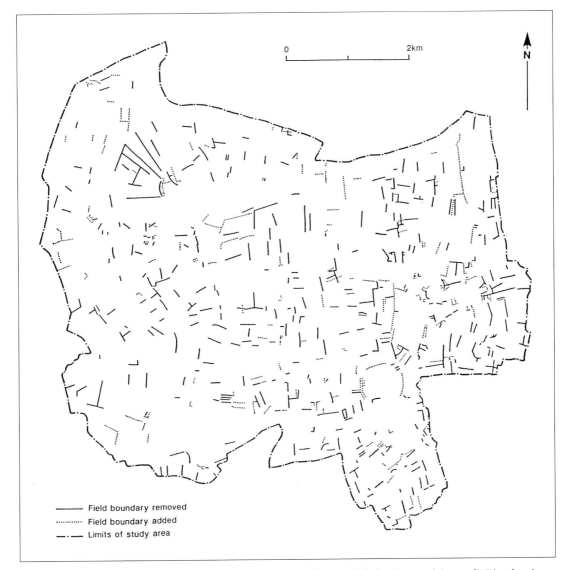

14. Field boundaries in the parishes of Burston, Gissing, Shelfhanger, Winfarthing, and (part of) Diss showing changes c.1840–1880. Source: tithe award maps and first edition OS 6″.

hedges, the high banks, the scrub or the bottoms where a fox or weasel might hope to find a night's lodging ... all these things have vanished.[52]

(v) *Levels of investment*

Feed, fertilisers and machines all required high levels of investment. One of Bacon's informants produced figures for a light land farm which showed the cost of cultivation rising from £1 15s. per acre in 1790 to £3 11s. in 1820.[53] Another set of figures, for an east Norfolk farm in the 1830s,

[52] A. Jessop, *Arcady: for better, for worse* (1878), p. 6.   [53] Bacon, *Agriculture*, p. 96.

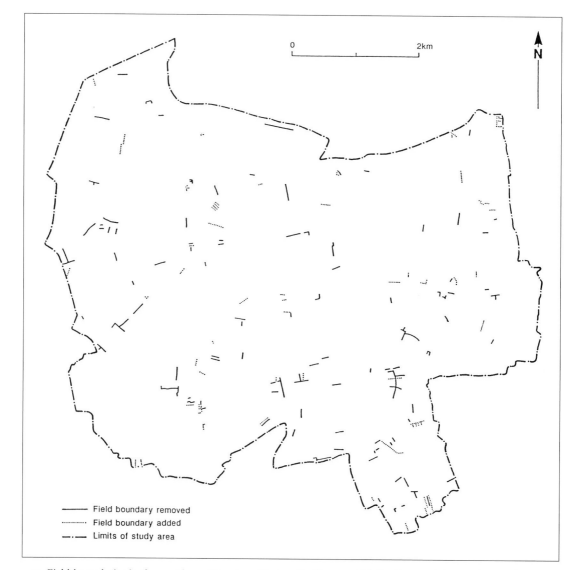

15. Field boundaries in the parishes of Burston, Gissing, Shelfhanger, Winfarthing, and (part of) Diss showing changes 1880–1945. Source: Ordnance Survey maps.

indicate an average expenditure of £4 12s. per acre. By 1861, according to Charles Wratislaw, the figure had risen to £9.[54] Much of this investment was of medium- or long-term benefit to the farm and the importance of establishing the tenant's rights to compensation for unexhausted improvements was emphasised by witnesses to the Select Committee on Agricultural Customs in 1847. Most contemporaries agreed that High Farming was only suited to large farms. It was not only the cost of cake and fertiliser, but also the need to buy large numbers of lean stock

[54] C. Wratislaw, 'The amount of capital required for the profitable occupation of a mixed arable and pasture farm in a Midland county', JRASE 22 (1861), pp. 167–88.

which prevented smaller farmers from fully embracing the new system. C. S. Read believed that High Farming was only to be found on farms of over 300 acres, and he asserted that 'The small farmer is rarely a high farmer'.[55] Nevertheless, the evidence reviewed here suggests that many of the elements of High Farming were more widely adopted. The use of oil cake and fertilisers, and the adoption of various forms of farm machinery, appear to have been universal, although doubtless varying in extent with the size of farm, and also with the character of the local soil, with inputs of fertiliser in particular being greatest in areas of lighter soil.

2. The elements of High Farming: the role of the landlord

Whilst the increase in tenant capital within the farming system has received much attention both from historians and from contemporaries campaigning for tenants' rights to unexhausted improvements, landlord investment has stimulated less interest. It is clear, however, that on most estates the 25 years after 1850 represented a peak in investment with drainage, reclamation and building projects under way throughout East Anglia.

(i) *Tile drainage*

Tile drainage was a permanent improvement, and thus generally recognised as the landlord's responsibility. Its importance was repeatedly stressed by contemporary commentators, Pusey for example arguing that 'Thorough draining is to the land as foundations are to a house'.[56] Between 1840 and 1855 over 10 per cent of the articles in the *JRASE* dealt with the topic.[57] Tile drainage became increasingly popular as the result of the development of workable pipe-making machinery in the 1840s, and the establishment of the land improvement companies from 1846. Between 1846 and 1870 £8 million was spent in Britain on drainage schemes approved for loans from the improvement companies. Yet most of this activity seems to have been concentrated in the Midlands and the North. Although some money was lent by the companies to East Anglian farmers for new buildings, little (to judge from the surviving ledgers) was advanced for drainage. This, combined with the comments of some contemporaries to the effect that there was little *tile* drainage on the East Anglian clays, has been taken by Phillips to show that agricultural advance in the region was 'faltering' in the second half of the nineteenth century.[58] The real reason, of course, was that under-drainage by bush drains was already well-established here, and existing methods were adequate for the needs of most farmers, given the comparatively dry nature of the East Anglian climate.[59] Tile drainage was an expensive investment which brought a return of perhaps no more than 3 per cent, on an outlay of around £5 per acre.[60]

This is not to deny that much land was drained by the new method in East Anglia in the

---

[55] C. S. Read, 'Large and small holdings', *JRASE*, sec. ser., 23 (1887), p. 27.

[56] Pusey, 'Progress'.

[57] Goddard, 'Information and innovation', pp. 165–90.

[58] Phillips, *Underdraining*, p. 243.

[59] It is surprising that Bacon's report on Norfolk makes little mention of under-draining, nor does it feature as a topic in the 160-odd questions addressed to farmers in his questionnaire. He included drainage as one of the important advances to be made on the heavy lands, but only alongside other improvements in their management, such as not working it when wet but instead 'leaving it as hollow as possible for the working of the elements'. Bacon, *Agriculture*, p. 112.

[60] Chambers and Mingay, *Agricultural Revolution*, p. 163.

middle decades of the century. Tile drains were, in particular, more effective at draining the less consolidated clays than bush drains, and the final stages of the arablisation of the clay soils of East Anglia probably depended upon their adoption. Tile drains were also increasingly employed in the Fens at this time. Certainly, more tile drains were laid in East Anglia than the records of the improvement companies suggest, for, on many estates, the work was carried out without recourse to loans. At Holkham, drainage was only listed as a separate item in the accounts from the 1850s, but throughout that decade expenditure could amount to over £2000 *per annum*. The agent for the Suffolk Tollemache estates stated in 1847 that he knew of several estates which were undertaking drainage schemes on their own account, and then charging tenants interest on the capital invested.[61] Elsewhere, he suggested, tenants sometimes carried out tile drainage on their own initiative, especially where, as on the Flixton and Tollemache estates, tenant right agreements allowed compensation for unexausted improvements. A Flixton tenant and land agent, one Mr Harvey, had tile-drained the whole of his 125 acre farm since 1840. The same source also, however, remarked that comparatively little tile drainage was currently being carried out, largely because allowances were only paid to the tenant up to four years after the improvement had been made: which, although appropriate for the less permanent benefits of bush drainage, did not provide adequate compensation for the more expensive business of laying tile drains.[62]

There is, however, some indication that the popularity of tile drainage increased in the 1850s and 1860s. It was only then that the improvement began to be adopted on some scale by large clayland estates, such as those of the Duke of Norfolk and the Adairs. The reasons for the increased enthusiasm was probably largely economic. Tile drainage systems – expensive to install but long-lasting – may have appeared a more appealing investment as the costs of labour rose in the second half of the century, although this development is also, no doubt, an indication of the willingness of landlords to take on more fixed capital expenditure in a period of rising rents, and of increasing *tenant* investment in working capital.

(ii) *Farm buildings*

More significant than the investment made in drainage was that in farm buildings: and it is in the accommodation for livestock that the greatest advances were made, with more and more attention being given to the housing of cattle. The aim was both to intensify manure production and to produce fatstock for the distant urban markets which, as already noted, were becoming more accessible as the rail network expanded. In addition, the design and layout of farm buildings was increasingly influenced, both directly and indirectly, by the changes in technology and rising labour costs. Thus, in particular, the barn generally became a small and insignificant component of the farm complex as portable threshing machines, working out in the fields, took over their function. As labour became more expensive, industrial principles of time and motion were increasingly applied to the design of farms. These dual requirements – for intensive livestock rearing and increased labour efficiency – coupled, crucially, with the need to attract

[61] Select Committee on Agricultural Customs, BPP   [62] *Ibid*, p. 68.
1847/8, VII, Q. 3290.

tenants with sufficient working capital – led to greatly increased expenditure on farm buildings in the mid-nineteenth century.

Some of the new buildings were elaborate 'model farms', built to a single plan at one time. These were, however, no longer normally designed (as those of the previous period had generally been) by architects, but by men who styled themselves 'agricultural engineers'. Interest in the design of improved farmsteads is manifested in a number of ways: in the Royal Agricultural Society's farm building competition, in articles in *JRASE*, and in books such as John Bailey Denton's *Farm Homesteads of England* (1863).[63] Most published designs involved not simply the housing of cattle in yards surrounded by shelter sheds, but also the building of ranges of loose boxes, often with a central feeding passage and with a turnip or cake house at one end. The logical culmination of this trend was for the shelter shed to be completely roofed over, so as to provide protection for both animals and manure. A farm of this kind, at Brome Hall, Eye, Suffolk, was illustrated in Denton's volume.[64] Although many farmers were wary of such designs, fearing that lack of ventilation could adversely effect the development of the cattle, covered yards gradually increased in popularity in East Anglia.

Yet it was not the erection of such substantial new buildings, or purpose-built 'model farms', which was the most important feature of the period. C. S. Read, writing in 1858, noted that there had been a more general improvement in farm buildings, with the widespread erection of new cattle sheds within or around existing yards. Even on the large landed estates on the light lands of Breckland or North-West Norfolk, piecemeal additions to the farm complex were more important than the erection of new farmsteads. On the Holkham estate, for example, prestigious buildings at Egmere, Model Farm and Longlands caught the contemporary eye, but there was hardly a farm amongst the seventy on the estate that did not receive new cattle sheds between 1840 and 1870, as well as a variety of other functional buildings.[65]

The scale of investment in this period on the large Breckland estates, in particular, is striking. Westmere Farm in 1869 consisted of two barns – a large wheat barn as well as the double barley barn which still survives – together with chaff and straw houses, a bullock shed, an open thatched shed on posts in the barley barn yard, a double open bullock shed, a cart horse stable for ten horses, a cow house for ten cows with calf crib, a riding horse stable for two horses, a gig house and wood house, a granary, a carpenter's shop, and a waggon lodge. There were, in addition, a number of clay and stud buildings, including a lean-to implement shed on the end of the granary, a chaff-cutting house on the end of the barn, a blacksmith's shop, a five-bay tumbril shed, and an open thatched shed and fenced yard for colts. The stack yard was surrounded by walls and there was an additional cattle yard and shed at some distance from the main farm complex, out in the fields.[66] The Waterend Farm premises were similarly impressive. They consisted of a large flint barn with a thatched roof; a lean-to open bullock shed with walled-in yard; two shut-up bullock boxes with a further yard, in front of the west doors of the barn; a second open bullock shed with a walled-in yard; as well as an open pig

---

[63] *JRASE* 7 (1850), pp. 186–310.

[64] John Bailey Denton, *The farm homesteads of England* (1863), p. 68.

[65] Wade Martins, *Great Estate*, pp. 132–3.

[66] This is a formidable collection of buildings, but ten working horses are not many for a 600 acre farm: an indication that much of the land was still uncultivated.

shed and yard. There was an open cattle shed with a granary above it and a five-bay waggon lodge adjoining a carpenter's shop. Horse accommodation included a stable for seven working horses and three riding horses, together with a harness house and gig house.[67]

The Walsingham estate accounts survive for the years 1859–1877.[68] Estate income from rents rose erratically from £7373 in 1859 to £9019 in 1873; by 1877 it had dropped back to £8642. The amount spent on buildings varied from year to year but was always above £630 and frequently above £1000: in other words, the estate generally invested over 10 per cent of its income in maintenance and improvement. No less than £1056 was spent at Mouse Hall Farm in 1854, £1395 at Waterloo in 1862 and another £1163 at Mortimer's in 1865.[69] In 1862, Lord Walsingham described in the *Norfolk News* how, since 1840, 'five new and large farm houses with necessary buildings have been erected and others enlarged and improved. The land is generally in a much better state of cultivation'.[70]

Indeed, the extent of arable land seems to have increased once again in the region, following the post-war slump, although it seems never to have returned to the levels of the Napoleonic peak. The Walsingham estate was not unusual in its willingness to invest in the poor Breckland soil in the middle and later decades of the century. The farms erected by the Rev. Benyon between 1825 and 1889 on the Culford estate, for example, were similarly impressive. All contained substantial yards, as at Neville House Farm and Culford Lodge. How far the willingness of landowners to pour money into what eventually proved to be a bottomless pit was motivated by sound economic considerations; how far they were swept along by the spirit of improvement which was opening up new lands across the empire, and believed that the great scientific developments of the age could allow man to overcome even the greatest physical obstacles, is a moot point. But either way, it is clear that the provision of farm buildings was here, as elsewhere, principally related to the amount of capital the landlord expected the tenant to put in, rather than directly to the fertility and potential productivity of the local soil.

Perhaps the most striking example of large-scale rebuilding in this period comes from the Hare estate, which covered about 10,500 acres in west Norfolk. Two thousand acres were occupied by peat fen, regarded until the 1840s as very poor land which had to be let with the 'upland' farms, because it was 'incapable from its poverty of separate occupation'. Between 1846 and 1849, under the agent John Wiggens, the fen land was more effectively drained and six new farms created. Plans in the estate records show groups of buildings – including barns, granaries, and turnip houses – ranged around yards: a distinctive feature is the provision of piggeries and food preparation rooms where the potatoes, for which the fens were already becoming famous, could be prepared for the pigs. After 1860 many of the buildings on the 'upland' part of the estate were also rebuilt and here features typical of this age of 'industrial' type farm buildings are in evidence: sliding doors which could be left open without danger of being blown closed, and hit-and-miss ventilator windows 'by which wind is excluded without excluding light'.[71] No

[67] NRO, WLS LXVII/9 479 X 9: again, seven horses for a farm containing 630 acres of arable as well as 36 of meadow and 400 of sheepwalk was very few indeed.

[68] NRO, WLS LX7/28 and 29 429 X 7.

[69] NRO, WLS XVIII/17 411 X.

[70] NRO, WLS XVII/7/23 410 X 8.

[71] John Wiggins, 'Survey, terrier and valuation, 1849': NRO, Hare 5370 221 X 6.

threshing barns were included, for by this time the farmers relied entirely on the services of portable threshing machines.

Large-scale rebuilding was also, in time, undertaken by some of the large clayland estates. In 1867 William Keary, the agent to the Holkham estate, was commissioned to write a report on the Duke of Norfolk's properties in south Norfolk (within what we have defined as the Central Clayland region). The farm buildings were of wood or clay-lump with thatched roofs: they were 'not adapted to the present mode of farming', having more barns than necessary but no suitable cattle housing. At Lodge Farm, Lopham, there were three barns and a good new cow shed, but 'little accommodation for grazing cattle'. The time had come 'when a considerable outlay must be made if this property is to be raised to a condition worthy of its hereditary owner'.[72] Charles Lenny's 1864 report on the Earsham estate, also in south Norfolk, was surprisingly similar. The buildings here were totally dilapidated and 'in several cases an entire reinstatement is absolutely necessary'. The farms were 'impoverished from a lack of buildings'.[73]

The high rents this rich land could command had presumably discouraged investment in buildings: rents per acre on the Flixton estate had risen from between 7s. and 14s. in 1750 to between £1 and £1 4s. in 1845, while on the Earsham estate they had increased from between 10s. 6d. and £11 6s. in 1810, to between £1 4s. and £2 in 1864. As higher investment demands were made of farmers in the years after 1840, however, and as agricultural techniques changed, clayland landowners were eventually obliged to undertake rebuilding. Lenny claimed that the fertility of the Earsham farms was suffering because hay was being sold off the farms, which lacked the buildings needed to over-winter large numbers of stock: as a result, insufficient manure was being produced and returned to the fields. Keary acknowledged that the Duke of Norfolk's lack of expenditure meant that he kept a higher proportion of the rent: but it also ensured that only poorer tenants with low levels of capital were prepared to farm there.[74]

Soon after Lenny's report the home farm at Earsham was rebuilt: a fine house was erected alongside a model farm on a rectangular plan with a barn, cartsheds, bullock sheds and stables surrounding a horse yard and covered cattle yard. Similarly, the Duke of Norfolk built a completely new farm at Lopham Hall, South Lopham, in the 1860s. The emphasis – as we would expect by this date – was on cattle accommodation, and the farm was provided with only a small barn. These show-pieces aside, nearly all the farms on the two estates gained some new buildings in the 1860s, particularly cattle sheds. Sometimes these were integrated with the old structures, taking the form of shelter shed wings added to existing barns, thus forming the typical E-shaped steading as at Fersfield Hall. Elsewhere, as at Shelfanger Hall and Place Farm, Kenninghall, they were separate, free-standing structures.

Nevertheless, we should not exaggerate the extent to which the clayland estates threw them-selves wholeheartedly into refurbishment in the 1850s and 1860s. Improvements were largely directed towards the larger farms; and on some estates little seems to have been done. An undated survey of the Adair's Flixton estate, for example – probably drawn up around 1870 – shows that farm buildings remained in a poor condition. Of a farm in South Elmham St Cross the survey states, 'farm buildings inferior and deficient of proper shedding as at many other

72 NRO, Smiths Gore 20.10.78 no.225, 152D.   74 NRO, Smiths Gore 20.10.78 no. 225, 152D.

73 NRO, MEA 3/539.

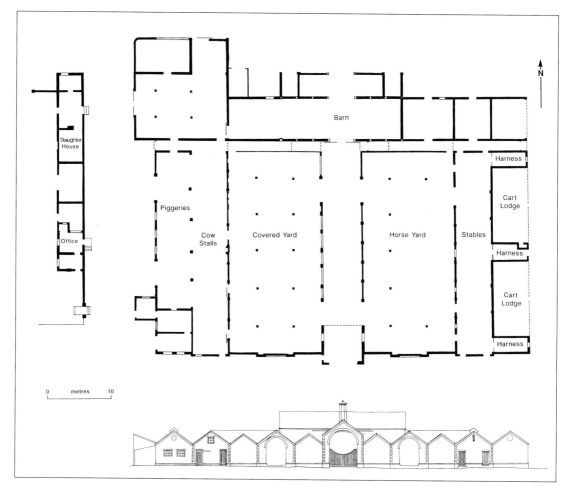

16. A model farmstead at Combs, Suffolk, built in 1867.

farmsteads with yards exposed to cold winds'.[75] The total cost of the necessary repairs would be £6000.[76] It is not surprising, perhaps, that the surveyor found the farmsteads here deficient, as between 1844 and 1879 there was only one year (1845) in which, out of an estate income of nearly £20,000 a year, as much as £2,000 was spent on building and repairs (the sum was between £1,000 and £2,000 in eight of these years, and below £500 in five).[77] It is noteworthy that rents here rose from between £1 and £1 4s. per acre in 1845, to between £1 6s. and £2 8s. in 1870: clearly, tenants could be found for this fertile land even when the latest in building technology was not on offer. Nevertheless, even here improvements were eventually made. The Flixton survey probably provided the impetus behind an application made to the Land Improvement Company in 1872 for loans towards new buildings and cottages. As a result numerous new farm buildings were erected.

[75] ESRO, HA 12/D4/26.
[76] ESRO, HA 12/D4/26.

[77] ESRO, HA 12 D38/8.

What was happening in the Central Claylands was also occurring in the other clayland regions: where large landed estates existed they belatedly embarked on extensive, if generally piecemeal, rebuilding schemes. One of the greatest spenders must have been the 12,000 acre Evans-Lombe estate in the Dissected Clays region of mid-Norfolk. Although no estate documents survive, field survey evidence shows that almost all the buildings on the 50-odd farms were rebuilt in the middle decades of the nineteenth century. Particularly striking are the six cattle yards built for the 1200-acre Field House Farm at Swanton Morley, and the elaborate covered yards at Park Farm, Bylaugh (Figure 17).[78] And it was not just the few large estates on the claylands which were involved in rebuilding schemes. Even quite small proprietors could, on occasions, erect imposing ranges, even true 'model farms'. One striking example is at Combs near Stowmarket, designed in 1867 by the local architect Mr Andrews for the Webb family, who had made their wealth as owners of the local tannery (Figure 16). After producing several versions of the plan, the buildings as finally erected comprised two yards divided by a central passage entered through an imposing arch with a cupola above. On one side were stables and horse yards with an outward-facing cart lodge; on the other were covered cow yards with outward-facing piggeries. An elaborate tiled dairy near the house would process the milk and provide the waste products to be used as pig-feed. This was an exceptional complex, and although some other small estates – especially on the claylands – attempted ambitious schemes, most were content with piecemeal rebuilding, and in particular with the addition of improved cattle housing. Even the smallest proprietors might thus invest in new buildings, embracing what Holderness has described as a 'fashion for conspicuous investment'.[79]

Indeed, there is hardly a farm within East Anglia which was not affected in some way by rebuilding in this period. As C. S. Read wrote of Norfolk in 1858: 'all over the county there are excellent new premises and the general aspect of the old ones is decidedly better than 15 years ago'. Much the same was true of Suffolk, where in 1874 it was noted that cattle were mostly kept in 'covered yards and comfortable sheds'.[80] Comparison of the layout of farmsteads shown on the tithe maps of the early 1840s with those on the 25″ Ordnance Survey maps of the 1880s in sample areas across Norfolk – embracing all the principal soils types and farming regions – brings home the point forcibly. In the 1840s half the farm layouts were irregular, with a further 20 per cent L-shaped but only 10 per cent E or U-shaped, presumably enclosing cattle yards. By the 1880s, however, more than half were E or U-shaped and only 10 per cent were irregular, indicating a major shift towards shelter sheds arranged around yards suited to more intensive yard feeding.[81]

This scale of rebuilding shows that far from 'faltering' in East Anglia in this period, investment was continuing at a high level. It has been argued by some historians that as farming systems became more intensive, with more tenants' working capital needed, the role of the landlord in investment declined. But the farm building evidence, in particular, does not support this view. The need to attract tenants with sufficient capital was stronger than ever, and only good, modern ranges of buildings could do this, and thus command enhanced rents. William Biddell, reporting

78 Wade Martins, *Historic farm buildings*, p. 152.

79 B. A. Holderness, 'The Victorian Farmer', in G. E. Mingay (ed.), *The Victorian Countryside* (2 vols, 1981), p. 233.

80 Biddell, 'Agriculture', p. 26.

81 Wade Martins, *Historic farm buildings*, p. 199.

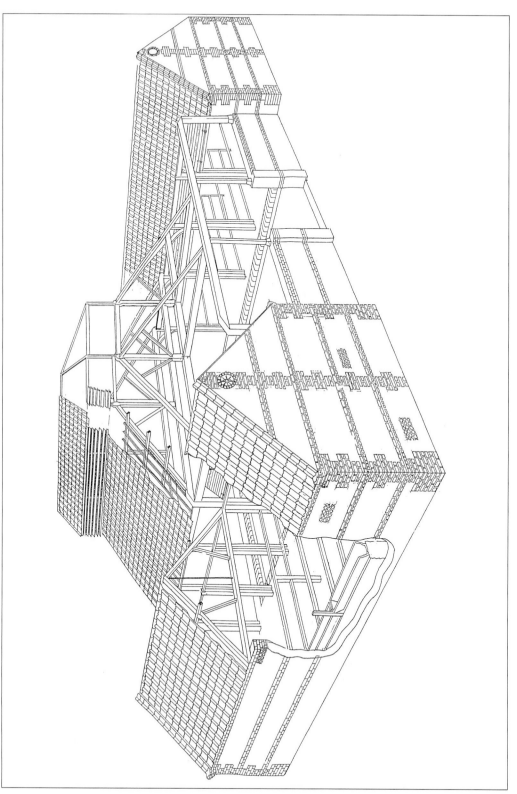

17. Covered cattle yard at Park Farm, Bylaugh, Norfolk.

on the Hengrave estate farms in 1860, typically described a farm of 240 acres which was let for £312 *per annum*, 'but consider how much more it might be worth if the premises were good'. Three years later, Robert Rodwell described another farm on the Hengrave estate: 'the buildings are excellent and add considerably to the value of the occupation'.[82]

Some of the finance for this work came from loans advanced by the various land improvement companies established between 1847 and 1860. The take-up rate for these was, however, relatively low in East Anglia and little use seems to have been made of this facility before the 1870s; indeed, most borrowing took place on the very eve of Depression. Viscount Townshend and the Marquis of Cholmondeley borrowed £2000 for farm buildings and £2000 for reclamation,[83] and £1300 for farm buildings,[84] respectively in the 1870s. Small sums went to Fenland estates in Stow Bardolph and Wiggenhall for the erection of new buildings (a total of £2000 between 1864 and 1875)[85] and £473 for buildings in Upwell and Welney in 1874.[86] Rather larger sums were spent in Breckland, with just over £10,000 being borrowed for buildings on farms in Thetford, Brettenham, East Wretham, Livermere and Hockham in the 1870s. The Marquess of Bristol borrowed £2396 in 1875. One of the largest borrowers was Lord Stafford who invested £6077 of Improvement Company money in his farms in Bawburgh and Costessey and £400 in cottages, between 1878 and 1880.[87] In the clayland districts various sums were borrowed by large estates, mainly for building rather than drainage: the largest borrower here was the Flixton estate, which drew on £19,353 for building between 1875 and 1879.[88]

Nevertheless, these were relatively small sums, which place East Anglia near the bottom of the league table of borrowers. The bulk of 'improvements' were funded from estate income. Indeed, surviving figures for East Anglian estates generally show expenditure on improvements increasing in the middle years of the nineteenth century. Edward Kerrison reputedly spent over £121,000 on his Oakley Park and Brome Hall estate in north Suffolk between 1853 and 1882, 'borrowing nothing', financing everything from estate income.[89] At Holkham, similarly, expenditure in the 1850s rose to over £10,000 in many years, over 25 per cent of total estate income.[90] On the Walsingham estate expenditure was particularly high between 1859 and 1878, often amounting to over 10 per cent of estate income (£500 per annum) and frequently approaching 20 per cent.[91] Between 1857 and 1869 Mr Preedy, agent to the LeStrange estate, Hunstanton, presided over its improvement from 'one of the most dilapidated in the country to one that compared favourably with neighbouring properties',[92] with between 8 per cent and 15 per cent of estate income in most years being ploughed back into the farms.[93]

(iii) *Drainage of fen and marsh*

The period from 1830 to 1880 also saw ever-greater levels of investment in the drainage of marshes and fens. Only a minority of this was carried out by individual estates: most was the

[82] WSRO, 449/3/13.
[83] PRO, MAFF 66/5.
[84] PRO, MAFF 66/35.
[85] PRO, MAFF 66/4, 8 and 12.
[86] PRO, MAFF 66/34.
[87] PRO, MAFF 66/4 and 16.
[88] PRO, MAFF 66/34.

[89] BPP, 1882, p. 179.
[90] Wade Martins, *Great Estate*, pp. 86, 94.
[91] NRO, WLS LXVII/9.
[92] Roe, *Norfolk Agriculture*, p. 155, quoting NRO, Le-Strange box 14.
[93] Wade Martins, *Historic farm buildings*, p. 134.

work of various Drainage Commissions, representing groups of landowners. In the Fens, the High Farming period saw further extension of the arable acreage, accompanied by the construction of new steam drainage engines and the improvement of existing ones, in particular the replacement of large, heavy beam engines with lighter 'grasshopper' engines and centrifugal pumps.[94]

In the Norfolk Broads similarly, the middle decades of the century saw increasing investment in drainage technology. As noted in chapter 2, large numbers of drainage mills were erected on the silt marshes during the first decades of the nineteenth century, partly as a consequence of enclosure acts and the establishment of drainage commissions. These were, however, fairly simple structures, with common sails and tail poles: more modern machines, with patent sails and fantails, did not appear until the late 1830s. In 1840 the drainage mill at Burgh St Margaret – which had been established following the enclosure of the commons here in 1804 – was blown down in a storm, and the Drainage Commissioners

> Resolved and agreed that a new Tower should be erected and that the same should commence from the present Foundations of the old mill at the top of the door ... the tower shall be built on the best and most improved principle so as to carry the machinery with self acting winding tackle and patent sails.[95]

The new mill was over nine metres high to the curb, and other mills on this new model erected in the High Farming period, such as Limpenhoe Marshes Mill (TG 395019, of 1832) or Dilham Dyke Mill, Smallburgh (TG 344248, of 1847) were of similar stature. Some were taller: Runham Five Mile House (TG 478098, 1849) stands over 12 metres to the curb; Hardley Marshes Mill (TG 387024: 1874), over 13 metres; while Berney Arms Mill (1865) has a total height of 22 metres. Some of these tall, sophisticated structures were equipped with two scoop wheels, some with particularly large scoops, but from the 1850s many were provided with the new and more powerful turbine pump, invented by Appold in 1851, examples of which were also added to many existing mills. Small brick tower mills continued to be erected, however, to drain limited areas of fen ground and there was a proliferation of cheap wooden windpumps, the so-called hollow post mills and skeleton mills.[96]

As well as seeing new varieties of drainage mill, the period also saw a further increase in the numbers of mills in Broadland. By the 1880s, to judge from the first edition Ordnance Survey 25" maps, there were over a hundred, although this probably represents a decline from an earlier peak. Mills had proliferated in the areas of fen and peat ground in the upper reaches of the Broadland rivers, reflecting numerous (but ultimately abortive) attempts at improving the quality of grazing here during the High Farming period. On the silt soils, in contrast, there had been some reduction in numbers since the 1820s. In part this was because the more powerful mills being erected in the middle decades of the century could drain more extensive areas of marsh; in part it was because of the adoption here of steam drainage.

Steam drainage began in Broadland in the 1830s or 1840s: Bacon in 1844 describes various

---

[94] R. L. Hills, *Machines, mills and uncountable costly necessities* (1967), pp. 136–54.

[95] NRO, MC 554 16–19, 774 X 9.
[96] Williamson, *Norfolk Broads*, pp. 125–133.

improvements carried out higher up the Yare, at Surlingham, and in particular at Buckenham, where:

> Sir William Beauchamp Proctor has within the last four or five years been greatly improving the drainage of the large tract lying between that place and the new Cut, by the erection of a steam mill, that will in a very few years render them very valuable grazing grounds.[97]

He also refers to a steam mill erected near Yarmouth by Mr Baker (probably Benjamin Heath Baker, who owned Scare Gap Farm at the time of the Tithe Award survey in 1840) which was so effective that when a friend went out to visit it on the day it first began to work, he found it had stopped: not through mechanical breakdown, but because in the course of a few hours 'it had so entirely drained the tract, that the ditches were empty'.[98] By the 1880s there were around thirty steam pumps operating in the district. Nevertheless, wind drainage mills were still being extensively refitted, and even constructed anew into the early years of the twentieth century. West Somerton Mill (TG 464202), for example, was built from scratch in the late 1890s; Martham Mill (TG 442192) was constructed in 1908, and extensively altered in 1912; while Horsey Mill (TG 457221) was demolished, and entirely rebuilt, in the same year.[99] Both drainage commissioners and private landowners often preferred to invest in the 'old' technology, rather than in the new. Even before the onset of agricultural recession Drainage Commissions were often uneasy about investing in steam. In 1873 the Burgh and Billockby Drainage Commissioners met to determine

> Whether it would be expedient that Steam drainage should be carried out in connection with the existing Drainage … inasmuch as the present drainage by means of the existing mill is inadequate.[100]

Tenders were put out for a steam engine and turbine pump: but when the bids came in at between £878 and £1007 the plan was dropped, and instead the millwright Daniel Rust was instructed to make an estimate of the 'cost of a new wheel of 3 feet increased diameter and to raise the laying shaft 6 inches and also to give an estimate for constructing a rigger to turn such Wheel by means of a portable engine'.[101] Wind drainage continued to be viable because most of the drained areas in Broadland were – unlike the Fenlands in the west – on silt rather than peat soils, and remained, for the most part, under pasture. Not only did less shrinkage of the surface occur, but in addition the dominant form of land use ensured that a far higher water-table, more easily maintained by wind drainage, could be tolerated.[102]

As with the extensive ranges of cattle housing provided on East Anglia's farms during the same period, the refinement of drainage in Fens and Broads clearly reflects the willingness of landowners to invest in agriculture – and especially in livestock production – in the classic High Farming period.

---

[97] Bacon, *Agriculture*, p. 294.
[98] *Ibid.*

[99] Williamson, *Norfolk Broads*, pp. 133–36.
[100] NRO, MC 554 19, 774 X 9.

3. High Farming: conclusion

High Farming unquestionably raised levels of production in East Anglia far beyond those attained during the previous period of 'Agricultural Revolution'. The *profitability* of this high-input/high-output system is, however, less easy to assess. John Hudson of Castle Acre made a fortune, but information about the generality of farmers in East Anglia in this period is scarce: very few farmers were good book keepers and, in all probability, rarely knew themselves the precise profits they were making.[103] Moreover, figures that were produced for surveys or Royal Commissions were usually doctored to prove a point. Those presented in Bacon's survey, for example, nearly always show a small loss, although one 300-acre farm in east Norfolk is said to have made an average annual profit of £500 on an investment of £1500.[104] Valuations of the Home Farm at Merton between 1850 and 1869 show dramatic swings between a profit of £814 in 1868 and a loss of £250 in 1860. Outgoings included over £1000 *per annum* in artificial fertilisers, roughly equivalent to the cost of labour in many years. Figures for other Walsingham farms over the same period similarly suggest that little profit was made.[105] Most mid-nineteenth century farmers nevertheless believed that the key to increased productivity, and therefore to prosperity, lay in the progressive application of science to agriculture. John Hastings' reply to the final question of Bacons' 1843 questionnaire, 'Has production reached its highest level?', was robust: 'This will develop itself in proportion as knowledge increases'. The High Farming of mid-Victorian England was very much a state of mind which exhibited that same confident faith in progress which was to be found in so many fields, rather than a wholly rational system of agriculture based on careful considerations of profit and loss.

It is clear that many elements of the High Farming system had their roots in the eighteenth century: neither underdrainage, nor intensive cattle feeding, nor mechanised threshing were innovations of the 1840s, and even the use of oil cake seems to have been widespread by 1820. The increasing adoption of these methods, however, and their gradual elaboration into a coherent 'system' also involving such novel practices as the use of artificial fertilisers, was a consequence of a range of inter-related forces operating in the middle decades of the century. These included improved transport, large-scale industrialisation in other parts of England, and advances in chemical sciences and technology inspired, for the most parts, by developments outside the agricultural sector. In addition, however, some of these developments were probably related to rising labour costs and to changes in the nature of the labour market.

In spite of what some historians have suggested, in East Anglia (at least) landlords played a crucial part in the elaboration of the new system, providing in particular the necessary buildings. As agriculture became more capital-intensive, the provision of up-to-date facilities became ever more important: for although tenants were not difficult to come by in the prosperous

[101] NRO, MC 554 19, 774 X 9.

[102] Williamson, *Norfolk Broads*, pp. 131–6.

[103] A Norfolk farmer told Sir Daniel Hall in 1919, 'It is impossible to show that any single item on a farm pays by itself; it is the whole system taken together which succeeds or fails' (quoted in Jones, *Agriculture and Industrial Revolution*, p. 197). A witness to the 1893 Royal Commission into Agriculture stated that very few farmers knew how much they had lost. 'They just kept going from year to year' (BPP 1894, Royal Commission on Agriculture, Q. 1595).

[104] Bacon, *Agriculture*, pp. 97–9.

[105] NRO, WLS XVIII/17 411 X.

mid-century years, the age-old problem of attracting men with sufficient capital was now even more acute. Such men required and expected, in particular, buildings suitable for the intensive feeding of cattle which was so much part of the High Farming system, even in this intensively arable region.

CHAPTER V

The Achievement

1. Introduction

In this chapter we will examine the *effects* of the momentous changes which we have been describing. We will attempt to assess the extent to which productivity increased in the years between 1700 and 1870, and to identify which of the various 'improvements' outlined in the previous sections were most responsible for these gains.

There are two main ways of measuring agricultural productivity. Agricultural historians have been most interested in *yields per acre*: that is, the amount of grain or other crops which can be produced each year on a standard area of land. More recently, however, some have emphasised the importance of *labour productivity*: that is, the amount of labour required to produce a given volume of crop.[1] One of the distinctive features of English agrarian experience in the eighteenth and nineteenth centuries was that ever larger quantities of foodstuffs were produced even though the percentage of the population involved in agriculture was falling. It is, however, surprisingly difficult to make any confident statements about labour productivity at a local or regional level, and the reasons for this need to be briefly discussed.

The first is that it is hard to establish the size of the workforce on any one farm, even when detailed records survive. In part this is because some workers do not figure in the farm accounts, because they were not paid in cash. The most important of these were farmers of small acreages who worked intermittently for their larger neighbours, sometimes in a managerial capacity, and who were often repaid by loans of labour and equipment. Such men were part of the group of small 'peasant' farmers recently discussed by Howkins.[2] Randall Burroughes' farming journal mentions a number of such men.[3]

Excluding such people, the labour force falls into three categories: yearly hired servants; day labourers; and piece workers.[4] Unfortunately, the majority of surviving labour books record only one type of worker. For example, the very complete accounts for the home farm at Earsham, spanning the years 1797–1807, rarely include tasks such as harvesting, sowing, marling and threshing, presumably because these were carried out on a piecework basis.[5] Piecework – that is, employment of individuals or groups to carry out some specific task – was, as we shall see, increasing in importance in East Anglia in the later eighteenth and early nineteenth centuries, as the practice of yearly hiring declined: and this produces further difficulties in

[1] M. Overton and B Campbell, 'Productivity change in European agricultural development', in Campbell and Overton (eds), *Land, labour and livestock*, pp. 7–17.

[2] Howkins, 'Peasants, servants and labourers', *AgHR* 42 (1994), pp. 49–62.

[3] Wade Martins and Williamson, *Randall Burroughes*, pp. 32–8.

[4] For a general discussion of the agricultural workforce, see A. Armstrong, *Farmworkers. A social and economic history, 1770–1980* (1988). For further discussion of the East Anglian material, see S. Wade Martins and T. Williamson, 'Labour and Improvement. Agricultural change in East Anglia, c. 1750–1870', *Labour History Review* 62 (1997).

examining patterns of employment. Because of increasing casualisation many farmers would themselves have been hard put to say precisely how many men they employed throughout the year. Bacon asked just this question in his questionnaire of 1843 but it was frequently left unanswered, or received only a vague reply. On one farm of 400 acres, for example, 'upwards of 20 men' were said to be employed. All Bacon's correspondents said they 'put out' all the work they could, so the numbers of labourers said to be employed does not necessarily represent the total workforce engaged on the farms in question.[6] The 1834 Commission into the Poor Laws similarly enquired how many labourers were needed in the various parishes investigated, but the question was only rarely answered.[7]

In a similar way, the figures given in the censuses from 1851 to 1881 concerning the numbers of labourers employed are hard to interpret. The number will have been influenced by the number of working-age sons and daughters still living at home; moreover, the figures include only *regular* workers employed at the time of the census (between 30 March and 7 April), and thus once again take no account of piecework or gang labour. Nevertheless, these figures are useful because they at least show the extent of variation in the number of workers employed. Areas where only one labourer was employed for every 40 acres or more generally fall into two categories: those where small family farms predominated, such as the Fens; and those where extensive, mainly pastoral farms existed, such as Breckland. The figures suggest that the average number of acres per labourer on a medium-sized farm of between 80 and 200 acres was between 20 and 30, but with regional variations suggesting that more manpower was employed on the heavier land than on the lighter. This is confirmed by contemporary observers. Thus, according to William and Hugh Raynbird in 1853, sixteen labourers and two boys were required to work a 400-acre heavy land farm in Suffolk (i.e., one worker per 25 acres);[8] while 950 labourers were, according to the Earl of Leicester in 1866, needed to work an estate of 37,000 acres (i.e., one man for every 38 acres, on mainly light land, large-scale arable farms).[9] Glyde used the figures from the 1851 census for Suffolk to produce a table of the number of labourers employed on farms in Suffolk,[10] which shows the same wide variations (again related in part to soil type). Sixteen farms of between 100 and 125 acres employed only one labourer while most (191) employed four, but 27 had as many as ten. The replies to the questionnaire produced in connection with the 1834 Poor Law Commission suggest that the number of labourers required by the farmers of various parishes varied from one labourer for 20 acres, to one for 35.

Such variations make it difficult to estimate 'average' levels of labour productivity, compounding the problems posed by pieceworkers and family labour. For an earlier period, such generalisations are even more problematic, given the nature of the surviving evidence. Moreover, even if such information was available it is clear that patterns of employment were not determined simply by economic considerations, but also by wider social ones. In particular, they were effected by paternalist concern about unemployment, and by anxiety about the Poor Rates and civil unrest – worries sharpened by the disorders of 1822 and 1830, and by the frequent

---

[5] NRO, MEA 15–32

[6] NRO, MS 4363.

[7] BPP 1834, XXX, pp. 300–30, 455–81.

[8] Raynbird, *Rham's Dictionary of Farming*, p. 471.

[9] *Norfolk News*, 13 Oct. 1866.

[10] J. Glyde, *Suffolk in the Nineteenth Century* (1856), pp. 330–4.

outbreaks of incendiarism in the middle decades of the century.[11] In 1834 the two large farmers in Cockley Cley described how they always agreed to find work for the resident labourers; while in the Suffolk parish of Stradbrooke, Lord Stradbrooke described how 'The parish belongs to me, and although it is much over-peopled, I employ all'.[12] As late as 1856 Glyde could write, 'The rate payers of a parish are frequently induced to agree a division of the surplus labour according to the size of their farms to prevent their becoming paupers and the superior skill of the farmer in economising one of the chief costs of production is thus arbitrarily set aside'.[13] Such a situation must have been more prevalent before before the New Poor Law of 1834 and rural population growth began to level out in the 1850s. All that we can say for certain, in fact, is that at no time in the century after 1750 was there anything other than a substantial surplus of labour in the East Anglian countryside. This is an obvious point, perhaps, but one with important implications, to which we will return at a later stage.

2. The improvement of crop yields

The estimation of crop yields from the evidence of probate inventories has become a major feature of the agrarian history of the early modern period. The work of Mark Overton, Paul Glennie and Robert Allen has already been mentioned.[14] Overton's work is of particular importance in the present context, providing as it does the background and baseline against which the productivity increases of the eighteenth and early nineteenth centuries need to assessed. His calculations suggest that wheat yields rose from the late sixteenth to the early seventeenth century, but increased relatively little over the remainder of that century. In the late seventeenth and early eighteenth centuries, however, they rose again, to unprecedented levels by the 1720s and 1730s. Barley yields followed a similar path: although they increased faster than those of wheat during the seventeenth century, they too showed their most dramatic rise in the first four decades of the eighteenth century. In the period 1680–1709, average yields per acre of wheat and barely were 15.9 and 16.1 bushels respectively. Over the period 1710–1739, in contrast, the figures were 19.2 and 20.8 – a significant increase. Overton used published sources to chart subsequent developments. By the 1760s, according to information presented in Arthur Young's *Farmer's Tour*, wheat yields had reached 26.5 bushels and barley 32.5 bushels per acre. By 1802, according to the House of Lords *Report on the Dearth of Provisions*, they had dropped back to 22.4 and 32 respectively, and shortly afterwards – in 1804 – Young estimated that the average yields per acre from Norfolk were 24 bushels per acre for wheat and 34 for barley. By the 1830s there had been no real improvement (an average of 23.3 bushels per acre for wheat, and 32 for barley, are recorded in the tithe files), but the *Reports of the Poor Law Inspectors* of 1854, which apply to Norfolk only, suggest further increases, to 30 bushels per acre for wheat and 38 for barley.

Closer inspection of this information allows the chronology of the increase in yields to be refined slightly: but before we do this the problems with one of these sets of figures must be

[11] J. E. Archer, *By a Flash and a Scare. Incendiarism, animal maiming, and poaching in East Anglia, 1815–1879* (1990).

[12] BPP 1834, XXX, pp. 316, 476.

[13] *Ibid*, p. 350.

[14] Overton, 'Estimating crop yields'; Overton, 'Determinants'; Glennie, 'Measuring crop yields'; Allen, 'The two English Agricultural Revolutions, 1450–1850'.

highlighted. The average yields for the 1760s, derived from Young's statistics, should probably be dispensed with. Even a cursory perusal of the text of the *Farmer's Tour* reveals that most of the figures are for individual farms, and that these are an unrepresentative sample, selected for their exemplary husbandry. Only once or twice does Young give what he believes to be the average yields for a particular *district*. If these former figures are ignored, then the pattern becomes clearer, and at the same time some intriguing differences in the trends for wheat and barley emerge. For *wheat*, the period of greatest increase was not, in fact, the classic period of the 'Agricultural Revolution', from *c.*1750 to 1830, but rather the periods before, and after. Wheat yields rose by more than 20 per cent in the first four decades of the eighteenth century, but by only *c.*14 per cent during the rest of the century, and by a mere 4 per cent between 1800 and the 1840. Thereafter growth accelerated, with yields perhaps increasing by as much as 28 per cent during the next decade and a half. The pattern for barley is strikingly different. Yields rose fast in the first four decades of the eighteenth century – perhaps by as much as 25 per cent – but, unlike those for wheat, they continued to rise throughout the century, with gains of around 35 per cent between *c.*1740 and *c.*1800. Thereafter there was little if any significant increase until after *c.*1840, when they resumed their upward trend, although less markedly than for wheat.[15]

Before exploring further the significance of such figures, it is worth noting the problems associated with the concept of the 'average yield'. Individual yield figures derived from particular documents cannot in themselves be taken as representative of a period, given that in practice yields fluctuated considerably from year to year in response to the vagaries of the weather. More important, however, is the fact that Norfolk and Suffolk display considerable variations in soils and topography. Eighteenth- and nineteenth-century commentators were well aware of these variations, and of the effect they could have upon the calculation of 'averages'. Kent in the 1790s argued that the average wheat yield for Norfolk was 3 quarters an acre, but added that 'in very light parts of the county, the farmer is glad to get two quarters'.[16] Thomas Beevor, commenting on this view, was more pessimistic:

> As there is a great deal of land in the county, sown with wheat, which is light and poor to produce above 12 or 14 bushels per acre; it is apprehended, that 2½ quarters, per acre, is rather above than under the general average for the whole county.[17]

'Average' figures may thus mask considerable regional variations, and may mask differences in the scale of improvement from region to region.

Unfortunately, there is relatively little evidence which can be used to chart the development of yields: and even less when some attempt is made to study this issue on a regional basis. For the start of the period we can use probate inventory evidence to some extent, although given the difficulties in interpreting this material we have employed only those inventories which give figures from which the expected yields per acre can be *directly* calculated: a tiny minority. The bulk of the argument that follows is based on a scatter of evidence provided by correspondence, memoranda books and diaries, and by tithe accounts, all of which occasionally give yields per

[15] Overton, 'Determinants', pp. 301–4.   [17] *Ibid*, p. 59.
[16] Kent, *Norfolk*, p. 56.

acre of the principal crops.[18] In addition, some of the published evidence from the end of the century can contribute to a regional breakdown of yields – thus, for example, Arthur Young presented the record kept by John Adey Repton of the yields of wheat from his farm at Oxnead over the period 1771 – 1800.[19] While evidence relating to cereal yields does thus exist, it does so in only small quantities. As a result, the kind of detailed regional analysis employed in earlier chapters is not possible, and in the discussion that follows four main groups of regions will be considered, *viz.:* the *claylands* (i.e., the Southern and Western Clays, the Central Claylands, and the Dissected Clays); the *acid soil regions* (the Sandlings, Breckland, and the Northern Heathlands); the *Flegg Loams*; and *North-West Norfolk.* Even lumped together like this, the available data is insufficient to allow any form of statistical analysis, and in reality provides only a somewhat impressionistic picture. What is important, however, is not so much the absolute yields achieved in any region in any period, but rather the relative differences in the extent to which these improved from region to region.

(i) *The Claylands*

Table 1. *Wheat yields, Clayland districts*

Carlton Forehoe, 1699 probate inventory: 4.2 combs per acre).[20]

Hindolveston, 1731 probate inventory: 5 combs per acre.[21]

Kirstead-cum-Langhale 1742, tithe account: 7 combs per acre.[22]

Kirstead-cum-Langhale 1748, tithe account: 6 combs per acre.[23]

Hedenham 1758, tithe account: 4 combs per acre.[24]

Stansfield 1760, tithe account; average of 15 records = 3.8 combs per acre.[25]

'Average' yield for claylands in *c.*1770 (retrospective estimate by Glyde, mid nineteenth century); 6 combs per acre, maximum.[26]

*c.*1770, district estimates by Arthur Young (from the *Farmers Tour*):
> Between Yarmouth and Beccles: 4 combs per acre
> Hadleigh/Lavenham/Stowmarket area: 8 combs per acre
> Between Ipswich and Hadleigh: 6.5 combs per acre
> Average: *c.*6.2 combs per acre.[27]

Mattishall 1783, tithe account, estimated average yields: 5 combs per acre.[28]

---

[18] The latter source also records agreed values given in lieu of tithes taken in kind, and while most of these take the form of lump sum compositions made for entire farms, or standardised compositions agreed with the parish as a whole, a few are clearly the result of individual bargains struck between farmer and incumbent, based on the estimated value of the crop. Even these, however, are subject to similar sources of error as the probate inventory calculations, and have – reluctantly – been ignored here.

[19] Young, *Norfolk*, pp. 252–3; 301–2.

[20] NRO, INV II, 157.
[21] NRO, INV I, 114
[22] NRO, PD 300/14.
[23] *Ibid.*
[24] NRO, MF/RO 36/2.
[25] WSRO, FL 627/3/18.
[26] Glyde, *Suffolk in the nineteenth century*, p. 338.
[27] Young, *Farmer's Tour*, II, pp. 165–7.
[28] Gonville and Caius College, Cambridge, Smith notebook.

Mattishall 1785/6, tithe account, estimated average yields: 6 combs per acre.

Mattishall 1787/8, tithe account, estimated average yields: 6 combs per acre.

Mattishall 1788/9, tithe account, estimated average yields: 5 combs per acre.

Mattishall 1789/90, tithe account, estimated average yields: 5 combs per acre.

Wymondham 1795, Randall Burroughes' farming journal: 4.5 combs per acre.[29]

Hasketon 1797, farm cropping account: 3 combs per acre.[30]

Hasketon 1798, farm cropping account: 3 combs per acre.[31]

Wymondham 1799, Randall Burroughes' farming journal: 6.5 combs per acre.[32]

Hasketon 1799, farm cropping account: 3 combs per acre.[33]

Hasketon 1800, farm cropping account: 8 combs per acre.[34]

Redgrave/Wortham 1791–1801, farm notebook: 98 combs 3 bushels of wheat off eight acres = 12.3 combs per acre.[35]

Area around Beccles 1801 predicted yields from the *House of Lords Report*: 5 to 6 combs per acre.[36]

Area around Norwich, 1801: predicted yields from the *House of Lords Report*: 5 to 6.5 combs per acre.[37]

*c.*1804: Arthur Young's estimates in the *General View*:

    Watton area: 6 combs per acre.

    Langley area: 7 combs per acre.

    Wymondham: 5 combs per acre.[38]

Stansfield *c.*1805, tithe account: average of 19 observations = 4.32 combs per acre.[39]

    1829: 5 combs per acre.

    1830: 7 combs per acre.

    1831: 5 combs per acre.

    1832: 7.5 combs per acre.

    1833: 7 combs per acre.

    1834: 9.5 combs per acre.

    1835: 10.5 combs per acre.[40]

Clayland districts in general *c.*1837 tithe file data: 6–7 combs per acre.[41]

[29] Wade Martins and Williamson, *Randall Burroughes*, p. 17.

[30] ESRO, HA24/50/19/3.26.

[31] *Ibid.*

[32] Wade Martins and Williamson, *Randall Burroughes*, p. 17.

[33] ESRO, HA24/50/19/3.26.

[34] *Ibid.*

[35] ESRO, HD79 AD4/3.

[36] PRO, HO 42/55, 305.

[37] *Ibid.*

[38] Young, *Norfolk*, p. 300.

[39] WSRO, FL 627/3/21.

[40] WSRO, FB76 C1/10.

[41] Kain, *Atlas*, pp. 51, 80.

Suffolk claylands *c.*1848, average figures from Raynbirds, *Suffolk Agriculture*:
    Risbridge hundred: 7–8 combs per acre.
    Risbridge hundred: 8 combs per acre.
    Hoxne hundred: 8 combs per acre
    Blackbourne hundred: (i) Light clay: 7–8 combs per acre.
                   (ii) Heavy clay: 5–6 combs per acre.[42]

East Anglian claylands generally *c.*1850, from Caird's *English Farming*: 8 combs per acre 'on the better description of heavy lands'.[43]

Suffolk claylands generally 1856, from Glyde's *Suffolk*: 8 combs per acre.[44]

The figures presented above pose considerable problems of interpretation, not least because the East Anglian claylands do not constitute an homogenous topographic zone. Nevertheless, an overall pattern can be discerned. In the second half of the eighteenth century wheat yields increased, on average, from around five to around six combs per acre, and by the late 1830s yields of between six and seven combs seems to have been the norm. To judge from the information presented by Glyde, the Raynbirds, and Caird – together with a handful of stray figures from individual farms – further gains were made over the following decade or so; by *c.*1850 average yields were between 7 and 8 combs per acre.

Table 2. *Barley yields, Clayland districts*

Carlton Forehoe 1699, probate inventory: 4 combs per acre).[45]

Hindolveston 1731, probate inventory: 5.4 combs per acre.[46]

Kirstead-cum-Langhale 1740, tithe account: 2.5 combs per acre.[47]

Kirstead-cum-Langhale 1742, tithe account: 10 combs per acre

Kirstead-cum-Langhale 1748, tithe account: 6 combs per acre

Stansfield 1760, tithe account: Average of 15 records = 4.4 combs per acre.[48]

c. 1770, district estimates from Young's *Farmers Tour*:
    Between Beccles and Yarmouth: 5 combs per acre
    Between Ipswich and Hadleigh: 8 combs per acre
    Hadleigh/Lavenham/Stowmarket: 8 combs per acre
    Average: 7 combs per acre.[49]

Mattishall 1783/4, tithe account: 8 combs per acre.[50]

Earl Soham 1785, diary: 11 combs per acre (noted as a particularly good crop).[51]

[42] Raynbirds, *Agriculture*, pp. 140, 142, 145, 148.
[43] Caird, *English Agriculture*, p. 171.
[44] Glyde, *Suffolk in the nineteenth century*, p. 338.
[45] NRO, INV II, 157.
[46] NRO, INV I, 114
[47] NRO, PD 300/14.
[48] WSRO, FL 627/3/18.
[49] Young, *Farmer's Tour*, II, pp. 165–7.
[50] Gonville and Caius College, Cambridge, Smith notebook.
[51] ESRO, HD 3651.

Mattishall 1785/6, tithe account: 5 combs per acre.[52]

Mattishall 1787/8, tithe account: 8 combs per acre.

Mattishall 1788/9, tithe account: 7 combs per acre.

Mattishall 1789/90, tithe account: 8 combs per acre.

Wymondham 1795, Randall Burroughes' diary: 7.5 combs per acre.[53]

Wymondham 1796, ditto: 9 combs per acre.

Wymondham 1797, ditto: 9.25 combs per acre.

Wymondham 1798, ditto: 6 combs per acre (noted as a drought year).

1801: predicted yields around Norwich (*House of Lords Rept*): 8 to 9 combs per acre.[54]

1804, Arthur Young's estimates in the *General View*:
>Watton area: 7 combs per acre.
>Langley area: 10 combs per acre.
>Wymondham: 9 combs per acre.[55]

Stansfield *c.*1805, tithe account: average of 14 observations = 5.4 combs per acre.[56]

Whatfield, glebe account:
>1829: 9.75 combs per acre.
>1830: 6.5 combs per acre.
>1831: 9.46 combs per acre
>1833: 11.3 combs per acre.
>1834: 7.73 combs per acre.
>1835: 9.8 combs per acre.[57]

Clayland districts in general *c.* 1837, tithe file data: 8–10 combs per acre.[58]

Suffolk claylands *c.*1848, from Raynbirds' *Agriculture of Suffolk*:
>Risbridge Hundred: 10 combs per acre
>Hoxne Hundred: 11 combs per acre
>Blackbourne Hundred: (i) Light clay: 10 combs per acre.
>>(ii) Heavy clay: 10 combs per acre.[59]

East Anglian claylands *c.*1850, from Caird's *English Agriculture*: 11 combs per acre 'on the better description of heavy lands'.

---

[52] Gonville and Caius College, Cambridge, Smith notebook.

[53] Wade Martins and Williamson, *Randall Burroughes*, p. 17.

[54] PRO, HO 42/55, 305.

[55] Young, *Norfolk*, p. 251.

[56] WSRO, FL 627/3/21.

[57] WSRO, FB76 C1/10.

[58] Kain, *Atlas*, pp. 51, 80.

[59] Raynbird and Raynbird, *Suffolk*, pp. 140, 142, 145, 148.

The figures for barley are more difficult to interpret, in part because barley was more susceptible to excess rainfall than wheat on these heavy soils. In 1860, for example, George Rope of Blaxhall in Suffolk commented:

> The wettest and coldest summer to this time I ever remember. The corn ripens very slowly … The wheat and barley on the mixsoil lands, well manured, promises exceedingly well, but on the cold clays and wet lands the barley crop will be very bad, thousands of acres in Suffolk will not produce 3 combs per acre and a large portion will not pay for harvesting.[60]

Nevertheless, it is again possible to obtain a general idea of the pattern and scale of improvement. In the first half of the eighteenth century barley yields rose slowly to around five and a half combs per acre, but by the 1780s and 1790s had improved dramatically, to around eight combs per acre. A slower rise thereafter took them to between nine and ten combs per acre by the middle of the nineteenth century. Barley yields on the clays thus approximately doubled in the century after *c.*1700, with the fastest increase occurring in the second half of the eighteenth century.

(ii) *Acid soil areas (Breckland, Northern Heathlands and Sandlings)*

Table 3. *Wheat yields, acid soil districts*

Cressingham 1624, glebe account: 3.3 combs per acre.[61]

Cressingham 1625, glebe account: 1.5 combs per acre.

Cressingham 1640, glebe account: 0.6 combs per acre.

Horsham St Faiths 1682, inventory: 2 combs per acre.[62]

Thorpe St Andrew 1689, probate inventory: 2.15 combs per acre.[63]

Oxburgh 1709, probate inventory: 1.375 combs per acres.[64]

Capel St Andrew 1709, probate inventory: 3 combs per acre.

Hempstead 1732, tithe account: ten acres of wheat 'valued at 2 combs per acre'.[65]

Hempstead 1743, tithe account: ten acres of wheat 'valued at 2 combs per acre'.[66]

Sturston 1780: 'cereals' = 4 combs per acre 'allowing for seed'.[67]

Henham 1793, farm accounts: 3.2 combs per acre.[68]

Henham 1794: 3.7 combs per acre.

Henham 1795: 6.3 combs per acre.

Henham 1796: 2.4 combs per acre.

[60] Thirsk and Imray, *Suffolk Farming*, p. 44.
[61] NRO, PD 132/22.
[62] NRO, NRS 16023
[63] NRO, INV III, 83.
[64] NRO, INV 70/8.
[65] NRO, NRS 20993 69 X 3.
[66] *Ibid.*
[67] NRO, WLS XXIX/2/30 416 X 4.
[68] ESRO, HA 11 C/628.

Henham 1797: 5 combs per acre.

Henham 1798: 3.9 combs per acre.

Henham 1799: 3.5 combs per acre.[69]

Area around Thetford 1801, predicted yields in the *House of Lords Report*: 3 to 3.5 combs per acre.[70]

Felbrigg 1802, glebe account: 5.75 combs per acre.[71]

Felbrigg 1803, glebe account: 6 combs per acre.[72]

1804, Arthur Young's estimates in the *General View*:

    Westwick: 6 combs per acre.

    Scottow: 6 combs per acre.

    North Walsham: 6 to 7 combs per acre.

    Haveringland: 5 to 7 combs per acre.

    Heydon: 5 combs per acre.

    Hackford, Reepham etc: 7 combs per acre.

    Average: *c.*6 combs per acre.[73]

Langford 1821, farm account: 3 combs per acre.[74]

Acid soils districts in general *c.*1837, Tithe File data: 4–6 combs per acre.[75]

Henham 1839, Richard Girling's farming journal: 7.5 combs per acre.[76]

Kessingland 1841, Richard Girling's farming journal: 9 combs per acre.[77]

Henham 1843, Richard Girling's farming journal: 10 combs per acre.[78]

Henham 1844, Richard Girling's farming journal: 12 combs per acre.

Henham 1847, Richard Girling's farming journal: 12 combs per acre.

Thingoe Hundred, Suffolk, 1849, from Raynbirds' *Suffolk Agriculture*: 7 combs per acre.[79]

Sudbourne 1855, farm account: 5 combs per acre.[80]

Sudbourne 1856, farm account: 7.2 combs per acre.[81]

Tottington *c.* 1860, estate valuation: 7 combs per acre.[82]

Once again, difficulties arise from the fact that the constituent regions – the Northern Heathlands, Breckland, and Sandlings – contain a rather varied range of soil types. Breckland was the most marginal of these regions: the Sandlings slightly less so; the Northern Heathlands the

[69] *Ibid.*
[70] PRO, HO 42/55, 305.
[71] NRO, WKC 5/233.
[72] *Ibid.*
[73] Young, *Norfolk*, p. 301.
[74] NRO, Petre Box 17/9.
[75] Kain, *Atlas*, pp. 51, 80.

[76] ESRO, JA 59.
[77] *Ibid.*
[78] *Ibid.*
[79] Raynbird and Raynbird, *Suffolk*, p. 143.
[80] ESRO, HA 28/50/23/4.4 (1–4).
[81] *Ibid.*
[82] NRO, WLS LX/9–18.

least, contained some pockets of fairly reasonable soils. Nevertheless, the broad pattern of development is clear enough – and in stark contrast to that observed in the clayland areas. During the first part of the period studied here wheat yields were remarkably low, and show no sign of an upward trend. The first eight records, covering the period before *c.* 1750, suggest an average yield of little over two combs per acre. By the last decades of the century significant gains had been made, with yields generally between four and five combs per acre – in other words, yields probably doubled on these soils in the second half of the century. Improvements continued to be made in the first half of the nineteenth century, gradually closing the gap with the clayland areas: by the 1840s and 1850s yields had reached 7 or even 7.5 combs per acre. Indeed, at Hengrave in the Suffolk Breckland in 1853 6.4 combs per acre was considered a poor yield. Overall, in the century after 1750 wheat yields in the acid soil areas of East Anglia probably trebled, an increase in productivity which was not matched by any other region.

Table 4. *Barley yields, acid soil districts*

Cressingham 1624, glebe account: 2.85 combs per acre.[83]

Cressingham 1625, glebe account: 2.82 combs per acre.

Cressingham 1627, glebe account: 2.875 combs per acre.

Colverston 1680, glebe account: 0.83 combs per acre.[84]

Horsham St Faiths 1682, probate inventory: 4.0 combs per acre.[85]

Oxburgh 1709, probate inventory: 2.125 combs per acre.[86]

Henham 1793, farm account: 3.48 combs per acre.[87]

Henham 1794, farm account: 6.2 combs per acre.

Henham 1795, farm account: 4.6 combs per acre.

Henham 1796, farm account: 5.6 combs per acre.

Henham 1797, farm account: 5.6 combs per acre.

Henham 1798, farm account: 7.4 combs per acre.

Henham 1799, farm account: 6.6 combs per acre

1801, predicted yields around Thetford: 6 to 8.5 combs per acre.[88]

Felbrigg 1802, glebe account: 7.8 combs per acre.[89]

Felbrigg 1803, glebe account: 7.8 combs per acre.

1804: Arthur Young's estimates in the *General View*.
   In Breckland generally: 5–6 combs per acre in a bad year, six to 8 in a good:
        implies an average of *c.*6–6.5 combs per acre.

[83] NRO, PD 132/22.

[84] NRO, KNY 575.

[85] NRO, NRS 16023.

[86] NRO, INV 70/8.

[87] ESRO, HA 11 C/628.

[88] PRO, HO 42/55, 305.

[89] NRO, WKC 5/233.

North Walsham: 8–9 combs per acre.

Scottow: 8 combs per acre.

Haveringland: 7–8 combs on the poorer land, 9–10 on the better.

Cawston: 10 combs per acre.

Hackford: 10 combs per acre.

Heydon: 8 combs per acre.

Thurning: 7–8 combs per acre.

Average: 8.2 combs per acre.[90]

Felbrigg 1805, glebe account: 7 combs per acre.[91]

Felbrigg 1808, glebe account: 5 combs per acre (specifically described as a 'poor crop').[92]

Langford 1821, estate account: 5.4 combs per acre.[93]

Henham 1845, Richard Girling's farming journal: 10.8 combs per acre.[94]

Henham 1846, Richard Girling's farming journal: 8 combs per acre.[831]

Thingoe Hundred, Suffolk, 1849, Raynbirds' estimates in *Suffolk Agriculture*: 9 combs per acre.[95]

Henham 1851, Richard Girling's farming journal: 9.5 combs per acre.[833]

Sudbourne 1855, farm account: 9 combs per acre.[96]

Sudbourne 1856, farm account: 9.3 combs per acre.[97]

Tottington 1860, farm valuation: 6.6 combs per acre.[98]

As with wheat, seventeenth and early eighteenth-century barley yields were pitifully low: only one record for the period before 1750 exceeds four combs per acre, and the average is around two and a half. By the end of the eighteenth century, however, when data becomes relatively abundant, yields had improved markedly. Seven records from Henham in the 1790s suggest an average of around five and a half combs per acre, but yields may have been rising fast at this time because the House of Lords Committee estimated that the 1801 harvest would produce, even in the region around Thetford (in the heart of Breckland), something in the order of 6–8.5 combs per acre. Young in 1804 reported yields as high as 10 combs per acre in parts of the Northern Heathlands; while four records from Felbrigg in the Northern Heathlands;, from the period 1802 – 1808, give an average yield of 6.9 combs per acre – and this includes one record (1808) of five combs per acre, explicitly described as 'a very poor crop'. That the latter figure was, nevertheless, perhaps double the average yields obtained a century earlier is ample testimony of the scale of the increase these poor lands had witnessed. Further gains in the course of the nineteenth century brought average yields to around nine combs per acre. Yields for barley in acid soil areas thus rose even more than those for wheat. Moreover, there are some

[90] Young, *Norfolk*, pp. 252–3.
[91] NRO, WKC5/233.
[92] *Ibid.*
[93] NRO, Petre Box 17/9.
[94] ESRO, JA 1/59.
[95] Raynbird and Raynbird, *Suffolk*, p. 143.
[96] ESRO, HA 28/50/23/4.4 (1–4).
[97] *Ibid.*
[98] NRO, WLS LX/9–18.

indications of differences in timing, in that wheat yields appear to have risen most rapidly in
the 'High Farming' era, while those for barley exhibit a more even rate of improvement over
the whole period studied here.

(iii) *The Flegg Loams*

Table 5. *Wheat yields, Flegg Loam region*

Thurne 1706, probate inventory: 6.25 combs per acre.[99]

Ormesby 1724, probate inventory: 6 combs per acre.[100]

Martham 1729, probate inventory: 4.55 combs per acre.[101]

Flegg district 1760s, estimates from Arthur Young's *Farmers Tour* of 1771: *c.*7 combs
per acre.[102]

Oxnead, Repton's yields published in Arthur Young's *General View* of 1804:
       1773–1777: average 5.6 combs per acre.
       1778–1782: average 6.55 combs per acre.
       1783–1787: average 7.2 combs per acre.
       1788–1792: average 7.45 combs per acre.
       1793–1797: average 7 combs per acre.
       1798–1800: average 7.4 combs per acre.[103]

1801, predicted yields around Yarmouth: 6 to 7 combs per acre.[104]

1804, estimate in Arthur Young's *General View*: 'Average of Flegg hundreds': 7 to 8
combs.[105]

Flegg loam district *c.* 1837, tithe file data: mainly 6 to 8 combs per acres.

Although the records are sparse, they suggest a different pattern to that exhibited by the regions
so far discussed. In the first half of the eighteenth century average wheat yields in Flegg were
between five and six combs per acre. By the end of the century, although he recorded some
phenomenal yields on individual farms, Young considered the *average* to have been between
seven and eight combs per acre. This is slightly higher than the figure for the area 'around
Yarmouth' (i.e., principally the district of the Flegg loams) predicted by the returns to the 1801
House of Lords enquiry, of between six and seven combs. In the 1830s, according to the tithe
files, wheat yields were still generally between six and eight combs per acre. In this region of
fertile soils the effects of the 'Agricultural Revolution', and in particular of 'High Farming',
were muted.

[99] NRO, INV II, 157.
[100] NRO, INV IV, 20.
[101] NRO, INV IV, 150.
[102] Young, *Farmer's Tour*, II, pp. 137–8.
[103] Young, *Norfolk*, pp. 301–2.
[104] PRO, HO 42/55, 305.
[105] Young, *Norfolk*, p. 300.

Table 6. *Barley yields, Flegg Loam region*

Thurne 1706, probate inventory: 7.5 combs per acre.[106]

Ormesby 1724, probate inventory: 5.6 combs per acre.[107]

Martham 1729, probate inventory: 3.8 combs per acre.[108]

Oxnead, Repton's yields published in Arthur Young's *General View* of 1804:

    1773–1777: average 7.6 combs per acre.

    1778–1782: 8.45 combs per acre.

    1783–1787: 8.55 combs per acre.

    1788–1792: 9.15 combs per acre.

    1793–1797: 8.65 combs per acre.

    1798–1800: 9.125 combs per acre.[109]

Predicted yields around 1801, Yarmouth district: 9 to 10 combs per acre.[110]

1804, estimate in Arthur Young's *General View*: average for Flegg, 9–11 combs, but as much as 14 at Happisburgh and Walcott, and in sporadic years far more.[111]

Flegg Loam district *c.* 1837, tithe file data: mainly 10–11 combs per acre.

This rather sparse evidence suggests a more significant improvement, with yields of around five and a half combs per acre in the early eighteenth century more or less doubling by 1800. To judge from the evidence of tithe files, however, there was little subsequent increase: most parishes recorded average yields of 10–11 combs per acre at this time.

(iv) *North-West Norfolk*

Table 7. *Wheat yields, North-West Norfolk*

North Creake 1675, probate inventory: 6.5 combs per acre.[112]

Snettisham 1711, probate inventory: 4.6 combs per acre.[113]

Shernbourne 1719, probate inventory: 4 combs per acre.[114]

Heacham 1721, probate inventory: 5 combs per acre.[115]

Kettlestone 1795, glebe account: 3.9 combs per acre.[116]

Kettlestone 1796, glebe account: 5.8 combs per acre.

Kettlestone 1797, glebe account: 5.6 combs per acre.

[106] NRO, INV II, 157.
[107] NRO, INV IV, 20.
[108] NRO, INV IV, 150.
[109] Young, *Norfolk*, pp. 252–3
[110] PRO, HO 42/55, 305.
[111] Young, *Norfolk*, p. 252.

[112] NRO, INV III, 144.
[113] NRO, INV IV, 221.
[114] NRO, INV 74b, 33.
[115] NRO, INV 74A, 222.
[116] NRO, PD 610/22.

Kettlestone 1798, glebe account: 8.7 comb per acre.

Kettlestone 1799, glebe account: 3.9 combs per acre

Kettlestone 1800, glebe account: 5.2 combs per acre.

1801, predicted yields around Kings Lynn 1801: 4–4.5 combs per acre.[117]

Kettlestone 1803, glebe account: 5 combs per acre.[118]

1804, Arthur Young's estimates in the *General View*:
    Burnham Westgate: 5 combs per acre.
    Holkham: 6 combs per acre.
    Holme: 'some very rich land': 8 to 12 combs, sometimes more'.
    Mr Hills Farm: 6 combs per acre.
    Snettisham: 8 combs per acre.
    Houghton: 5 combs per acre.
    Hillington: less than 4 combs per acre.[119]
    Average: *c.*6.5 combs per acre.

Langham *c.*1810, farm account:
    3 combs per acre (former heathland).
    5 combs per acre ('Middling land').
    7 combs per acre ('best land').[120]

North-West Norfolk *c.*1830, Caird's retrospective estimate of 1852 in *English Agriculture*: *c.*5.5 combs per acre.[121]

North-West Norfolk *c.*1837, tithe file data: mainly 4–6 combs per acre, but some parishes 6–8.

North-West Norfolk 1832–1839, estimate in Caird's *English Agriculture*: 6.25 combs per care.[122]

North-West Norfolk 1839–1846, estimate in Caird's *English Agriculture*: 7.25 combs per acre.

North-West Norfolk 1847/1848, estimate in Caird's *English Agriculture*: 9 combs per acre.

North-West Norfolk 1850, estimate in Caird's *English Agriculture*: *c.*10 combs per acre.

The available figures for North-West Norfolk are, like those from Flegg, somewhat sparse. Yields of around five combs per acre in the period up to the 1720s compare well with those for the years around 1800, variously estimated at between four and six and a half combs. Caird, writing in the 1850s, believed that local yields as late as the 1820s had been in the order of five and a half combs per acre, and this figure appears to be confirmed by the tithe files, which show that in the late 1830s average yields generally remained at less than 6 combs per acre, only a few

[117] PRO, HO 42/55, 305.
[118] NRO, PD 610/22.
[119] Young, *Norfolk*, p. 302.

[120] Parker, *Coke of Norfolk*, p. 97.
[121] Caird, *English Agriculture*, p. 171.
[122] *Ibid*

coastal parishes attaining more than this. However, the period *after c.*1830 saw a further and more rapid increase, or so contemporaries believed. Caird for example described how, on one farm in North-West Norfolk wheat yields for the period 1832 – 1839 averaged 6.25 combs per acre, but those for the following seven years leapt to 7.25, and those for the two years 1847/8 averaged no less than 9 combs per acre. Indeed, he noted that on some farms yields of as much as ten combs per acre were not uncommon. Similarly, C. S. Read, writing in 1856, believed that over the previous fifteen years wheat yields in this region had increased by around 2 combs per acre.

The available information for barley yields suggests a rather different pattern. The few available figures suggest that in the early eighteenth century yields of around 3 combs per acre were usual. By the early nineteenth century average yields were nearly three times this figure. In marked contrast to the pattern for wheat, however, there was little further improvement during the High Farming era: C. S. Read, while describing the major increases in wheat yields in the region, added that those for barley had 'not perceptibly increased'.

Table 8. *Barley yields, North-West Norfolk*

Swaffham 1708, probate inventory: 3 combs per acre.[123]

Snettisham 1711, probate inventory: 2.625 combs per acre.[124]

Shernbourne 1719, probate inventory: 3 combs per acre.[125]

Kettlestone 1795, glebe account: 8.28 combs per acre.[126]

Kettlestone 1796, glebe account: 6.37 combs per acre.

Kettlestone 1797, glebe account: 9.47 combs per acre.

Kettlestone 1798, glebe account: 9.3 combs per acre.

Kettlestone 1799, glebe account: 8 combs per acre.

Kettlestone 1800, glebe account: 8.6 combs per acre.

1801, predicted yields around Kings Lynn: 7–9 combs per acre.[127]

Kettlestone 1803, glebe account: 7.57 combs per acre.[128]

North-West Norfolk 1804, estimates in Arthur Young's *General View*: 8–10 combs per acre.[129]

Langham, *c.*1810, farm account:
    4 combs per acre (former heathland).
    6 combs ('Middling land').
    9 combs ('best land').[130]

[123] NRO, INV III, 45.
[124] NRO, INV IV, 109.
[125] NRO, INV 74b, 33.
[126] NRO, PD 610/22

[127] PRO, HO 42/55, 305
[128] NRO, PD 610/22
[129] Young, *Norfolk*, pp. 251, 254.
[130] Parker, *Coke of Norfolk*, p. 97.

North-West Norfolk *c.*1837, tithe file data: mainly 6–8 combs per acre, but in some coastal parishes as high as 11.

Burnham 1832–1839, information in Caird's *English Agriculture*: 7.75 combs per acre.
Burnham 1839–1846, information in Caird's *English Agriculture*: 8.25 combs per acre.
Burnham 1847–1849, information in Caird's *English Agriculture*: 11.25 combs per acre.[131]

The figures presented above are too few to be treated in a statistically rigorous way, but they do nevertheless suggest the broad regional groupings discussed here displayed different scales and chronologies of improvement. Were it possible to break the 'clayland' and 'acid soil' groups down still further, into their constituent regions, doubtless the degree of diversity would become still more apparent. Diversity is compounded by the fact that, in each regional group, the yields for wheat and barley generally exhibit markedly different trajectories. The overall pattern of development during the period of the 'Agricultural Revolution' can, however, be summarised fairly simply. Taking first the yields for wheat: while Flegg and North-West Norfolk displayed relatively minor increases, and the claylands exhibited steady growth, the acid soil areas saw a phenomenal improvement, with yields rising throughout the period at a rate of perhaps 1 per cent *per annum*. Yields for barley, in contrast, increased in all regions, although principally in the clayland and acid soil regions. Such diversity of experience, and in particular the fact that the more significant increases occurred in the more agriculturally marginal acid soil areas, was obvious to contemporaries. Thus C. S. Read observed in 1858 that:

As often happens, the greatest improvements have been made on some of the worst land. Naturally fertile soils have produced good rents and have grown good crops for centuries: it is on the lighter description of land that modern agriculture has chiefly progressed.[132]

This, however, was only partly true, for the claylands – always considered intrinsically fertile land – also witnessed a significant, if less dramatic, increase in cereal yields.

3. The impact of the new rotations

Improvements in yields per acre in the eighteenth century have usually been explained in terms of the new rotations, featuring turnips and artificial grasses or clover.[133] These had a significant impact on fertility because they increased the amount of nitrogen in the soil. In most medieval farming systems nitrogen was simply returned to the ploughsoil through breaking the course of cropping at intervals, with a year-long 'fallow': the spontaneous weed growth would be ploughed back in, thus restoring some nitrogen to the soil, and (more importantly) foraging livestock would dung the land. The new systems of cropping which developed in the post-medieval centuries raised the amounts of soil nitrogen in two ways. Legumes fixed atmospheric nitrogen directly; root crops increased the amount of stock which could be kept through the

131 Caird, *English Agriculture*.
132 Read, 'Recent Improvements', p. 266.
133 Sheil, 'Soil Fertility'.

134 Wade Martins and Williamson, *Randall Burroughes*, pp. 12–13.

winter, and thus the amounts of manure entering the soil.[134] The result of these developments, according to Sheil, were far-reaching:

> Increased use of leguminous crops as fodder for animals resulted in a greater input of nitrogen to the soil, and this facilitated an increase in the growth of extractive crops such as cereals. Perennial forage legumes fix about twice as much nitrogen as pulses and, together with the switch from grass-dominated permanent grassland to rotational grasses and clover, resulted in a massive rise in the recurrent input of nitrogen.[135]

But it was not simply the use of the new crops *per se* which was important. It was the scale on which they were used, and the ways in which they were incorporated within rotations. In most versions of the improved rotations the nitrogen fixed by the clover was utilised rapidly by the cereal courses, instead of (as in convertible or 'up and down' farming systems) accumulating to no good purpose over several years.

Mark Overton has argued that the rapid rise in cereal yields which the probate inventory evidence suggests occurred in the late seventeenth and early eighteenth centuries cannot easily be ascribed to the adoption of these new crops and rotations because – to judge from the same source – neither turnips nor clover were being cultivated together on a sufficient scale to have made the required difference.[136] The rather different body of evidence examined here suggests that this is an oversimplification. Improved rotations of various kinds *were* widely adopted in East Anglia in this period, and must certainly have been an important factor in increasing yields: by the 1750s, the use of clover was widespread and turnips were only absent from field rotations in places where environmental constraints – waterlogging or soil acidity – or institutional ones – especially the foldcourse – prevented their cultivation. To some extent it might be argued that the increase in yields which occurred in the second half of the eighteenth century simply reflects the gradual removal or amelioration of the various factors limiting the further spread of 'improved' rotations. But there is one problem with this explanation. The main way the new crops improved yields was by increasing the numbers of animals which could be kept, and thus the amount of manure which could be applied to the land. But so far as the evidence goes, the ratio of livestock to arable acres in East Anglia did not significantly increase, and may even have fallen, in the period between *c.* 1750 and 1820.

This might appear a surprising assertion to many readers, not least because it would reverse the trend apparent in previous periods, studied by Overton and Campbell. They employed a combination of manorial accounts and probate inventories to suggest a near doubling of livestock densities between 1250 and 1740, much of which took place between the late sixteenth and the early eighteenth centuries: between 1584–1599, and 1710–1740, densities rose from 54.1 livestock units per 100 sown acres, to 67.9.[137] Subsequent developments in stocking densities are less easy to trace, not only because the evidence is sparse but also because it often represents a snap-shot of the situation at a certain point in time, whereas in reality the numbers of livestock on a farm could fluctuate markedly from month to month, and even from week to week. Cattle were bought in as a short-term speculation when prices were low and the farmer had a few

135 Sheil, 'Soil Fertility', p. 76.
136 Overton, 'Determinants', pp. 313–15.

137 Campbell and Overton, 'A new perspective', pp. 83–8.

turnips to spare: those who fattened stock were constantly buying and selling through the winter as, on the one hand, animals were ready for market, and on the other as the supply of fodder fluctuated. Nor is it always clear how far the stock appearing in particular records were being grazed on open heaths and marshes, rather than solely on the enclosed land of the farm itself.

In this context, the records relating to a tithe dispute in Flixton in the 1790s are particularly informative. These describe the numbers of stock kept on three farms, and the details of their movements, between November 1791 and June 1792.[138] On one farm twelve bullocks were kept on hay in a paddock at Flixton from March to April, and then moved to a neighbouring parish. Four were sold in early June and the rest moved on again. Twenty Scots and eleven Irish bullocks were kept on the Waveney marshes from April 1792 through the summer, and five steers were at Flixton for the whole year.[139] In a similar way, grazing within a farm might be leased out to another individual: at Henham in 1794, although many sheep were kept on the home farm, some of the stubbles were let to other graziers.[140]

Nevertheless, the available evidence does allow us to make some general observations about stocking densities. The most interesting evidence comes from the Central Claylands. In the late seventeenth and early eighteenth centuries, to judge from Overton and Campbell's figures, most farms had between 0.6 and 1.2 livestock units per cropped acre, although a minority had slightly more.[141] Only the ratio between the numbers of livestock and the *cropped* acreage can be calculated from probate inventories, of course, because the total area of the farm (including meadows and pasture), and any right of common grazing attached to it, are not given in this source. As we have seen, on clayland farms in this period only around 33 per cent, and often as little as 25 per cent, of the acreage was under cultivation, the rest of the land taking the form of permanent pasture or long grass leys. Actual livestock densities, in other words – that is, the number of livestock kept on a farm divided by its total acreage – must have been in the order of 0.15 – 0.4 units per acre. It is interesting to compare these figures with those which can be calculated from the information provided by Sir John Walsham for the average numbers of livestock kept in various parts of East Anglia in 1854. These indicate that clayland farms had, on average, between 0.2 and 0.35 livestock units per acre: clearly suggesting that there had been no increase, and probably some reduction, in stocking densities during the eighteenth and early nineteenth centuries. But the figures are, in fact, more intriguing than this, for the later eighteenth century saw a steady reduction in the area of grassland on the clays, and a doubling of that under cereal crops. Even if the number of animals per acre had doubled, in other words – which it clearly did not – the quantity of manure supplied to each cropped acre would only have remained the same.

This surprising conclusion is supported by fragments of documentary evidence. A tithe account for Stansfield, drawn up in *c.*1760, provides figures from which stocking densities can

[138] ESRO, E1/3/57 and 58.

[139] ESRO, HA 12 E1/3 57 and 58.

[140] ESRO, HA 11/6/28

[141] See the map in Overton and Campbell, 'Norfolk Livestock Farming', p. 390. We have followed their method of calculating livestock densities, which was itself taken from J. A. Yelling, 'Probate inventories and the geography of livestock farming: a study of East Worcestershire', *Trans. Institute of British Geographers* 51 (1970). This calculates stocking units according to the nutritional needs of the livestock in question: total stocking density = (horses × 1.0) + (oxen, cows, bulls × 1.2) + (immature cattle × 0.8) + (sheep × 0.1).

be calculated for ten farms: a total of 759 acres, 223 stocking units, or an average of 0.29 per acre.[142] By a remarkable coincidence, another account for the same parish, drawn up in *c.* 1808, gives figures for eight farms: a total of 678 cropped acres with 165 stocking units, an average of only 0.24 per acre.[143] The latter figure is higher than the total parish figures given in the Mattishall tithe account for the 1780s, of 0.14 units per acre; higher than the 0.102 implied in Randall Burroughes' journal for 1799; but much the same as the 0.26 units per acre which can be calculated from the detailed, month-by-month figures for three farms submitted in connection with the tithe dispute at Flixton in the 1790s, referred to above.[144] There are many problems with these figures, we freely admit, but it seems unlikely that the ratio of livestock to sown acres increased significantly on clayland farms in the century after 1750.

Although we have less direct evidence, it is clear that the situation was similar on the lighter lands of East Anglia. In North-West Norfolk, for example, probate inventories suggest that most farms had between 0.3 and 0.6 livestock units per cropped acre in the early eighteenth century. Most parishes here had, however, between a quarter and a third of their land under permanent grass at this time – the extensive heaths and sheepwalks – so that the real stocking density must have been around 0.25–0.4 units per acre. The probate figures, moreover, are probably distorted by the exclusion of large numbers of sheep grazed in the foldcourse flocks, so these figures may be a serious underestimate. Bearing this in mind, it is difficult to believe that there had been much improvement when Walsham recorded – for the Docking Union, which comprises the major part of this region – stocking levels of only 0.21 units per acre.[145] And this, needless to say, was at a time when the area under arable cultivation had been greatly increased, through enclosure and reclamation.

In spite of frequent claims that increases in yields in the eighteenth century resulted from higher stocking densities, consequent on the adoption of new rotations, there is little evidence to support this assertion. In fact, what the improved rotations really achieved was an expansion of the cultivated acreage without a concomitant diminution in the numbers of animals being kept.

We have already noted that the total cultivated acreage of the two counties probably increased by over 50 per cent in the period 1750 – 1820. The cultivation of root crops and turnips, combined with the stall feeding of cattle, allowed this increased acreage to be kept fertile. Not only was more manure produced, but it was used more effectively. This was particularly true of cattle dung. Half the nitrogen and more than half the potassium is contained in the urine, and when simply dropped in the field most is simply leached away. In a yard or feeding shed a much higher proportion is retained, absorbed by the bedding. The same is true of the dung, half the nitrogen in which volatises within 48 hours if dropped directly on the ground.[146] The gradual adoption of oil cake during the first three decades of the nineteenth century may have increased stocking levels, but again it was the quality of manure which was emphasised by

[142] WSRO, FL 627/3/18.

[143] WSRO, FL 627/3/21.

[144] Gonville and Caius College, Cambridge, Smith note-book; Wade Martins and Williamson, *Randall Burroughes*, p. 10, 25; ESRO, HA 12 E1/3 57 and 58.

[145] *Reports of Poor Law Inspectors on Agricultural Statistics (England), 1854*, in BPP 1854–5, LIII.

[146] L. S. Thompson, *Soils and fertility* (second edn, 1957), pp. 190–8.

contemporaries: Bacon thought 'the increased use of artificial feeds for fattening' had enhanced the quality of farmyard manure by between 20 and 40 per cent.[147]

In short, the continued spread of the new rotations may have been a significant factor in raising yields in the period after 1740, but – assuming that the above calculations are at least roughly correct – it is hard to believe that it was the only or main factor. Indeed, rather than ascribe increases in productivity to one particular cause or set of causes, the evidence reviewed so far suggests that they were achieved by a combination of factors, which varied from region to region: factors which included changes in the farming framework, as much as in farming practice.

4. Changing the environment

(i) *Improvement on the Claylands*

The increase in cereal yields on clayland farms in the period c.1750–1840 – from approximately five to seven combs per acre for wheat, and five to 8½combs for barley – were almost certainly due in large measure to improvements in drainage. As modern research has shown, poor drainage retards crop growth in a number of ways.[148] Fields which lie wet for much of the winter do not warm up so rapidly in the spring as drier land: implements cannot be got on to them so quickly, and cultivation starts later. More significantly, waterlogged crops do not take up nutrients well, and their root structure is poorly developed: the removal of stagnant surface water allows root systems to develop to a greater depth.

> In the development of crops the early stages of growth are of great, even vital importance and on this growth soil temperature has a potent influence. Its response to increasing sunshine in the spring is greatly influenced by drainage conditions.[149]

Drainage also helps soil structure: the pore space within the soil is increased, and aeration improved. Paradoxically, this increases the amount of water which can be taken up by the plant, and reduces the natural droughtiness of clay soils, because the roots can derive moisture from a greater depth.

Not only would improved drainage have benefited cereal crops directly. It was also a necessary precondition for the successful adoption of the new rotations; for turnips are particularly susceptible to waterlogging, and the tightly-packed nature of permanently or seasonally water-logged soils makes it difficult to 'pull' the crop, so that it has to be fed off in the field. This can itself increase problems with structure and drainage, for large numbers of animals (especially if closely folded) serve to compact the soil.

Contemporaries had no doubt that drainage increased clayland yields in the century after 1750, and it is surprising that modern historians have so neglected its effects. '... Draining has been effected at enormous outlay', wrote Glyde in 1856, 'but from the great increase in production, no one questions the propriety of the expenditure'.[150] Glyde specifically asserted that it was because of underdrainage that average yields on the clays for wheat had increased, between

---

[147] Bacon, *Agriculture*, p. 111.
[148] Robinson, *Fream's Agriculture*, pp. 36–9.

[149] *Ibid*, p. 36.
[150] Glyde, *Suffolk in the nineteenth century*, p. 338.

1770 and 1850, from 24 bushels per acre to 32: a rise, that is, of *c.*33 per cent.[151] The Raynbirds, too, emphasised the central importance of underdrainage in the improvement of Suffolk agriculture: as did their various correspondents. 'Draining and the peculiar system of drill husbandry have rendered it [the claylands] one of the finest corn districts in England'.[152] According to Caird, 'The chief characteristic of Suffolk agriculture is the success with which heavy land farming is carried on … Drainage is of course the primary improvement on this description of land'.[153] And it was not just agricultural writers who voiced such a view. The rector of Stansfield in Suffolk in 1808, for example, commenting on the local farming population, remarked favourably of one young man that he had 'at great expense with land drains on his farm which is the most effective method in this country to get good crops'.[154] The improvement was a particularly attractive one because, although the cost was high, the benefits were almost immediate: as the agent for the Ashburnham estate asserted in 1830, those who undertook to underdrain their land were 'reimbursed by the first crop'.[155]

Poor drainage, rather than nutrient-deficiency, was the main problem facing farmers on these inherently fertile soils; and the period of maximum increase in yields appears to coincide with that in which the practice of underdrainage spread most rapidly. Once this improvement had become widespread the potential for further improvement in yields was limited. Neither Caird, nor the Raynbirds, nor Glyde, make much reference to the use of artificial fertilisers in this region in the middle decades of the nineteenth century, emphasising instead their importance on the lighter lands of East Anglia. Significantly, yields did not rise so markedly here in the 'High Farming' period as they did on the lighter, acid soils. It is also noteworthy that it was the yields for barley, rather than those for wheat, which displayed the most dramatic improvement in the course of the eighteenth and nineteenth centuries. This is just what we would expect, if drainage was a key factor, for barley is more susceptible than wheat to the effects of waterlogging.[156]

Drainage was the crucial improvement on the clays, but other changes to the farming environment may have helped to boost yields. Claying was widely carried out when fields were converted from pasture to tillage, but also occasionally in other circumstances. Arthur Biddell of Hill Farm, Playford, noted in 1817 how he had:

> Thrashed 6 comb wheat & 3 Pecks from Lollys – 1c. 3¾b grew upon 2 stetches that had no clay upon them and 4c. 1¼b on 4 stetches that had been clayed in the Dec[em]b[e]r & Jan[ua]ry of 1815 and 1816 – shewing an advantage by the clay, in the produce of wheat after the rate of about 3 bushels per acre.[157]

In part, claying served to neutralise the soil acidity which resulted from the effects of a high natural water table: significantly, it was usually carried out in association with schemes of underdrainage. We would also draw attention to the widespread rationalisation of field boundaries, and the reduction in the quantity of hedgerow timber, which occurred in clayland areas in the period after 1750. While the scale of these changes can scarcely be compared with the 'prairification' of the eastern counties which has occurred since the Second World War,

[151] *Ibid*, p. 349.
[152] Raynbird and Raynbird, *Suffolk*, p. 7.
[153] Caird, *English Agriculture*, p. 152.
[154] ESRO, FL 627/3/21

[155] ESRO, HB4/2.
[156] Hanley, *Practical Farming*, p. 109.
[157] Thirsk and Imray, *Suffolk Farming*, p. 40.

the nature of the benefits would have been similar. Large amounts of hedgerow timber would have damaged field crops, both through overshadowing and through 'drip'. In addition, some kinds of hedgerow trees (most notably ash and elm) throw out long superficial rootstrands into the adjacent fields, robbing the soil of nutrients.[158] Reducing the number and size of hedges might also have brought improvements in vermin and weed control. Whatever the precise effects of removing excess trees and hedges, contemporaries were clear that it increased yields, and thus the value of farms. In 1750 it was thought that marling and cutting down trees would together raise the rental value of Flixton Park Farm from £156 to £200.[159]

(ii) *Improvement on acid soils*

The key improvement on the acid lands of East Anglia was marling: this was the foundation stone of the 'Agricultural Revolution', and contemporaries knew it. Almost all lighter land in England is to some extent acidic: but this is especially true in East Anglia, where such soils are mostly developed over base-poor substrates. The easily-exchangeable bases held by soil colloids are steadily leached – that is, removed in solution by rainwater, which is slightly acid due both to the CO_2 in the atmosphere, and to the various decay products of humus. 'Light, sandy soils have the lowest capacity for holding exchangeable lime and, being freely drained, lose this lime rapidly by leaching. It is therefore on such soils that soil acidity most commonly occurs'.[160] The normal loss of lime from cultivable soils is from

> 1 cwt to 4 cwt (as CaO) per acre per year. Besides these losses from the soil by natural drainage, the crops themselves extract amounts of lime each year, since it is an essential plant constituent, and if the crop is not returned to the soil again by ploughing in, a certain amount of lime is removed from it.[161]

Lime is essential for plant growth. In addition, high soil acidity enhances the solubility (and hence the availability) of certain harmful elements, such as aluminium and manganese, and encourages a number of fungal pests and diseases. Moreover, as with underdraining on the clays, marling not only increased yields in its own right. It also allowed the cultivation of key crops on a scale which would otherwise have been impossible. Turnips are liable to fail completely on sour land, and are particularly prone to attack by finger-and-toe disease.[162] Red clover is also susceptible to acidity, and often fails to reach the seedling stage.[163] We should also note that lime benefits the soil environment more generally, by encouraging a variety of important micro-organisms. In particular, nitrogen is converted into nitrites by soil bacteria which are highly susceptible to acidity. The state of soil acidity was thus of crucial importance in the adoption of the new rotations, for without a healthy microbe population any increased applications of farmyard manure resulting from the new rotations would have been pointless: they could simply not have been broken down. This explains the significance of Bacon's words, that Norfolk husbandry was a 'union of high manuring and an appropriate application of the calcareous soils'.[164] Equally important, perhaps, was the fact that the presence or absence of

---

[158] R. P. Wright (ed.), *The standard cyclopedia of modern agriculture and rural economy* (1908), p. 252.

[159] ESRO, HA 12/E1/5/86.

[160] Robinson, *Fream's Agriculture*, p. 33.

[161] *Ibid.*

[162] *Ibid*; Hanley, *Practical Farming*, pp. 92–9.

[163] *Ibid*, p. 109.

[164] Bacon, *Agriculture*, p. 267.

such bacteria also effects the extent to which clover fixes atmospheric nitrogen in the soil. In short, not only could the key crops of the agricultural revolution not have been successfully cultivated on acid soils without extensive marling: even if they could have been, few of their principal benefits would have been realised.

We have already noted that the most significant recorded increases in yields per acre in eighteenth-century East Anglia occurred on the acid soils. Contemporaries certainly believed that much of this improvement was the result of marling. Bacon for example quoted an account of a farm in Threxton, on the edge of the Norfolk Breckland. 'In the interval between 1732 and 1742, six thousand three hundred and seventy-eight loads of marl were carried on this farm' resulting in an increase in production from 442 combs of all crops (peas, tares, rye, wheat, barley and clover seed) to 1648 combs (the acreage of the farm is unfortunately not given, nor a break-down of the increases of the different crops).[165]

All this is not to deny the importance of the new rotations. Indeed, their role in raising yields – through increasing manure production – was doubtless greater here than in the claylands, for nutrients are more easily leached out of these light soils and thus need constant replacement. In this context, it is noteworthy that in the nineteenth century the use of artificial fertilisers was a more important feature on light lands than on heavy.

We have already noted that although cereal yields rose steadily on these acid soils throughout the eighteenth and early nineteenth centuries, those for barley seem to have increased slightly more than those for wheat. In part this may have been because barley was more vulnerable to excess acidity than wheat: 'Barley is one of our most lime-sensitive crops, and to attempt the production of a malting sample on sour soil is to assay the impossible'. But it was also, as Read explained, because of the crop's position in the four-course rotation, which ensured that it always received more manure than wheat, following as it did the well-dunged turnip crop (wheat was autumn-sown, before the winter muck-spreading season).[166] It was not until artificial fertilisers came into widespread use, as a top-dressing in the spring, that wheat yields increased at a faster rate than those for barley. Barley did not respond well to ever-higher inputs of fertiliser. As Read observed,

> This grain will not bear more forcing; even now too much stimulant is frequently applied, the crop lodges, destroys its own quality, and kills the grass seeds.[167]

(iii) North-West Norfolk and Flegg

Flegg and North-West Norfolk were both areas in which increases in wheat yields were comparatively muted during the eighteenth and early nineteenth centuries, with only barley showing significant improvement. In the case of Flegg the reasons are fairly straightforward. The light loams characteristic of the region required no draining and are naturally highly fertile. The fattening of bullocks on turnips was already well-established here at an early date, and there was thus little scope for further increases in soil nitrogen through additional inputs of manure. Some benefit could be gained from marling, for the soils here are in places mildly acidic, and this practice was widespread by the later eighteenth century. The impact of this, the only

---

[165] Bacon, *Agriculture*, pp. 268–76.
[166] Read, 'Recent Improvements', p. 276.
[167] *Ibid*, p. 277.

significant improvement available to Flegg farmers, is reflected in the fact that barley yields showed a greater improvement than those for wheat in the second half of the eighteenth century. The yields of neither crop improved much in the course of the nineteenth century, however. This was not a region where lack of soil nutrients was a significant problem, and high inputs of artificial manures could be positively harmful, leading to 'lodging', especially in the case of barley.

The lack of significant increases in wheat yields in North-West Norfolk is more difficult to explain and, given the prominence of this region in conventional accounts of the 'Agricultural Revolution', somewhat surprising. The explanation probably lies in the region's topography – in the contrast between the fertile calcareous loams of the lower ground and the poor acid soils of the uplands. The scope for improvement on the former soils through underdraining was nil, and only limited through marling. The gains to be made through adopting the new rotations perhaps not that great, for this long-established arable land had always received the night tathe of the vast foldcourse flocks. At the same time, *average* yields from the region as a whole were depressed by the expansion of arable farming on to the poorer soils of the acid uplands. Extensive marling and intensive manuring allowed these areas to be profitably cultivated, but they always produced poorer crops than the older-cultivated land, as contemporaries were well aware: at Langham Farm in *c.*1810 a barley yield of only four combs per acre was recorded from 'former heathland', in contrast to the six combs from 'Middling land' and nine from the 'best land'.[168] The fact that barley yields increased significantly while those for wheat did not presumably indicates, once again, the crucial importance of marling on the acid soils of the uplands.

There was a contrast here with the situation in most other light-land regions of East Anglia, such as Breckland or the Northern Heathlands. Here, there was always less of a contrast between the best and the worst soils: *all* were (and are) relatively marginal because of inherent acidity, and all can therefore be improved through a combination of intensive marling and large-scale applications of manure. The very worst soils in these regions, moreover, were only under the plough for a relatively short period, the boom years of the Napoleonic Wars, and then reverted to grass. Average yields within these regions therefore increased markedly from their low level at the start of the eighteenth century, while improvements in North-West Norfolk were less striking.

This contrast between calcareous valley soils, and acid uplands, may also explain why yields in North-West Norfolk began to rise more rapidly during the nineteenth century, and especially in the period of 'High Farming'. There were no further attempts at enclosure or reclamation here – the entire area, more or less, was now under the plough – so that average yields were no longer being depressed by the breaking in of more marginal land. In this period substantial applications of artificial manures allowed massive increases in wheat yields, on calcareous and acid soils alike, although improvements in barley were, as noted above, more marginal.

---

[168] Parker, *Coke of Norfolk*, p. 97.

5. Expanding production

Yields increased dramatically in the period, but the greatest gains were made on the poorest lands, where they rose from abysmally low levels. Indeed, in terms of yields per acre, the eighteenth century saw, not so much an *overall* increase in productivity, but an evening-out of regional variations as the yields from areas of poor, acid soil caught up with those from more fertile and heavier land. By the Victorian period, following the abandonment of some of the most marginal land brought into cultivation during the Napoleonic War years, yields for wheat and barley were much the same in all districts, at around eight and ten combs per acre respectively. Given that the areas of poorest, most acid soils had, in 1700, been turning in yields less than a third of these, the achievement was great indeed.

Nevertheless, it was probably the expansion of the cultivated acreage which contributed most to increased grain production in East Anglia. As we have seen, the area of land under arable cultivation in East Anglia may have risen in the period *c.*1700–1850 from *c.*40 per cent to *c.*65 per cent. Against this, it should be noted that the resultant increase in production was less than these bald figures imply, for expansion was only made possible by the adoption of forms of rotation which involved *less intensive* courses of cereal cropping. Whereas in most parts of East Anglia in the late seventeenth century rotations had featured two cropped years in three, rising in some cases to three in four or even four in five, by 1850 many farmers were employing the Norfolk four-course, or its five-course variant, and were therefore taking only two cereal crops every four years, or three in every five. As we have no precise information about the relative proportions of land farmed under systems of differing intensity in either period, the actual extent to which the area of land under cereal crops at any one time changed remains obscure: but it is clear that it did not rise by the same amount as the changes in the raw arable/pasture ratio might suggest. A reasonable estimate would be that in *c.*1700 around 70 per cent of the arable acreage was under cereal crops each year: John Walsham's figures show that by the 1850s this had fallen to *c.*56 per cent. If we accept these broad calculations, it seems likely that the area of farmland under cereal crops in any one year increased, in the period 1700–1850, by around 28 per cent.

This is a significant increase, but it certainly underestimates the true impact on cereal production. This is because the greatest increase in the cultivated area occurred in the Fens and in the various clayland regions, which contain East Anglia's most naturally fertile soils (other than those found in Flegg, where there was little increase in the cropped acreage in this period). These soils could sustain intensive cropping with much lower inputs of manure and, later, fertilisers than the light soil areas, where yields were generally lower. It was the shift from pasture to arable which occurred in this period on these fertile lands which, more than anything else, made East Anglia the grain-basket of nineteenth-century England.

The evidence presented in this volume confirms, therefore, that increases in grain production were achieved both by raising yields per acre, and by increasing the sown acreage. Yet it may also suggest that the relative contribution made by these two developments changed over time. Up until the second half of the eighteenth century increased production was mainly achieved by raising output on existing arable land, probably for the most part by adopting new crops and rotations. From the 1760s, the main gains were achieved through expanding the sown acreage, although yields per acre continued to increase, largely perhaps because of underdraining, marling and other changes to the farming framework. The continued spread of the new crops and rotations also doubtless benefited yields but their real significance was that they allowed stocking levels (and thus manure inputs) to be maintained even as the area under pasture steadily declined. After *c.*1840 the expansion of the arable acreage slowed down: the main increases in production were now once again achieved by raising yields per acre, partly though further refinements in drainage, but largely through the use of materials produced outside the farm which could, directly or indirectly, raise soil fertility: artificial fertilisers, and oil cake.

CHAPTER VI

The Improvers

1. Landlords and tenants

Traditionally, the story of the Agricultural Revolution has emphasised the key role of land-owners, and especially the owners of large estates in North-West Norfolk: most notably Charles, Second Viscount Townshend, who owned Raynham from 1687 until 1738; and Thomas William Coke, who inherited Holkham in 1776. Such men reclaimed land on a grand scale, set an example in new farming methods, and actively encouraged their tenants to adopt new practices. There were dissenting voices from this orthodoxy as early as the eighteenth century: Marshall argued that 'improvement' really began with the smaller tenants and owner-occupiers of north-east Norfolk.[1] Nevertheless, the traditional view still commands widespread support.[2]

Although it is sometimes implied that landowners and tenants worked together to improve the productivity of agriculture, in reality their economic interests were different. The tenant's interest was in winning the maximum amount of produce from the soil during the duration of his tenancy; the landlord's main concern was with the long-term value of his property; and the balance of power between the two was largely determined by the overall profitability of agriculture. At times of recession, when it was difficult to attract tenants, the landlord had to take on the costs of most permanent improvements himself, and was in no position to dictate to the tenant over matters of farming. In 1740 the agent at Flixton reported that he could not collect the rent. He had threatened 'the tenants with distraining on them, which they tell me I may do and take the farms in hand, in which case I am sure I would be worse off'.[3] When agricultural prices were rising, in contrast, the landowners were in a better position to pass costs of improvement on to tenants, and also to demand husbandry practices which would enhance the long-term value of the land.

East Anglia became, in the course of the period studied here, an increasingly arable region, and while (as we have seen) the profits to be made from livestock remained central to the economy of many farms, grain prices were the main determinant of farm profitability by the later eighteenth century. The early eighteenth century was a time of fairly static arable prices, but in the period after 1750 prices rose, although even so there were sporadic slumps, like that in the 1780s.[4] Profits rose fast during the Napoleonic Wars. The 1820s, however, brought another downturn: a particularly serious one for farmers who had borrowed heavily during the boom years. The number of farm sales advertised in the *Norfolk News* rose dramatically. Even the

---

[1] Marshall, *Rural Economy*, I, p. 2.

[2] For the classic statement of this orthodox position, see Riches, *Agricultural Revolution* and its restatement in Chambers and Mingay, *Agricultural Revolution*.

[3] ESRO, HD 148/7/14/1.

[4] Thomas De Grey of Merton described how 'Our

farms in the open country have suffered much from two dry summers and winters unusually severe'. They were worth 20 per cent less than three years previously and the tenant at Langford had failed. NRO, WLS XXIX/2/19 416 X 4.

stock of Mr Purdy of Castle Acre, a well-known Holkham tenant, was sold to pay off creditors in October 1822.[5] By the late 1830s, however, conditions were improving again, and confidence returned, although there was recurrent anxiety about the imminent repeal of the Corn Laws. There was in fact no recession following their repeal in 1846, although the years from 1848 to 1852 saw a steady, if unspectacular, fall in prices. The 1850s, however, saw a sustained return of prosperity and confidence, and 'High Farming' continued to flourish, until the Depression of the late 1870s.

Rents closely mirrored farm prices. On the Wolterton estate, for example, those for the Burnham and Barsham farms rose from £2102 in 1760 to £5217 in 1817: insufficient records survive to be sure that the area of the estate had remained constant in the intervening years, but the trend is clear enough.[6] Conversely, in the immediate post-War years reductions had to be made: in 1822 rents here were reduced by 20 per cent. On the Holkham estate rents similarly went down dramatically at this time, by 6 per cent between 1820 and 1829.[7] The 1830s and 1840s saw, however, a sustained recovery in rental incomes: in general it was said that rents rose by between 10 per cent and 20 per cent between 1834 and 1843.[8] There was some pause in this trend during the late 1840s and early 1850s, and on some estates – as at Chediston, in Suffolk[9] – reductions were made. But for the most part the middle decades of the century saw a steady upward trend. On the Heydon estate, where rents had risen fast during the Napoleonic Wars and dropped dramatically in the 1820s, they were rising again by 1840, and rose steadily thereafter to a peak in 1878.[10] The pattern on the Earsham estate was similar, while on the neighbouring Adair estate rental income nearly doubled between 1838 and 1878, from £10,711 to £19,465. These figures confirm more general estimates, from the Royal Commission on Agriculture of 1882, that rents rose by around 25 per cent in East Anglia between 1852 and the 1880s.[11]

It was not only rents which were effected by the character of farm profitability, but the whole character of the landlord/tenant relationship. In 1722, during one of the worst periods of the early eighteenth-century recession, the agent at Glemham (Suffolk) wrote that there were a great many farms to let: 'I fear landlords must comply with their tenants upon terms not altogether agreeable, if times hold this bad'.[12] During the slump of the 1780s Thomas de Grey described to his brother how 'An advantage is certainly taken of the times and even this present season is much against the interests of the landlord. I hear of farms to be let in every part of the country'.[13] He went on to describe recent negotiations with Abel Smith, a prospective tenant: 'The Norfolk farmers have long ceased to be humble dependants; we must therefore bear with their language which is to be treated on equal terms. If you wish to be master of your estate, you must reject Mr Smith; if you wish for ease and less profit, you must accept him on the best terms that can be made'.[14] Walsingham was still unsure as to whether to accept Smith, and in his next letter, De Grey persisted: 'The time has been when landlords dictated to their

[5] Wade Martins, *Black Faces*, p. 38.
[6] Wolterton Hall archives, WOLT 3/3/1.
[7] Wade Martins, *Great Estate*, p. 101.
[8] NRO, MF/RO 10.
[9] Thirsk and Imray, *Suffolk Farming*, pp. 96–7.
[10] NRO, BUL 16/4, 705 X 6; 16/276/1–12 X 5; 11/66 615

X 6; 11/68 615 X 6; 11/288 614 X 8; 11/290 617 X 2.
[11] BPP, 1882, XIV, p. 179.
[12] ESRO, HA 49/4/14.
[13] NRO, WLS XXIX/2/20 416 X 4.
[14] NRO, WLS XXIX/2/23 416 X 4.

tenants, but that has passed long ago ... I know not how to advise – in one of the Norwich papers of last week only there were 27 sales of the various stock of farmers'.[15] In times of recession the tenant thus called the shots; in times of boom, as in the decades either side of 1800, landlords were in the position of strength. This neat relationship becomes less apparent in the middle decades of the nineteenth century. This was another period of high prices, but 'High Farming' demanded high levels of investment both from the landowner and from the tenant, and the need to attract farmers with the necessary capital became more pressing than ever.

2. The lease

According to the traditional view of the East Anglian agricultural revolution, leases were the key instrument through which landowners influenced the farming practices of their tenants: and these were pioneered by the great estates, especially in North-West Norfolk. Only gradually did smaller landowners elsewhere follow their example. Leases could be used to promote 'improved' farming in three ways. Firstly, they could – unlike yearly tenancies at will – provide the farmer with a measure of long- or medium-term security, and thus give him an incentive to invest in improvements. Secondly, they could be used to frame co-operative ventures of land reclamation and improvement: as Kent put it in 1796, 'Without leases no marling to any extent would have been undertaken, nor so much ground brought into cultivation by one-third as there now is'.[16] Thirdly, leases could formally stipulate practices which were beneficial to the farm, by – for example – laying down a particular course of husbandry which the tenant was to follow.

Contemporaries were convinced of the importance of leases: in Kent's words, 'That leases are the first, the greatest and most rational encouragement that can be given to agriculture admits not of a doubt ... In this county it is rather the fashion to grant leases, which in great measure accounts for the improvements that have taken place in it'.[17] Some modern historians have supported this view. In 1953 Habbakuk listed the lease and its covenants as one of the main ways in which landlords could influence farming on their estates, albeit within certain limits.[18] Others, however, have been more cautious, suggesting that leases were merely a 'loose framework' within which the landlord and tenant could work, and that in a system in which landlords required good tenants just as farmers required good landlords, a system of annual tenancies could be just as secure.[19] In the case of eighteenth-century Nottinghamshire it has been suggested that leasehold tenants were not characterised by any greater propensity to improve than those with annual tenancies.[20]

Nevertheless, those who have studied the early development of leases on the two legendary Norfolk estates of Raynham and Holkham have argued an important role for them. James

[15] NRO, WLS XXIX/2/23 416 X 4.

[16] Kent, *Norfolk*, p. 123.

[17] *Ibid.*

[18] H. J. Habbakuk, 'Economic functions of English land- owners in the seventeenth and eighteenth centuries', *Explorations in Entrepreneurial History*, 9 (1953), pp. 92–102.

[19] C. Clay, 'Landlords and estate management in England', in *Agrarian History*, V (ii), p. 229.

[20] J. V. Beckett, *The Aristocracy in England, 1660–1914* (1986), p. 615.

Rosenheim in his analysis of the leases issued by 'Turnip' Townshend at Raynham saw 'lease-based control over tenant practices' as 'an essential element of Townshend's successful managerial regime [which] begins to explain his reputation as an innovative agriculturalist'.[21] Townshend's 'reliance on leases to bring tenants to his view of husbandry was indeed a far-sighted innovative and effective strategy'.[22] Parker similarly emphasised the precocity of lease agreements on the Holkham estate in the early decades of the eighteenth century. In Parker's words, 'The terms of leases are of great importance. They provide evidence of the standards of cultivation the landlord was setting for his tenants. The progress and technical changes in the clauses dictating how the land was to be used are evidence for the progress of farming'.[23]

These assertions are, however, made in the absence of comparative studies of other East Anglian estates; and an examination of the evidence relating to these suggests, in fact, that neither Holkham nor Raynham were especially innovative in their use of the lease. By the late seventeenth century leases were widely used by landowners to improve their estates: in 1694 the agent for an estate at Horsford thus informed the landlord that he intended letting all the farms by lease 'for as long as they are tenants-at-will there will be no care taken to improve the estate'.[24] Some leases survive from as early as the sixteenth century, such as the six-year lease for the demesne of Sapiston Grange, granted in 1567, which stated that the farmer promised to leave fallow every third year land in the furlongs called Arckerhill, Sowerbotome and Sowerbomsens.[25] Such vague prescriptions continued to be usual well into the following century: indeed, many leases contained no husbandry clauses at all: one of 1628 from Nacton in the Sandlings, for example, simply instructed the tenant to maintain hedges and keep buildings in repair;[26] while another, 30 years later, merely required the tenant not to plough up pasture or sell manure.[27] More usual are two leases from the 1690s for farms in Carlton and in Great and Little Thurlow (Suffolk), which contain only the stipulation that the land should lie fallow after two crops: terms repeated, for example, in leases of 1684 and 1694 for farms in Barrow in Breckland.[28] Roughly contemporary leases from the LeStrange estate in North-West Norfolk – nineteen in all, spanning the years from 1680 to 1699 – are just as general, although they were mostly granted for longer periods than those just discussed – two were for terms of no less than 21 years.[29]

On many estates vague or limited prescriptions continued to appear in leases well into the eighteenth century. One of 1727 for Thorndon in north Suffolk, for example, simply states that the tenant 'will in every third year summertill the same according to the course of good husbandry in that country, and even as late as 1759 a lease here simply stated 'not more than two crops without summerlay'.[30] It is possible that in many cases – particularly where leases relate to farms in Breckland or North-West Norfolk – husbandry details *had* to be vague because open-field systems remained in operation, and the organisation of cropping was still to some extent communally organised so that detailed cropping prescriptions would have been difficult to follow. This may explain why, by the end of the seventeenth century, leases from certain

[21] Rosenheim, *Townshends of Raynham*, p. 151.

[22] *Ibid*, p. 154.

[23] Parker, *Coke of Norfolk*, p. 54.

[24] Essex RO, D/DL/C4/1.

[25] ESRO, HD 535/907/1.

[26] ESRO, HA 93 3/42.

[27] ESRO, HA 93 3/43.

[28] WSRO, HA 540/2/47, 49, 507/3/583 and 584.

[29] NRO, LeStrange KA 12.

[30] WSRO, 613/631/3; ESRO, HA 535/2/52.

districts, where communal organisation (even of open-field land) had always been weak, had begun to include more detailed prescriptions. Thus, the single surviving seventeenth-century lease from the Blickling estate – for a seven-year tenancy of Abbey Farm in 1666, a property scattered across the open fields of Horsham St Faiths in the Northern Heathlands – stipulates that at the end of the term the farm was to be left with 20 acres 'lying conveniently together' under turnips, tilled and sown in 'a husbandlike manner at seasonable times in the year, that is to say about midsummer time'. Fifteen acres was also to be 'summertilled in the fourthe earth' (fallow that had been ploughed four times).[31] Other equally early leases from this region are similarly detailed, most notably the fine series from Thorpe Market, drawn up by the Rant estate (later absorbed into the Harbord's Gunton estate).[32] All except one of the twelve leases granted before 1700 are for terms of five or seven years; the exception is for seventeen years. The earliest, granted in 1662, contains no detailed husbandry clauses; but one of 1665 includes a description of how the farm should be left at the end of the final (fifth) year. Ten acres were to be under pea, buck or vetch stubble, next to be sown with winter corn; and 10 acres were to be in pasture of two years lying. All the fodder produced was to be fed to stock on the farm, and all the resultant muck was to be spread and not sold: all that produced in the final year of the lease was to be put on the land destined for winter corn.

There are six Thorpe market leases for the 1680s, all of which include similarly detailed prescriptions. Turnips are first mentioned in a lease of 1690: two acres were to be sown with the crop in the final year of the tenancy (compared with the ten to be left in pea stubble and ten in pasture of one and two years lying respectively). In a seven year lease granted in 1709, ten acres were to be sown in turnips in the last year, 18 in clover seed, ten in olland of two years' lying, ten in peas stubble to be sown in winter corn, 26 in pasture of three years' lying, six in wheat stubble sown on a new break and seven in barley stubble sown after wheat. Thereafter the crop figures regularly in leases issued by the estate, in gradually increasing quantities.[33]

Leases for fairly long terms of years, with detailed husbandry clauses which include references to turnips, were by no means unusual in the early eighteenth century. Thus a 1711 lease for a farm in Gorboldisham on the edge of the Breckland laid down that not more than two crops were to be grown in succession before 'summerlanding or growing turnips in a husbandlike manner'.[34] A note in a 1723 lease for a farm on the Felbrigg estate in the Northern Heathlands states that 'whereas tis said in the old lease that not above 3 crops of corn shall be sown before the land is lay'd down with clover or non such and that he may sow turnip seed between any of the three crops of corn. Now the meaning is that he may have liberty to sow one crop of turnips besides three crops of corn before it is laid down as aforesaid'.[35] The earliest surviving lease from the Heydon estate, from 1724, similarly instructed the tenant of Beer House Farm 'not to sow more than three crops whereof one is turnips, before laying down to three years olland'.[36]

This is the first in a book of leases from the 1720s, 1730s and 1740s which survives from the

---

[31] NRO, MSS 16,023.
[32] NRO, Gunton archives, uncatalogued.
[33] NRO, Gunton archives, uncatalogued.

[34] NRO, MC 421/4.
[35] NRO, WKC 5/95/3.
[36] NRO, BUL 310 617 X 4.

Heydon estate in the Northern Heathlands.[37] Whilst all (nine from the 1720s, 23 from the 1730s and 22 from the 1740s) have much in common, there are variations which suggest that some at least were negotiated individually with tenants. Some were for 21 years but most were for shorter terms: by the 1730s seven years was the commonest term, generally increasing to 14 years by the 1740s. Like the Thorpe Market leases, those from Heydon include quite detailed prescriptions regarding the management and maintenance of the farm. Typical is a seven-year agreement for a holding in Cawston, granted in 1747.[38] At the end of the lease the tenant was to leave '15 acres of olland of two years' lying, 15 acres of olland of one year's lying having been sown with 8lb of clover and a bushell of nonsuch per acre, 10 acres mucked and summertilled on the third earth and sown with turnips at a rate of 1½ pints per acre, and once howed, 10 acres of summerley on olland of 2 years' lying tilled on the third earth, mucked and made ready to sow with wintercorn'. The tenant was not to sow 'above two crops whereof turnips was one' before laying the land down to grass for two years.

Holkham and Raynham did not, therefore, pioneer long leases with detailed husbandry clauses. These were in widespread use in the first half of the eighteenth century: Rosenheim's statement regarding a particularly detailed Raynham lease of 1717, that 'the lease terms outstrip in precision any known Norfolk leases of this date and show Townshend as already unmistakably in the vanguard of agricultural improvement' is clearly incorrect.[39] All this, however, brings us to a more fundamental question: were leases anyway of much importance in moulding the practices of farmers?

Some answer to this question is provided by documents relating to the Norfolk parish of Shotesham, on the northern edge of the Central Clayland region, which include both a fine series of early and mid-eighteenth century leases and detailed tithe accounts. The leases, for the Fellowes estate, have comparatively conservative husbandry clauses.[40] They stipulate that not more than two crops of grain were to be grown before fallowing. The cultivation of turnips is nowhere explicitly demanded before the late 1740s when two leases, one of 1747 and one of 1749, required that 12 and 20 acres of turnips should be left on the respective farms.[41] Yet turnips were unquestionably being grown on a large scale in the parish at this time: to judge from the tithe accounts they figured prominently in the fields of almost every farm on the Fellowes' estate.[42] Indeed, it is sometimes possible to compare what a tenant was actually growing on his farm, with what the lease demanded of him. Henry Moor of Shotesham Hall Farm was given a 14 year lease in 1733.[43] This stipulated that no more than two cereal crops were to be grown in succession, after which the land was to be fallowed. The tithe books, however, show that turnips were already a major crop on the farm; that bare fallows were gradually eradicated during the course of the tenancy; and that by the end of the lease most of the arable land was cultivated under the improved five-shift system. Similarly, Whitwood Farm was bought by William Fellowes, owner of the Shotesham estate, in 1733 and a nine-year lease was granted to R. Pooley.[44] He was already the tenant here, and had been since at least 1728. The lease stated

[37] NRO, BUL 617 X 4; NRO, BUL 11/310.
[38] NRO, BUL 11/311 617 X 5.
[39] Rosenheim, *Townshends of Raynham*, p. 152.
[40] NRO, FEL 382–430.

[41] NRO, FEL 406.
[42] NRO, FEL 490–492.
[43] NRO, FEL 394.
[44] NRO, FEL 400.

that not more than two cereal crops should be grown in succession and that a summerlay should follow the barley course. In fact, Pooley simply continued what had been his practice over the previous years: following erratic 'improved' rotations which seldom included fallows, but frequently featured turnips. The terms of the lease, in other words, simply made no difference to his farming.

Husbandry prescriptions thus provide a poor guide to the development of farming methods: and landlords did not necessarily set the pace of agrarian change by including them in leases. But leases can be misleading in another way. Even where landlords *were* trying to improve the character of their tenants' husbandry, their prescriptions might simply be ignored, either because the farmers had a more practical knowledge of local conditions, or because they were attempting to wrest more out of the ground at the expense of longer-term soil fertility. As the Raynbirds emphasised in 1849, few farmed on the Suffolk clays in the 1840s 'strictly according to covenants, except by not sowing two white corn crops following; in fact it is impossible. Seasons will not always admit of ploughing a certain number of times at certain intervals'.[45] On the Earsham estate in south Norfolk, within the Central Clayland region, a field book showing the crops grown on the Earsham and Denton farms between 1773 and 1778 can be compared with the terms of a lease for Hill Farm, Earsham granted in 1773.[46] The latter stated that not more than one crop of grain should be grown without summerlaying to clover, and that the clover should remain for at least 18 months. However, the field book shows that two and in some cases three successive grain crops were grown, and that clover frequently remained in the fields for only one year. Presumably these deviations from the tenancy agreement were made with the knowledge of the landlord, who perhaps cared less than modern historians about the precise course of husbandry adopted. Indeed, some contraventions to old-established prescriptions might be to his advantage. The Earsham home farm accounts for the 1780s and 1790s show the owner buying fields of turnips from his tenants, in spite of the fact that the selling of fodder crops was expressly forbidden in the estate leases.[47] While such deviations might be allowed, however, they needed to be monitored. On the Middleton estate a cropping book for the parish of Henley was begun in 1769 specifically 'to know if your tenants use the land according to the covenants in their leases and take no more than 2 crops before they summerlay the same or sow with clover or turnips which is not esteemed a crop'.[48]

The development of East Anglian leases in the period up to the late eighteenth century can now be briefly summarised. Firstly, the granting of leases with detailed husbandry clauses, and for a moderate number of years, was by no means unique to the famous Holkham and Raynham estates in the first half of the eighteenth century. It appears to have been common practice and the pioneering role of these estates must, in this respect at least, be discounted. Secondly, where 'improved' practices were demanded in leases there is no guarantee that these were being followed by the tenants. More importantly, where they were *not* demanded this does not mean that they were not being practised anyway by local farmers. The lease was thus not a tool by which 'improved' practices were imposed by enlightened aristocrats on an unwilling tenantry.

[45] Raynbird and Raynbird, *Suffolk*, p. 127.
[46] NRO, MEA 3/537, 518.
[47] NRO, MEA 3/13.
[48] ESRO, HA 93/3/53.

The principal feature of the development of leases in the later eighteenth and early nineteenth centuries is that they became more restrictive, standardised and demanding in their terms. They began to make prescriptions regarding elements of husbandry about which earlier leases had remained silent: stipulating, in particular, routine applications of marl and, less frequently, underdrainage. Formerly these had appeared but rarely as a condition of tenancy agreements, and then usually in the context of land reclamation and at least in part funded by the landlord. By 1800 marling in particular was commonly demanded as a routine part of land management, and was no longer subsidised by the landlord. A typical lease of 1802 thus stated that all the land on the farm was to be marled with 25 loads per acre in the first 12 years of the lease, and was to be dressed with a mixture of marl and dung before the turnip crop in the ensuing years.[49] More important, perhaps, were changes in the character of husbandry prescriptions. As we have seen, there were significant changes in the character of rotations during the late eighteenth and early nineteenth centuries.[50] On estates where 'improved' rotations had not formerly been stipulated, they were now almost universally demanded; and it was the four-course, rather than other kinds of turnip-based rotation, which was usually insisted upon. Husbandry prescriptions thus became increasingly standardised, and simplified: and even where the *terms* did not significantly change, their *expression* generally did. On the Earsham estate in the south Norfolk claylands, for example, the leases for the 1760s and 1770s were often very detailed:[51] typical is an example of 1760 which stated that the tenant was to

> lay down to summerlay in a husbandlike manner with clover upon the first crop after a good summertilth and turnips well-mucked and continue the same laid down by the space of 18 months at least before the breaking up the same again ... it is declared and agreed that peas set on clover stubble sown next after a good summertilth and turnips well mucked shall not be deemed a crop as to hinder the taking of one crop of corn in succession after the same.[52]

From 1788, however, such leases were replaced by ones which stipulated a similar four-course shift, but in much simpler terms. A quarter of the arable was to be in clover, and a quarter in summertilth followed by turnips. Only one crop of cereals was to be grown before a break crop, and the clover was to stand for a year to 18 months before being ploughed (peas and beans – especially suited to such heavy land – were not to be counted as a corn crop in the rotation). From 1811, Earsham leases simply stated that the arable was either to be worked in four shifts (corn or pulses → turnips → summer corn → clover lay); or else the tenant was to take two crops of corn or pulse and then fallow (again a reflection of the particularly tenacious soils found on parts of this estate).[53]

The trend towards greater standardisation, and greater simplicity, while not universal, is evident on most of the larger estates and was epitomised by the 'model' leases produced by William Marshall and Nathaniel Kent. In 1787 William Marshall published what he claimed to be 'a pretty faithful outline of the modern Norfolk lease',[54] presumably based on his direct experience as agent of the Gunton estate, whilst also drawing on information from elsewhere.

[49] NRO, BUL 293/9.
[50] See above, pp. 99–115.
[51] NRO, MEA 3/515–527, 668 X 7.

[52] NRO, MEA 3/515.
[53] NRO, MEA 3/538.
[54] Marshall, *Rural Economy*, II, pp. 71–80.

As well as keeping the hedges, gates and buildings in repair, refraining from breaking up meadows and lopping timber, the tenant was not to take more than two crops of corn without a whole year's fallow, a crop of turnips twice hoed or a two-year lay. All the straw, hay, etc. was to be consumed on the farm and the dung was to be spread on the fields. The number of acres of turnips, and of 'olland' of one and two years, to be left at the end of the lease was also stipulated. Nathaniel Kent's lease – which his firm, Kent, Claridge and Co. had provided for Thomas William Coke and no doubt other clients – was quoted by him in 1796. A six-course shift was laid down 'of which one shift shall be turnips or vetches fed off with sheep, two other shifts in grass seeds (which shall not be broken up till the same have lain two years) one other shift in wheat and the remaining two shifts in lent grain'.[55] These trends were taken further by the Holkham agent, Francis Blaikie, after 1816 with the development of the famous 'Holkham lease'. Several different, but nevertheless standardised, shifts were devised to suit the variety of soils on the estate. These included a four-, five- or six-course shift, longer periods of lay being required on poorer soils.[56]

The range of alternatives proposed by Blaikie was unusual, however. By the early nineteenth century husbandry covenants in leases generally laid down a simple four-course rotation. On many estates a printed form was devised. Typical was that used on the Langley estate in the 1820s which stipulated a rigid clayland version of the standard Norfolk four-course. A quarter of the land was to be 'well-wrought summer tilth on which shall be taken no other crop but turnips, beet, cabbages, parsnips or carrots'; a quarter was to be under barley or oats after summertilth; a quarter sown with clover; and a quarter with wheat after layer.[57]

Given that improved rotations, drainage and marling were all standard practice on East Anglian farms by the late eighteenth century, the increased attention paid to such matters in leases clearly cannot reflect landowners' efforts to foster 'improvements' on apathetic tenants. Rather, they reflected the changing balance of power between the two principal groups within agriculture. When, in the early and middle decades of the century, landlords found it difficult to attract farmers of ability and capital, prescriptions were bound to be limited in scope and often variable in character, the result of individual negotiations. As agricultural prices rose towards the end of the century, however, landowners were now in the commanding position: able to insist on the best farming practices, particularly those thought to effect the long-term fertility of the soil.

Leases continued to be seen as a fundamental aspect of good estate management throughout the first half of the nineteenth century. Questions 164 to 175 of Bacon's 1844 questionnaire dealt with leases. Most of the 77 farmers who replied were happy with a system of long (14–21 years) leases, and with the standard restrictions which they generally contained. Individual answers concerning husbandry clauses ranged from 'absolutely necessary' to 'they are of little consequence where men are disposed to act honourably'. In summarising his replies, Bacon wrote that Norfolk farms were 'almost entirely held on lease'. Their lengths varied from 8, 12 and 21 years and the terms generally bound the farmer to the four-course system.[58]

Already by the 1830s, however, leases were being abandoned in some parts of East Anglia, generally where estates were small and owners absentees: most notably, in the Central Clayland

55 Kent, *General View*, pp. 223–5.
56 Parker, *Coke of Norfolk*, p. 54.
57 NRO, MF/RO 117/9.
58 Bacon, *Agriculture*, p. 35.

region. Tenancies-at-will, verbal undertakings which committed a farm for a year but which could be terminated by either party at six month's notice, were increasingly favoured. Indeed, on the Ashburnham estate leases had been completely abandoned as early as 1830.[59] By 1841 the majority of tenants on the Bramford estate were holding by yearly tenancies.[60] The experience of the post-Napoleonic War slump had engendered a degree of caution among farmers, and there was considerable uncertainty surrounding the effects of the repeal of the Corn Laws. The Raynbirds in 1849 thought that 'few farmers have leases … some landlords will not give leases and many farmers will not hire on leases, from the fluctuation of prices and danger of free trade' on the heavier Suffolk clays.[61] With the development of 'High Farming', moreover, there was increasing opposition to standardised prescriptions. The growing use of oil cake and artificial fertilisers allowed the sacrosanct principles of the four-course to be broken, and as early as 1844 one of Bacon's respondents said that he saw no objection to two successive straw crops being taken if the tenants 'were prepared to go to the expense necessary'.[62] The high rates of investment now demanded of farmers began to redress the balance of power between tenants and landlords, and attention focused on the issue of the tenant's right to compensation for unexhausted improvements. The Select Committee on Agricultural Customs looked into this question in 1847–48, and included two East Anglian agents amongst its witnesses. Mr R. B. Harvey, land agent and tenant of the Flixton estate, stated that allowances for unexhausted improvements had been part of the agreements between landlord and tenants there since 1840, and that these were more important to improvement than leases. The agent to the Tollemache estate took very much the same view.[63]

Caird in 1851 found that there was a dislike of leases among tenants, but thought that the system of yearly tenure was 'inferior to that of leases with liberal covenants when fairly and judiciously tried'.[64] Nevertheless, in an article surveying farming customs and covenants across Britain written in 1868, Clement Cadle wrote that most Norfolk and Suffolk farms were still held on leases.[65] He noted, moreover, that the majority of East Anglian leases still contained detailed husbandry provisions. Most, indeed, normally stipulated a four-course rotation. This he considered quite unnecessary, given the recent developments in farming: limiting the number of grain crops which could be taken during any five year period would have been sufficient protection of the landlord's interest.

On the Holkham estate tenants were being given permission to depart from the terms of their leases and grow more grain, using artificial manures, as early as 1860.[66] But more typical was the view of the agent at Earl Stonham (Suffolk) in 1851: 'I think no deviation from the four-course should be allowed, but under special circumstances of high farming and then only by permission and to a small extent'.[67] Many landlords and agents would have agreed. Charles

[59] ESRO, HA 1, HB4/2.
[60] ESRO, HA 61/436/896.
[61] Raynbirds, *Agriculture*, p. 127.
[62] NRO, MF/RO 10.
[63] BPP 1847/8, VII, p. 68.
[64] Caird, *English Agriculture*, p. 509.
[65] C. Cadle, 'Farming customs and covenants of England', *JRASE*, sec. ser. 4 (1868), p. 168.

[66] Wade Martins, *Great Estate*, p. 121. An unusual clause proposed for a Walsingham lease bound the tenant to spend £40 a year on artificial manure which was all to be used on turnips. The prospective tenant did not object to buying the fertiliser, but did not want to be restricted to using it all on turnips; he wanted to put some on his wheat.
[67] ESRO, HA 93/3/676.

Lenny's 1864 report on the Earsham estate noted that the 'courses of cropping' followed by the tenants were 'very unequal'.[68] For the proper management of the estate he thought that 'leases with judicious covenants under proper restrictions' were necessary, and he laid down a standard rotation to be followed on all the farms.

Nevertheless, leases seem to have declined steadily in popularity through the 1850s and 1860s, and even when they continued to be used, husbandry clauses generally became less restrictive. Indeed, in the early 1870s husbandry clauses were abandoned altogether on the Holkham estate, and tenants were allowed to farm as they wished until the final years of the term, when the land had to be returned to a standard rotation: although if the agent ever thought that a farm was in a bad state, he had the power to re-impose a strict cropping pattern.[69] With the onset of depression landlords everywhere found it impossible to enforce the terms of leases; by the end of the century annual tenancies were normal on most East Anglian estates.

3. The large estates and reclamation

The popular image of the agricultural revolution involves not only the adoption of new crops and rotations, but also the expansion of productive agricultural land at the expense of 'waste': and it is here that large estates – great landowners and their large capitalist tenants – certainly did play an important role. As already noted, leases were not only used to encourage improved husbandry techniques, but also to frame co-operative schemes of land reclamation, converting tracts of heath and sheepwalk into productive arable land.

It is important to emphasise here that large estates did not dominate the countryside in all areas of East Anglia. Eighteenth and nineteenth-century writers were well aware of the marked contrasts in the size of landholding which were to be found across the two counties. C. S. Read, for example, noted in 1858 that 'the land of West Norfolk is chiefly held by large proprietors; in the east there is hardly one estate of any great size',[70] an observation that is broadly backed up by the statistics in the *Return of Owners of Land* (1876). A similar contrast existed in Suffolk, between the clayland 'core' of the county, where land was mainly held in small estates, often by absentee landowners; and the acid soil fringes, Breckland and the Sandlings, in which large proprietors predominated. The regions dominated by large estates thus corresponded with the areas of poorest soils: areas of acid sands and gravels, especially Breckland, North-West Norfolk, the Northern Heathlands and the Sandlings. It was only in areas where land was cheap that really large estates could be built up in the course of the post-medieval period. Farms also tended to be larger on such soils, partly because these had always been, by their very nature, arable rather than cattle-rearing or dairying areas, but mainly because more land was needed to make a reasonable living than in more fertile districts. In addition, landowners had long been aware that it was the large-scale farmer who had the capital necessary to maintain or enhance the value of this marginal land. Hence the steady increase in farm size effected by the large estates in the course of the period studied here. As early as the 1680s a new tenant for a farm in South Creake was recommended to Horatio Townshend on the grounds that he was 'thought to be a ritch fellow' who could bear the expense of farming there.[71]

[68] NRO, MEA 3/539.
[69] Wade Martins, *Great Estate*, pp. 75–6.
[70] Read, 'Recent Improvements', p. 226.
[71] Rosenheim, *Townshends of Raynham*, p. 95.

It was in these light soil regions, of great estates and large farms, that the most striking feats of land reclamation took place, as open heaths were replaced by grids of hawthorn hedges surrounding neat arable fields. Writers like Young were irresistibly drawn to such scenes:

> All the country from Holkham to Houghton was a wild sheep walk before the spirit of improvement seized the inhabitants … Instead of boundless wilds and uncultivated wastes inhabited by scarce anything but sheep, the country is all cut into enclosures, cultivated in a most husband-like manner, well peopled, and yielding an hundred times the produce that it did in its former state.[72]

The visual impact of such large-scale and dramatic transformations of the landscape, so much in keeping with the ideals of this age of improvement, goes a long way towards explaining the fame of the aristocratic pioneers. Yet we need to view these achievements with some scepticism. In North-West Norfolk, reclamation began in the first half of the eighteenth century and was for the most part successful: elsewhere, however, the conversion of heathland and sheepwalk to arable met with more limited success. Indeed, the extent to which land improvement schemes were anyway motivated by purely economic considerations may be doubted. Agricultural historians sometimes forget that great landowners were not only interested in agriculture: estate management was motivated by a more complex range of considerations. In these marginal areas the landscape was transformed not only by enclosure and reclamation, but also by large-scale tree-planting, and by the creation of elaborate and extensive parks and gardens. Indeed, involvement in agricultural improvement was itself a fashionable pastime, as much social and ideological as economic in character. Schemes of reclamation were not necessarily motivated by rational cost-benefit analysis. When in 1774 Thomas de Grey bemoaned the costs of enclosing the heaths at Tottington in Breckland, he observed candidly that the 'great expense … would but ill answer, unless there was a real satisfaction in employing the labourers and bringing forth a ragged dirty parish to a neatness of cultivation'.[73]Indeed, it is noteworthy that the word 'improvement' was applied indiscriminately to both land reclamation and agricultural innovation, *and* to landscape gardening. Some forms of 'improvement' fall uncomfortably between these two broad areas of activity, such as architect-designed 'model farms', where the expense involved in building can hardly have been justified in economic terms. Notable East Anglian examples include William Kent's buildings at Robert Walpole's home farm at Houghton[74]; the Soane stables and dovecote on Sir William Jerningham's home farm at Costessey[75]; the gothic buildings, possibly by James Wyatt, on the Earl of Stradbrooke's home farm at Henham[76]; a Soane cowhouse at Marlesford Hall[77]; and the neo-classical buildings illustrated by Loudon on W. Colhoun's farm at Wretham Hall[78]; and at Starston Place.[79] When Thomas Coke massively expanded Holkham Park in the 1780s and 1790s, the centre-piece of the landscape was the Great Barn, setting for the famous sheep-shearings. The surrounding parkland consisted of a mixture of arable land and clumps, carefully positioned both for aesthetic effect and for the benefit of the game. J. C. Curwen was particularly taken with the landscape here:

[72] Young, *Farmer's Tour*, II, p. 1.
[73] NRO, WLS XXLVII/19 415 X 5.
[74] J. M. Robinson, *Georgian Model Farms* (1980), p. 128.
[75] *Ibid*, p. 122.
[76] *Ibid*, p. 123.
[77] *Ibid*, p. 132.
[78] *Ibid*, p. 146.
[79] *Ibid*, p. 140.

What can be more beautiful than the diversified scenery which there presents itself? ... The effects of order and industry, combined with abundance, must be gratifying to every spectator.[80]

Conversely, when the large landowners in these light soil areas *did* act from purely economic motives they sometimes embraced policies which ran counter to the needs of agricultural improvement. Thus landowners for long guarded rights of foldcourse wherever these existed, in spite of the fact that these hindered the adoption of new crops and rotations by neighbours and tenants. Similarly, landlords might wish to protect their investment in hedgerow timber even though spreading branches caused damage to the tenants' crops. Lastly, we should note the extent to which the *non-economic* activities of great landowners might run counter to the needs of agricultural improvement. In particular, the needs of farming and game preservation came into frequent conflict. Among other misdemeanours, Abel Smith on the Merton estate was accused in 1786 of having 'cleared all the furze off Wether heath, which leaves it as naked as Lincoln Inn Fields for the protection of game, and threatens to plough up the whole heath unless he is given permission to plough 30 acres'.[81] In the 1850s Richard Girling blamed the Game Laws for farmers' problems: they allowed the game to 'eat off crops and grain in stacks', and as a result there were poor relations between landlords and tenants and 'the once happy England is reduced to beggary and want'.[82]

Yet there is a more important sense in which the achievement of large landowners in reclaiming heaths and sheepwalks needs to be qualified. It is true that the area under cultivation was massively expanded on these light lands, especially in the decades either side of 1800. But in many cases, cultivation could only be sustained with extraordinarily high inputs of manure, fertiliser, and marl; and was thus only viable while grain prices remained high. As we have seen, in Breckland, and to some extent in the Northern Heathlands and the Sandlings, the high water mark of arable expansion came in the Napoleonic War years; even then, some schemes of reclamation proved unsuccessful, and the post-war depression saw the reversion of much of the new arable land to rough grazing. Half a century later further retrenchment began, especially in Breckland, as agricultural depression set in. In the last two decades of the century extensive areas of land were either abandoned altogether or were farmed at very low levels of intensity. As one commentator observed in 1885, 'On the light soils, fields which once grew good crops of wheat and barley were put down to rye-grass worth 1s. to 2s. an acre and devoted to the rearing of game'. This was because 'when prices of corn were high and labour cheap it paid to fertilise these lands with clay ... spreading a hundred loads to the acre. At present, this is out of the question'.[83] Only in North-West Norfolk, where the soils were less marginal for arable cultivation, could the war waged against the heaths really be counted an unqualified long-term success.

The real success story of reclamation in eighteenth and nineteenth-century East Anglia did not concern these heathland areas at all, but the Fens: and, while some large estates (like that of the Hares at Stow Bardolph) certainly held land here, much was in the hands of small and

---

[80] J. C. Curwen, *General hints on agricultural subjects* (1809), p. 238.

[81] NRO, Petre Box 17, bundle 1.

[82] ESRO, JA 1/59.

[83] A. Wilson Fox, in BPP 1895, XIV, p. 310.

medium-sized proprietors, including many owner-occupiers. Moreover, while large sums of outside capital had brought about the initial drainage of the area in the seventeenth century, the conversion to arable which occurred here from the end of the eighteenth was largely the work of local farmers; while the subsequent development of improved drainage, employing steam pumps, was organised by large numbers of proprietors working through the organisational framework of Drainage Commissions. Above all, we should note that the greatest expansion of arable at the expense of grass – although the least visually dramatic – actually took place on the claylands of Norfolk and Suffolk and was principally the work of tenant farmers and small owner-occupiers; it was achieved against a background of initial hostility on the part of estate owners, and – certainly until the High Farming period – of chronic under-investment in drainage, farm buildings and other infrastructure. Contemporaries were mesmerised by the reclamation of heath and sheepwalk; but, as we have seen, it was the expansion of ploughland in the Fens and on the clays which, more than anything else, increased cereal production in the course of the eighteenth and early nineteenth century.

4. Farmers

The other key protagonists in the 'traditional' agricultural revolution were large 'gentlemen' farmers, usually tenants of the great estates but sometimes owner-occupiers. Such individuals were a particular feature of areas of lighter soil but were present to some extent even on the more fertile soils of Flegg or the claylands. Contemporaries had no doubt that they were the key innovators. Arthur Young's *Tour through the East of England*, published in 1771, is mainly concerned with such men: large-scale farmers like Mr Carr, who farmed 1000 acres at Massingham; or Mr Curtis with 1700 acres at Summerfield and Sunderland (near Docking). 'You must go to a Curtis, a Mallet, a Barton, a Glover or a Carr to see Norfolk husbandry. You will not among them see the stolen crops that are to be met with among the little occupiers of £100 a year in the eastern part of the county'.[84] When Young revisited the county in 1804, he again concentrated on such substantial 'gentleman' farmers, men characterised by 'a disposition ... that would not readily reject a proposal merely because it was new'. He listed 57 farmers whom he thought were at the forefront of improvement. By the 1840s, when Bacon wrote his book on Norfolk agriculture, the names had mostly changed, but there still remained a group of 60 or so farmers, all with extensive acreages, who were prepared to take the time to fill in his complicated questionnaire, and to explain the reasons behind their adoption of various 'improved' methods. Such sources tend to confirm the received view, of a small group of innovators in a sea of peasant ignorance. In Mingay's words, 'The progressive, market-oriented and scientifically minded farmer was ... surrounded on all sides by ignorance and prejudice'.[85]

In a more general sense, such views have been echoed by many modern sociologists. Grigg, for example, has identified three types of farmer, each responding differently to agricultural innovation; the 'early adopters'; the majority; and the 'laggards'. The early adopters tend to be the larger farmers, specialist producers and those with easy access to credit. The failure of an

---

[84] Young, *Farmer's Tour*, II, pp. 160–1.
[85] G. E. Mingay, 'Agricultural productivity and agri-
cultural society in eighteenth-century England', *Research in Economic History*, Supplement 5 (1989), p. 41.

innovation tends to have less serious consequences for these men than it would for members of the other groups. Such men are also likely to be well-educated, young (under 45) and of high social status. They learn about innovation through farming journals and agricultural societies, whilst other groups learn from their neighbours.[86] In addition to all this, many modern historians have assumed that, almost by definition, the large farms managed by such men were more productive and efficient than smaller units, not only in terms of labour productivity but also in terms of yields: large farms were able to invest more per acre than small and were perhaps run with a greater awareness of market conditions.[87]

In an East Anglian context, it is hard to challenge these views because it is precisely these kinds of individual and these kinds of enterprise which figure prominently in the documentary record. Large estates favoured large tenants; and it is the records of large estates, rather than small ones, which have generally survived to the present. Moreover, it was the educated and wealthy farmer who had the time, and the inclination, to keep a diary or farming journal. Randall Burroughes of Wymondham, who meticulously recorded the work on his farm from 1795–99, was both a farmer in his own right and the largest landowner in the parish.[88] He had been educated at Cambridge and his diary includes numerous Latin phrases. Similar in some ways, although a tenant rather than a landowner, was John Leeds of Billingford. His journal, which covers the years 1823–1827, begins with a laboriously copied out history of Britain, and numerous entries make it clear that he read widely from the religious and farming literature of his day.[89] Arthur Biddell of Playford, another important farming diarist, was likewise an exceptional man, who not only bred Suffolk horses and Norfolk sheep but also invented a scarifier which was manufactured by his wife's father, the agricultural engineer Robert Ransome. At various times he managed other farms and travelled, both locally and also to London and Scotland. A note in his day book for 1820 records how he lent out a copy of Byron's works, and of Mary Wollstonecroft's *A Vindication of the Rights of Women*: hardly, one might guess, the normal fare of the working farmer.[90]

Yet in spite of such biases in the available evidence, the simple view that the most significant improvements in farming practice were necessarily pioneered by large educated farmers can at least be questioned. On the one hand, it is evident that large gentlemen farmers might – like landowners – adopt fashionable practices which were in reality quite unsuited to the locality: the case of irrigated meadows, discussed in some detail above is a case in point.[91] On the other hand, there is no hard evidence that those innovations which really *were* successful in raising yields were first adopted by such men; nor, indeed, that smaller farmers were, of necessity and in general, characterised by ignorance and prejudice.

It is certainly true that educated opinion generally echoed the prejudices of Young and other agricultural commentators. But not invariably. The incumbent of Stansfield in Suffolk in the early nineteenth century typically described one tenant of a 40-acre farm as 'an ignorant old man as most of the little farmers are'.[92] But the descriptions given of other farmers in the

[86] D. Grigg, *The dynamics of agricultural change* (1982), pp. 154–5.

[87] For the classic statement of this position, see Mingay, 'Size of farms'.

[88] NRO, MC 216/1 668 X 3; Wade Martins and

Williamson, *Randall Burroughes*.

[89] NRO, Adcock 27.6.74.

[90] ESRO, HA 2/B2/3/1c.

[91] Above pp. 72–5.

[92] ESRO, FL 627/3/21.

neighbourhood tend to undermine this easy correspondence. Thomas Wade of Windolphs Farm, for example, only farmed 27 acres but was 'a good farmer and seemingly industrious'. John Raye only rented 40 acres but was 'a very industrious working young fellow' and as a result his fields were 'the best fields of any man'. Abraham Golding, an owner-occupier of 33 acres, was described as 'an industrious young fellow', and John Beeton, a tenant of 76 acres, 'a very industrious civil man'. The same source suggests that small farmers as much as large were keen to adopt innovations, especially underdraining. Moreover, as Mark Overton has shown, it was in the south and east of Norfolk – areas characterised by smaller farmers – that turnip cultivation was first adopted on a large scale. An examination of the exceptionally detailed tithe accounts for Shotesham in Norfolk for the 1720s, 1730s and 1740s similarly reveals no observable difference in the rate at which either turnips, or regular 'improved' rotations, were adopted on different sized farms.

Moreover, there is no very clear evidence that large farms were necessarily more efficient and profitable than small. Even the owners of large estates sporadically acknowledged that small farms might weather times of economic downturn better than large: during the slump of the 1780s Thomas de Grey of Merton noted that 'Landlords and tenants now feel the inconvenience of great farms because of the difficulty of finding those who have the capital for such an undertaking'.[93] Nor, more importantly, is it clear that smaller farms actually produced significantly lower yields than large, although the evidence is perhaps insufficient to argue the case either way. Small farms actually recorded higher yields on average than large ones, in all periods, because they were generally located in areas of more fertile soils – for the reasons already discussed. But comparisons *within* regions likewise fail to reveal any clear pattern of variation related to farm size. Small glebe farms, like those at Kettlestone or Felbrigg, recorded yields about average for their regions. More significantly, there was little difference between the average yields recorded in the tithe accounts for Mattishall in the 1780s – a parish in which over 85 per cent of the land was farmed in holdings of less than 150 acres – and those achieved around the same time on the 300-acre farm of the energetic improver Randall Burroughes, on identical soils in the nearby parish of Wymondham.

As modern sociologists have noted, the speed with which new methods and techniques are adopted depends on their character. The more complex an innovation, the less likely it is to be taken up: changes that can easily be fitted into an existing system are more readily accepted than those which involve major reorganisation.[94] The important point here is that the key innovations of the eighteenth and early nineteenth centuries – the cultivation of new crops, underdrainage, and marling – were neither complex nor disruptive. All, moreover, were the kind of improvement whose benefits were felt almost immediately.

5. Labour

East Anglia's Agricultural Revolution of the eighteenth and nineteenth centuries cannot, therefore, be convincingly explained in terms of some nebulous 'culture of innovation', percolating

---

[93] NRO, WLS XXXIX/2/19 416 X 4.

[94] The spread of innovation is considered in detail in Grigg, *Dynamics of agricultural change*, pp. 156–7.

down from the aristocratic pioneers, through the gentlemen farmers, to the broader ranks of agriculturalists. The key innovations which raised yields per acre – new rotations, marling, underdrainage – seem to have been adopted by small farmers as quickly as by large, and there is little evidence that such improved methods were, in reality, foisted on an unwilling tenancy by progressive and far-sighted landowners. Nor, indeed, is there any real evidence that large farms produced higher yields than small ones. Great feats of reclamation were achieved by large estates and their tenants in areas of light acid soil, but only at considerable expense: many of these new arable areas were subsequently abandoned, some even before the agricultural depression of the late nineteenth century. The really important increases in sown acreage – those on the claylands – were achieved in areas in which large estates were less prominent, by small proprietors and tenants rather than by large landowners, and often in the face of landowners' opposition. As one contributor to the Raynbirds' *Suffolk* noted:

> I cannot but look with surprise at the altered appearance of the country when I pass through and consider the enormous cost of the labour which has been expended by the *tenantry* in clearing, draining, and breaking up pastures &c.[95]

Rather than see the agricultural revolution in terms of enlightened aristocrats and capitalist innovators, therefore, it is perhaps more useful to conceptualise it in more straightforward terms: as the response of farmers of all kinds to the convergence of a number of definable economic factors.

There has been much discussion about the relative levels of investment – in stock, tools, infrastructure – made by landlords and tenants during the various phases of the 'Agricultural Revolution'. The three most important factors in raising yields and extending the cultivated acreage in the period before *c*. 1840, however – marling, draining, and the use of turnip-based rotations – did not in fact require much in the way of equipment or materials. What they *did* require, as the quotation from Raynbird emphasises, was large and recurrent inputs of *labour*. Trimmer thus calculated that a farm operating a four-course rotation needed 45 per cent more labour than one of equivalent size following a 'traditional' rotation in which a third of the land lay fallow each year.[96] Although across much of East Anglia such archaic rotations had been abandoned long before the eighteenth century, there is little doubt that the widespread adoption of turnips did increase labour demands. Their successful cultivation required much weeding and hoeing, at times of the year when the demands of the hay and cereal harvest were also acute. Without such attention not only would the turnips themselves fail to thrive but, in addition, they would not be able to fulfil one of their main roles – that of controlling summer weed growth.

> If, as is sometimes the case … weeds are allowed to grow, turnips can become anything but a cleaning and restorative crop. There is no particular virtue in a turnip as a 'cleaning' agent; the crop merely offers a chance of cleaning the land and building up fertility, and it is the management rather than the crop itself which is important.[97]

The transportation of muck from yard to field similarly involved much time and effort. In

[95] Raynbird and Raynbird, *Suffolk*, p. 127.

[96] C. P. Trimmer, 'The Turnip, the New Husbandry and the English Agricultural Revolution', *Quarterly J. of Economics* 83 (1969), pp. 375–95.

[97] Hanley, *Practical Farming*, p. 139.

addition, large inputs of labour were of more general importance in the 'improved' husbandry: 'the rich man keeps his land rich and clean', according to Young, with regular hoeing and multiple ploughing and harrowing to prepare a good seed bed. Dibbling, which began to replace broadcast sowing in the later eighteenth century, was probably a significant factor in raising yields as it allowed for hoeing between the dibbled rows: but this was again was a labour-intensive practice.

Farm accounts surviving from the Benhall Lodge estate in Suffolk for 1821–2 illustrate well the amounts of labour required by the routine tasks of the improved husbandry.[98] Ploughing consumed most labour – 330 man days – although this was spread across much of the year. Not far behind came the pulling of turnips, which took 285 man days concentrated in November and March. In six separate weeks during this period, between 20 and 30 man days, and in one November week 57, were spent lifting and topping turnips or fodder beet. The root crop also required hoeing, which took 72 man days from May to July. These figures go some way towards justifying Bacon's observation in 1844 that 'upon no other crop is so large an outlay made either in manure or labour'.[99] Carting and spreading muck occupied 155 man days between November and February. In contrast, drilling and sowing took 22 man days, although this figure does not include a small acreage of peas sown by piece rates, and the harvest was also contracted out.

The large-scale schemes of land improvement and reclamation, as well as the alterations effected to the basic chemical and physical structure of existing arable land, would also have been impossible without large supplies of cheap labour. Digging and spreading marl and installing bush drains were very labour intensive: the costs of the former were almost entirely in the labour bill, of the latter at least half. The records for Hill Farm, Playford in the first decade of the nineteenth century only describe the type of work done on piece rates, but they nevertheless provide some indication of the amounts of labour necessary for the principal 'improvements' of the period. Ditching, fencing, and digging drains accounted for 54 per cent of piece work expenditure, with a further 14 per cent going on marling and on the spreading of muck.[100]

Given all this, the relative abundance, and therefore cheapness, of East Anglian labour must have been of crucial importance in the region's agrarian development. The underlying reasons for this were demographic – the marked recovery of the population in the period after c.1750, following more than half a century of stagnation. Population continued to grow during the first decades of the nineteenth century, and most parishes in Norfolk and Suffolk experienced an increase of more than 33 per cent between 1801 and 1851.[101] The pressure on employment which this caused was exacerbated by economic factors. East Anglia was, in essence, a de-industrialising economy: the traditional textile industry, largely based in the countryside, gradually declined in the course of the eighteenth and early nineteenth centuries.[102] Initially, this meant a reduction in jobs for men, but by the nineteenth century the employment of women and children was also being effected: in 1834 at Costessey near Norwich it was reported that

[98] ESRO, HA 408 C2.

[99] Bacon, *Agriculture*, p. 214.

[100] ESRO, HA 2/B2.

[101] F. Grace, 'Population Trends', in Dymond and Martin (eds) *Historical Atlas*, pp. 80–1; J. Wright, 'Population Change 1801–1851', in Wade-Martins (ed.) *Historical Atlas*, pp. 132–3.

[102] D. C. Coleman, 'Growth and decay during the Industrial Revolution: the case of East Anglia', *Scandinavian Economic History Rev.* 10 (1962), pp. 115–27.

'formerly the women had spinning to do and brought in as much as the men', while in Beccles it was said that there was now 'no spinning or other employment for women and children who otherwise might earn 8s. or 10s. per week'.[103]

A growing labour surplus had a direct effect on the pay of labourers. In the middle decades of the eighteenth century wages in Norfolk and Suffolk were reasonably high. In the following decades, however, they consistently fell, and by 1800 both counties were in the 'average' wage category.[104] According to Young, labourers were paid between 1s. and 1s. 2d. a day on west Norfolk farms in 1767, a figure which had risen to only 1s. 6d. a day (10s. a week) by the 1790s.[105] Kent puts this figure in some sort of inflationary context in his *Agricultural Survey of Norfolk* when he states that although wages may have risen 25 per cent in the second half of the eighteenth century, the cost of living had risen by 60 per cent.[106] Young's figure for a Norfolk labourer's daily wage in 1804 was 1s. 4d. in the summer and 1s. 1d. in the winter, which differs slightly from the Suffolk rate of 1s. 6d. and 1s. 4d. These figures are broadly in line with those from the few surviving labour accounts for the period. The rate on the Home Farm at Earsham between 1787 and 1807 was generally 1s. 6d. a day, sometimes rising to 1s. 8d. and very occasionally to 2s.;[107] at Ringstead fifteen daily labourers received 10s. 6d. a week during the same period;[108] while at Hasketon they received 6d. per day.[109] Significantly, the two aspects of the Norfolk labourer that impressed Marshall in the 1780s were his capacity for hard work and the low wages he received. 'A Norfolk farm labourer will do as much for one shilling as some two men in many other places will do for eighteen pence each'.[110]

To some extent poor wages were offset by help in kind. In May 1790 the farmers of Earl Soham were selling wheat at a subsidised price to the poor;[111] Randall Burroughes sold his labourers meal at a price lower than the market rate in the particularly bad year of 1794–95, as did A. Bacon at Hasketon in 1800; and according to the Rev. Forby, Fincham farmers operated similar schemes.[112] Meals were provided by Burroughes when all the labourers worked together to bring in a stack for threshing, as well as during harvest. Moreover, although William Goodwin of Earl Soham recorded in his journal in September 1788 that 'The Gleaning Cause was given against the Gleaners because *all the crop* is of right his who sows and cultivates'[113] (he was referring to the test case of *Steel* v. *Houghton* which stated that there was no common law right to glean and that it could therefore only be at the farmers' discretion), the practice remained widespread. Randall Burroughes' men certainly gleaned in the 1790s. Gleaning continued to be tolerated well into the 1850s, Glyde for example reporting that between four and six bushels were collected by many labouring families.[114] Gleaning could make up 10 per cent of their income and only rarely did farmers try and enforce the ruling.[115] This was particularly true in

---

[103] BPP 1834, XXX, pp. 331, 457.

[104] E. H. Hunt, 'Industrialisation and regional inequality: wages in Britain, 1760–1914', *J. Economic History* 46 (1986), pp. 935–66.

[105] Young, *Norfolk*, p. 483.

[106] Kent, *Norfolk*, p. 165.

[107] NRO, MEA 3/15–32.

[108] NRO, LeStrange, supplementary box 2.

[109] ESRO, HA 24 50/19/3.26.

[110] Marshall, *Rural Economy*, I, p. 41.

[111] ESRO, HD 365/1.

[112] The Rev Forby, 'Reply to the editor's circular letter', *Annals of Agriculture* 26 (1796), p. 140.

[113] ESRO, HD 365/1.

[114] Glyde, *Suffolk in the nineteenth century*, p. 350.

[115] P. King, 'Gleaners, farmers and the failure of legal sanctions in England, 1750–1850', *Past and Present* 125 (1989), pp. 116–50.

Suffolk, to judge from the Poor Law Commission findings of 1834 (at Drinkstone, gleaning was said to be worth as much as 30s. to an average labouring family).[116] There were other perks. Randall Burroughes' men usually received a Christmas box of a shilling, while those working on hedging and ditching could take the trimmings for firing. Occasionally tools and harvest gloves were also provided by the farmer. Such acts of paternalism helped enforce, and to structure, the master/man relationship, legitimising endemic poverty with sporadic acts of kindness. The particular advantage to the employer was that in most cases the gift cost little or nothing: it would have been less economic to deal with the gleaned corn or the hedge trimmings in any other way. But such additional benefits, while of considerable social importance, would have had only a marginal effect upon the impact of low wages.

Yet the regional labour surplus had a more profound effect than that of simply bringing wage rates down. It ensured, as already noted, significant changes in the organisation and security of labour. Yearly hired servants in husbandry had traditionally been the most secure of workers. In the seventeenth century they had usually been given their keep in the farm house as well as a wage, but in the course of the eighteenth century living-in was becoming less usual and instead the men were given cottages or an allowance. Such men constituted, by the 1780s, only a small proportion of the agricultural workforce, normally those working with animals: horsemen, ploughmen or teamsmen, yardmen or shepherds. Not surprisingly, living-in lasted longest in the remaining pastoral areas of East Anglia, especially on the heaviest clays, where cowmen needed to be kept close at hand. A valuation of the Brandeston estate west of Wickham Market made in 1821 thus describes a 116-acre farm at Crettingham in Suffolk where there were 'men's sleeping rooms' over the pantry.[117] Similarly in the parish of Creeting, Badley Mill Farm house contained a servant's room and a man servant's room and a second farm in Badley contained three servant's rooms. Significantly, by 1830 one was no longer needed for a labourer, and was instead being used as a cheese loft.[118] In his survey of Suffolk in 1849 Raynbird noted that the custom of living in was 'still practised': but only on 'a few old fashioned small farms'.[119]

The decline in yearly hiring was accompanied by an increase in both daily hiring and piece working, by which individuals or groups of workers made a deal with a farmer to carry out some particular task, such as hoeing turnips, spreading muck or carting marl. The Rev Forby of Fincham in Norfolk in 1796 stated that 'we do all the work we can by the piece' while in Suffolk in 1813 'the great mass of work' was said to be 'done by the piece'.[120] Harvest was always done as a form of piecework, the farmer making a 'bargain' with a group of labourers, often after much negotiation. In 1795 Burroughes employed ten man and a boy at 7s. 6d. an acre which amounted to about two guineas per man. William Marshall gave the price of a harvest man as between 35s. and 40s. plus board 'be it long or short'.[121] Harvest usually lasted between four and six weeks and the harvest bargain often included an agreement to hoe the turnips if and when the cereals were too wet to cut, as on Samuel Gross's Alderton farm in July 1838.[122] But by the end of the century many other routine tasks were being carried out as piecework. We find farmers making bargains to dig marl, spread muck, hoe crops or carry out

[116] BPP 1834, XXX, p. 461.
[117] ESRO, HA 28/50/23/4.4 (1–4).
[118] ESRO, HA 28/50/23/4.4 (1–4).
[119] Raynbird and Raynbird, *Suffolk*, p. 72.

[120] Forby, 'Reply', p. 140; Young, *Suffolk*, p. 223.
[121] Marshall, *Rural Economy*, I, p. 184.
[122] WSRO, S1/8/3.2.

just about every other kind of task, other than ploughing and specialised tasks involving livestock, which continued, for the most part, to be done by yearly hired servants. The popularity of pieceworking continued into the nineteenth century. The Poor Law Commission of 1834 reported its use, especially in Norfolk and particularly on the larger farms, for a wide range of tasks, including threshing, hoeing, fencing, draining, ditching and harvesting.

Many farmers preferred piecework over daily hiring. There was widespread agreement that labourers on piece rates earned more than day labourers (Robert Hall, for instance, told Bacon that whilst day labourers earned 9s. to 10s. a week, those on task work made 10s. to 14s.): but, as Raynbird emphasised in 1846, they 'worked proportionately harder'.[123] Randall Burroughes calculated in 1796 that it cost 6s. to weed the barley in a field called Oak Close using labourers paid on piece rates: if the task had been performed by men hired by the day, it would have cost at least 8s.[124] It is important to emphasise again, however, that terms of employment were tempered by worries about poor rates, social unrest, and perhaps the health and efficiency of the workforce. Burroughes generally set the rate for a particular task at a level equivalent to a daily wage of about 1s. 6d. a day, also the guide figure followed by the Rev. Forby and his fellow farmers in Fincham. In December 1794, Burroughes paid 1s. 3d. per acre for 'halming the stubbles', but '12d. would have been quite sufficient as it would have produced to the men 1s. 6d. halfpenny per day besides the wood which would have been equal to 1s. 10d. per diem, the present rate of day wages being 1s. 4d. per diem'. Conversely, if the terms proved too hard, then the rate might be improved. For some ditching work, 'I pay'd the men one shilling per rod instead of 6d. as was agreed upon, the latter being too hard a bargain for them, so they earned eighteen pence a day'.[125]

As a result of this increase in both daily hiring, and in pieceworking, by the end of the century employment was generally spasmodic and irregular. The labour accounts for the Home Farm at Earsham, 1797–1807, for example, show that of the one to five men generally employed on a daily basis (up to nine at hay-making time), none continued in employment for more than a few weeks at a time.[126] Whether they were unemployed or working elsewhere when absent from the accounts it is impossible to say, but at the very least a degree of insecurity is suggested. Moreover, no names continue to appear throughout the entire period covered by the accounts. The situation at Earsham may not have been typical: Randall Burroughes' diary shows labourers in fairly steady employment (indeed, when the weather was too bad for field work he often found them other tasks, sometimes apparently of a token nature, around the farm). Nevertheless, none of the labourers mentioned in the first year of the diary, 1794, were still employed in the last year, 1799.[127]

The surplus of local labour brought disadvantages to the mass of the population, but clear advantages to the farmer. It allowed a high degree of flexibility in working arrangements, permitting him to tailor the supply of labour to his needs. Henry Blyth of Burnham Deepdale, answering Bacon's question in 1844 concerning the number of men he employed, candidly

---

123 H. Raynbird, 'Agriculture', in *White's Suffolk Directory* (1864).

124 Wade Martins and Williamson, *Randall Burroughes*, p. 34.

125 *Ibid*, pp. 34–6.

126 NRO, MEA 15–32.

127 Wade Martins and Williamson, *Randall Burroughes*, pp. 32–8.

replied: 'just exactly the quantity of men I want and for exactly the time it takes to do the work'.[128] It is clear that an abundance of cheap labour, and also the need to find employment for people who would otherwise need to be maintained on the Poor Rates, not only allowed but encouraged the adoption of particular forms of husbandry, and the instigation of various schemes of land improvement, which would otherwise have been impossible for the landowner or landowner. As we saw earlier, Thomas de Grey gave as one of the main motives for the reclamation of the heaths at Tottington in the 1770s the 'real satisfaction in employing the labourers'.[129]

Piecework and daily hiring continued to be the main forms of agricultural labour in East Anglia during first half of the nineteenth century, a period in which wages rose only slowly and fitfully, to judge from surviving farm accounts. At Earsham in Norfolk, for example, daily rates of 1s. 6d. in the period 1797–1807 had climbed to 2s. by 1832.[130] But wages varied from area to area: they also tended to fluctuate depending on the buoyancy of the cereal market. At Henham, Henry Girling described how weekly wages fell to 9s. in 1842, because of the state of the local economy, rising to 10s. in 1845 and 10s. 6d. two years later.[131] Bacon provided his own figures for the 40 years up to 1844, which indicated a rise of from 8s. to 12s. a week: although the replies given in his questionnaire are, in fact, generally in the region of 9s. to 10s. a week, and this is similar to the figure given by Glyde and Raynbird for the 1850s.[132] Agricultural pay rates thus appear to have risen only marginally in the first half of the century, although as the price of grain had dropped the improvement was perhaps rather greater in real terms. From the 1850s, however, there were significant improvements. In 1858 C. S. Read wrote that labour costs had gone up by as much as 20 per cent since Bacon's day: while this was partly due to the fact that 'more manual labour is employed than formerly, notwithstanding all the aid that machinery affords …', it was also because of rising wage levels.[133] The wages at Westmere Farm rose from 9s. a week in 1838 to 14s. a week in 1877: at Playford in 1860 many of the regular labourers were receiving £1 a week, that is, roughly double the average wage fifty years before.[134] It is also probable that in the second half of the century more work was carried out by day labourers, less by the piece: at Playford, for example, by 1860 only threshing and hoeing were carried out as piecework.

The slow relative improvement in wages and conditions from mid-century was principally due to the increased scarcity of labour, as regional population growth slackened after 1840, and as the local economy became more diversified, especially in the vicinity of the major towns and cities of Norwich, Yarmouth, Lynn and Ipswich. The extent to which the labourers' condition ameliorated should not of course be exaggerated. In 1856 Glyde thought there were 'many labourers frequently without work a day or two each week' and Hunt's research suggests that in the second half of the nineteenth century Norfolk labourers were still some of the worst paid in England, although in relative terms it seems that their position had improved considerably since the 1790s.[135]

---

[128] NRO, MF/RO 10.
[129] NRO, WLS XXLVII/19 415 X 5.
[130] NRO, MEA3/57 553 X 3.
[131] ESRO, JA 1/59.
[132] Raynbird, *Rham's Dictionary*, p. 471.

[133] Read, 'Recent Improvements', p. 292.
[134] NRO, WLS XXIX/2/30 416 X 4; ESRO, HA 2/B2.
[135] Glyde, *Suffolk in the nineteenth century*, p. 354; E. H. Hunt, 'Labour productivity in English agriculture, 1850–1912', *EcHR* 20 (1967), pp. 280–92.

Nevertheless, the development of a more balanced supply of labour is indicated by rising costs at the time of greatest demand. Harvest rates were already climbing by the middle of the century: Richard Girling at Henham paid six pounds each for his harvest team of 11 men and 4 boys in July 1847.[136] The previous year Raynbird calculated that for a farm of 240 acres, six harvesters were needed, plus women and boys, and the cost per acre would be £5 10s. Each man could expect £4 10s. plus 3 bushels of malt for five weeks' certain employment.[137] In 1854 the harvest at Sudbourne Farm took six weeks and cost the farmer a total of £51 2s. (six men at £7 2s. 4d. each, two boys at £3 12s. and one lad at £4 16s.).[138] These costs are more than double those of the later eighteenth century.

Doubtless this explains the gradual shift in the course of the nineteenth century away from reaping wheat, and towards mowing. In 1846 Raynbird reported that in Suffolk 'mowing wheat is a practice coming into use in preference to reaping'.[139] A man could mow about an acre a day, but only reap between a third and half an acre. The shift was part of a national trend, beginning in the Napoleonic Wars and gathering pace between 1835 and 1870.[140] And as we have seen, the middle decades of the century saw a general increase in mechanisation, with (in particular) the gradual adoption of threshing machines and reapers.

[136] ESRO, JA 1/59.
[137] Raynbird, 'Measured work', p. 126.
[138] ESRO, HA 28 50/23 4.4.
[139] Raynbird, 'Measured work', p. 126.
[140] Collins, 'Harvest Technology', pp. 453–73.

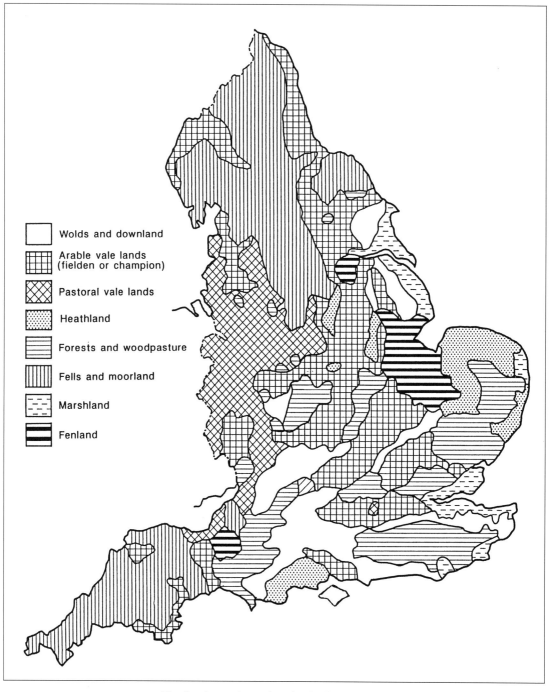

18. The farming regions of England, after Thirsk 1987.

Legend:
- Wolds and downland
- Arable vale lands (fielden or champion)
- Pastoral vale lands
- Heathland
- Forests and woodpasture
- Fells and moorland
- Marshland
- Fenland

CHAPTER VII

Conclusion

It is time to return to the principal questions posed at the start of this book. How, to judge from the East Anglian evidence, was the burgeoning population of Britain fed in the eighteenth and early nineteenth centuries? And why was East Anglia the acknowledged birthplace of England's 'Agricultural Revolution'? We have argued that agricultural change in this period is not best explained in terms of a 'culture of innovation' percolating down from landowners and educated farmers, to the broad mass of the farming community, but rather as a more general pattern of change, involving the widespread adoption of new techniques by farmers of all kinds. The new crops and rotations – adopted rather earlier than some recent commentators have allowed – were of key importance: but so too were a range of other techniques, especially marling and underdraining, which changed the chemical and physical structure of the soil. These and other developments, adopted on a large scale, permitted both an increase in yields and an expansion of the cultivated acreage.

It is important to emphasise that the expansion of arable was not the same as the 'reclamation' of 'waste'. Heaths and sheepwalks on light land had not been under-utilised and unmanaged. On the contrary, they had played a vital role in the old agriculture of the light lands, as reservoirs of nutrients. More importantly, the greatest and most successful expansion of ploughland was at the expense of long-enclosed and well-exploited pasture land in the Fens and claylands. It was thus a shift from pasture to arable, rather than simply the reclamation of unused or worthless land, which was the key feature of East Anglia's agrarian experience in this period. But this in turn was one aspect of a more fundamental, but much neglected, transformation of England's agricultural geography occurring in the century after 1750. One the one hand, it is clear that the area of ploughland was increasing in many parts of eastern England at this time – in the Fenlands of Cambridgeshire and Lincolnshire, on the Wolds of Yorkshire and Lincolnshire, even in the Weald of Kent. On the other, the arable acreage did not, contrary to what we might expect in this period of rapid demographic growth, increase in all regions. As arable expanded in the east of England, the acreage of grassland was increasing in many parts of the Midlands, and continued to expand even in the Napoleonic War years.

In the sixteenth and seventeenth centuries England had comprised a mosaic of farming regions, with some arable regions in the west and many pastoral ones – the Fens, the claylands of Essex and East Anglia – in the east (Figure 18). By 1850, this had largely changed, and something approaching the modern pattern – an arable south and east, a pastoral west – had emerged (Figure 19). Indeed, in the second half of the nineteenth century the latter distinction was, if anything, more marked, for arable was then extensive in certain areas, such as the Weald, in which pasture returned once again after the 1870s. The period conventionally labelled the Agricultural Revolution was, above all, the period which saw the emergence of England's modern agrarian geography.

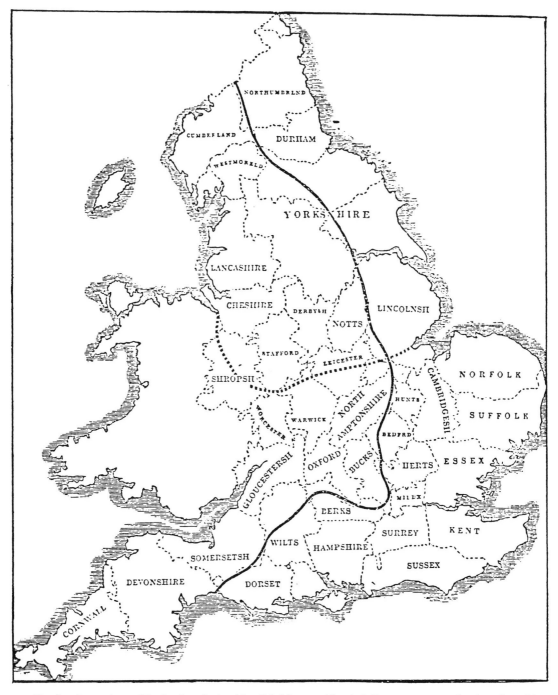

19. The farming regions of England as depicted by Caird in 1852. The dark line separates predominantly arable areas of England (to the east) from those principally devoted to livestock production (to the west).

Modern land-use patterns are an almost direct reflection of climatic factors, especially rainfall. The geography of early-modern farming regions, in contrast, was determined by more complex considerations – the poor quality of transport networks, and thus limitations on the movement of bulk grain supplies; and, above all, the character of local soils. The seventeenth, eighteenth and nineteenth centuries saw steady improvements in communications, and the development of a more integrated national economy – a favourite theme of commentators from Defoe onwards. And as we have seen, in the course of the eighteenth and nineteenth centuries the problems of soil acidity and poor drainage which had militated against arable farming in many eastern districts were overcome, and the adoption of the new rotations allowed the area of pasture to be massively reduced, yet manure inputs to be maintained.

The expansion of arable in the east began in the early and middle decades of the eighteenth century, and was associated, on both heavy land and light, with the cultivation of fodder crops, as farmers attempted to expand livestock production in line with market trends. An increasing interest in fattening store cattle led to the introduction of turnips into areas of traditional sheep-corn husbandry, especially North-West Norfolk, areas where alternative sources of fodder were in short supply; this in turn led to the enclosure, marling and ploughing of heaths and sheepwalks. But on the claylands, too, the arable acreage was expanding by the middle decades of the century, as farmers increased the production of bullocks by growing turnips and cabbages.

Nevertheless, it was the later eighteenth century which saw the real expansion of arable cultivation, both in light land areas and on the clays: and by the early nineteenth the Fens were also coming under the plough. Expansion of ploughland peaked during the Napoleonic War years, when cereal prices reached unprecedented levels; when, in Young's words, 'The scarcities and consequent high prices, brought immense sums into the county [of Norfolk], and enabled the farmers to exert themselves with uncommon vigour'.[1] While, as we have seen, there was some retrenchment of arable after the war, by 1850 East Anglia was a largely arable district, and yields on clay and acid soils had been transformed by the widespread adoption of underdrainage and large-scale marling.

The later eighteenth and early nineteenth centuries also saw a steady rise in yields per acre in East Anglia. This, like the expansion of the arable acreage, was the consequence of many factors, including the adoption of new crops and the spread of underdrainage and marling. Yields rose in all districts, but the greatest increases were in the areas of poorest land: overall improvement was thus the consequence of evening out earlier regional variations in productivity.

Both the expansion of tillage and the increases in yields depended crucially on the application of large amounts of labour. Marling, underdrainage, enclosure, the rationalisation of existing field patterns, and the new rotations themselves were all highly labour intensive. Increased inputs of labour also served to raise cereal yields more generally in this period, through better preparation of the seed bed, more careful sowing, more intensive weeding and the rest. The key point here is that East Anglia was a region in which labour became increasingly abundant, and in which increasingly casual patterns of employment developed in the course of the eighteenth and early nineteenth centuries. What had, in the early modern period, been a

---

[1] Young, *Norfolk*, p. 31.

densely-populated and industrialised region now became an over-populated rural one. A pool of under-employed workers could here be used flexibly to implement specific improvements, and was well adapted to the particular needs of the improved husbandry – with its high demands for labour, unevenly distributed across the farming year.

Norfolk and Suffolk were not, of course, the only areas of England in which agricultural wages fell in the later eighteenth century. As Hunt has pointed out, the East Anglian experience was part of a wider pattern:

> Between 1760 and 1800 the wages geography of Britain changed to the advantage of the industrialising areas. London remained a high-wage centre and wages were still high in some counties nearby. But southern counties more distant from London suffered a substantial fall in relative wages.[2]

But most other areas of declining agricultural wages were less suited, by nature of their climate, to arable farming. And of the exceptions, none were so susceptible to land use change, and to improvements in the essential nature of the agrarian environment, as East Anglia. The adjacent counties in the south east – Essex, Hertfordshire, Cambridgeshire – had long contained more arable land, tillage here being much less restricted by problems of waterlogging or acidity. The 'Agricultural Revolution' of the eighteenth and early nineteenth centuries was principally considered by contemporaries as a revolution in *arable* husbandry, and the scale of the transformation from arable to pasture was probably greater in Norfolk and Suffolk than in any other part of eastern England.

The Agricultural Revolution of the period c.1750–1840 thus represented a systematic transformation of the agricultural geography of England, involving a radical change in the essential physical and chemical nature of the natural environment, which was brought about by high inputs of labour. The same inputs of labour also, by allowing an intensification of existing farming practices (involving in particular rotations featuring turnips and clover), more generally served to increase productivity. Emphasising the importance of the labour supply during the period 1750–1820 allows us to see this 'Agricultural Revolution' as similar in essence to earlier periods of progress. Campbell, for example, has noted that the demographic explosion of the thirteenth century did not – as Postan had earlier postulated – lead to a decrease in yields per acre, as a consequence of the expansion of cultivation onto marginal land. Instead it led to an increase in yields, as an abundance of labour permitted more intensive methods of cultivation. In earlier periods, however, increased inputs of labour had been achieved at the *expense* of labour productivity: that is, by simply having more people working on the land, but less efficiently.[3] In eighteenth- and early nineteenth-century East Anglia, in contrast, it was achieved by making labourers work harder: using the abundance of labour to develop flexible patterns of employment. Due to the changes in patterns of landholding which had largely occurred in the period before 1750, the majority of the population were now effectively landless, and entirely dependent on wages. The decline of local industries ensured that no alternative form of employment existed on any scale.

---

[2] Hunt, 'Industrialisation and Inequality', p. 960.

[3] B. Campbell, 'Land, labour, livestock and productivity trends in English seignorial agriculture, 1208–1450', in Campbell and Overton (eds), *Land, labour and livestock*, pp. 178–182.

And this, of course, is the most important context in which we should consider the East Anglian agricultural revolution – that of the industrial revolution. The complex pattern of early modern farming regions may have disintegrated in the course of the eighteenth century, but the simpler regional geography that replaced it had a fundamental effect of the progress both of agriculture and of industry. Because large-scale industrialisation was largely a phenomenon of the north and west of England, and of the Midlands, a degree of *deindustrialisation* occurred elsewhere, especially in East Anglia. This, coupled with sustained population growth, led in turn to a high degree of labour productivity: and thus allowed the expanding cities to be fed. The industrial revolution, as much as the agricultural, thus rested – in the final analysis – on the exploitation and impoverishment of rural workers, especially those in East Anglia and adjacent regions: much as in the Third World today urbanisation and industrialisation are largely achieved at the expense of the countryside.

In the period of High Farming after *c*.1840, as industrialisation proceeded, as national and international transport networks improved, a new form of agriculture developed in the arable areas of England, as mechanical power and inputs of manufactured commodities were increasingly substituted for local materials and large inputs of labour. 'High Farming' took the tendencies of the earlier 'Agricultural Revolution' to their logical conclusion, affecting a further transformation of the natural environment, but it did so by breaking the earlier rules of the agricultural game. Farms now depended, not on their own resources, but on materials and inputs generated in the industrial sector, or brought in from elsewhere in the world. The classic closed circuit, labour-intensive system through which East Anglia had risen to fame was gone for ever.

Index